CRYSTALLOGRAPHY
and its Applications

CRYSTALLOGRAPHY
and its Applications

L. S. DENT GLASSER
Department of Chemistry
University of Aberdeen

Van Nostrand Reinhold (UK) Co. Ltd.

Published by Van Nostrand Reinhold (UK) Co. Ltd.
Molly Millars Lane, Wokingham, Berkshire, England

Library of Congress Cataloging in Publication Data
Glasser, L. S.   Dent,
   Crystallography and its applications.

   Includes index.
   1. Crystallography.   I. Title.
QD905.2.G55   548   76-831
ISBN 0-442-30135-9
ISBN 0-442-30136-7 pbk.

Preface

The uses of crystallography cover a wide spectrum. At one extreme lies the occasional recording of a powder pattern, usually for purposes of identification: at the other lies the full-scale structure determination that employs the whole range of modern automated equipment and powerful computers. Recently the glamour of the latter has tended to overshadow the many other ways in which crystallography can help scientists, and it is hoped that this book may help to redress the balance.

It is *not* intended here to provide a complete guide to crystal structure analysis, although the subject is briefly covered. There are many excellent texts available for those who intend to specialize in this field—some are listed in the Bibliography—and it is not my intention to compete with these in any way. Instead I am trying to emphasize the many other ways in which a knowledge of crystallography can be useful. In addition to discussing routine identification techniques, I have tried to point out such uses as studies of reactions in the solid state, applications to polymer science and the use of a knowledge of unit cell parameters to establish composition.

In writing the text I have had in mind two groups of people. On the one hand, I hope that it will be useful to the advanced undergraduate who would like a general introduction to the subject in all its aspects without undue emphasis on crystal structure analysis; in particular it should appeal to students following courses with an applied or materials science bias. On the other hand, I would hope that it might also be a useful practical guide for those research workers (industrial as well as academic), who without wishing to specialize in crystallography would like to use some of its techniques to help them along. Since a book of this length cannot hope to treat all aspects of the subject in depth, I have provided copious suggestions for further reading so that a reader, having established his or her area of interest, can then pursue the topic in more depth if desired.

The shape of the book has been determined by these considerations. The first chapter is devoted to providing a thorough grounding in the concepts used when talking about crystalline order. Subsequent chapters develop these concepts in relation to crystal optics, and powder and single crystal diffraction effects. The final chapters give a brief survey of the principal techniques used in crystal structure analysis, mainly with the aim of enabling the reader to understand and assess papers on the subject, and a short treatment of the complementary techniques of neutron and electron diffraction. The last chapter attempts to give a 'cost-benefit' analysis for the various techniques covered, to enable the reader to assess the information likely to be obtained against the effort likely to be expended.

I am grateful to those of my colleagues who have constructively criticized parts of the text, and in particular to Professor H. F. W. Taylor, especially for his comments on the chapter on crystal optics, and to Dr. J. A. Gard for his comments on the section on electron diffraction. I am also grateful to those of our honours students who read various parts of the manuscript and helped greatly by pointing out obscurities in the text. Any remaining errors, omissions or obscurities are entirely my own responsibility. The cover design is based on a high resolution electron micrograph of $Nb_{22}O_{54}$ kindly provided by Professor Sumio Iijima.

Finally I should like to thank my family for their help with proof reading, for comments (constructive and otherwise) and for putting up with me in general. Also my thanks to Mr. B. G. Cooksley and Mr. J. R. Price for their help with the photographs and Fig. 6.11, and to Miss Elma McGrath who typed, deleted and retyped successive versions of the manuscript with unflagging cheerfulness.

Contents

CHAPTER 1

Pattern and symmetry

1.1 The solid state

It is not easy to give a completely satisfactory definition of a solid; examples of 'borderline' materials can always be found. I shall use 'solid' to mean any material whose constituent particles (atoms, ions or molecules) are relatively fixed in position, except for thermal vibrations; 'fluid', on the other hand, will mean a material whose particles are in a state of constant translational motion.

A solid may be composed of particles arranged in a regularly repeating pattern (a situation difficult to achieve with any degree of permanence in a fluid) in which case it is said to be **crystalline**. A solid whose particles show no long-range order is said to be **amorphous**, and in many of its properties it will resemble a fluid whose particles have suddenly ceased to move; indeed, one school of thought does not regard such materials as solid at all, but classifies them as supercooled liquids. This idea has some merit when glasses are being considered (although even here it runs somewhat counter to common sense: most of us have enough faith in the solidity of glass to use it freely for containing liquids and will avoid bringing our heads into violent contact with large chunks of it) but there are many amorphous solids that are *not* supercooled liquids—charcoal for example. Moreover, if crystalline and solid are considered to be synonymous, how shall we describe the many semi-ordered materials whose structures are intermediate between amorphous and crystalline?

Let us therefore use the definition of a solid given in the opening paragraph, and regard the solid state as a continuum between the extremes of perfect order and complete disorder. The extreme of perfect order (Fig. 1.1(a)), in which the atomic pattern extends unbroken throughout the solid, is rarely encountered. More commonly small imperfections occur in the atomic pattern (Fig. 1.1(b)), which is thus broken up into small blocks of perfectly ordered material very slightly misaligned with respect to one another. Most crystals have this **mosaic block** type of structure; the blocks are large in comparison with atomic dimensions, but far smaller than the whole crystal. The misalignment between adjacent blocks is extremely small, usually only a few minutes of arc. The term **single crystal** implies a solid whose atomic pattern is broken only by small imperfections of this type. For many purposes we can treat such a crystal as if it were perfect, and for the present the slight imperfections will be ignored.

The extreme of complete disorder is also rare; most amorphous solids show at least some local order even though long-range order is lacking. Between the two extremes, many intermediate states are possible. A solid may, for example, consist of many crystals grown together in an interlocking mass, the relationships between their orientations being quite random (Fig. 1.1(c)); such a mass is said to be **polycrystalline**. Most metals are like this unless special efforts are made to grow them as single crystals. Other solids contain regions of order connected by regions of disorder; this type of structure occurs in many composite materials such as concrete, glass-ceramics and

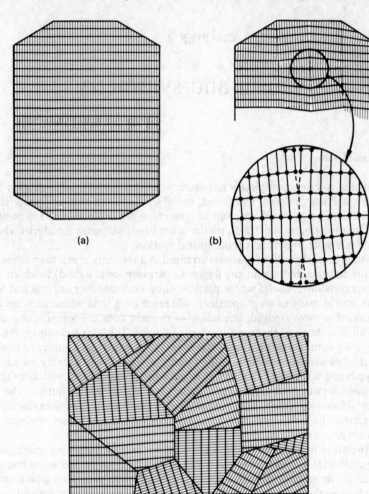

(a)   (b)

(c)

Fig. 1.1   Two-dimensional representations of crystalline order. (a) Perfect order. (b) Mosaic block structure, with a small portion enlarged to show how the discontinuities can arise at the atomic level; both the amount of misalignment and size of the blocks are somewhat exaggerated. (c) A polycrystalline mass.

paint films. Yet others show partial order throughout; for example they may have a regularly repeating pattern in only one or two directions—some polymers can have this sort of structure.

All materials interact to some extent with electromagnetic radiation, but the amount of information that can be obtained from such interactions varies enormously.

Amorphous solids, having no long-range order, behave towards incident radiation in much the same way as fluids. They absorb or transmit it equally in all directions, or **isotropically**, and if a particle scatters some of the incident radiation it does so virtually independently of the other particles. In contrast, the behaviour of crystalline materials towards radiation is modified by the ordered arrangement of their particles. Crystals may, for example, show **anisotropy** because different directions within the repeating pattern interact differently with the incident radiation. Such interactions with visible light form the basis of optical crystallography, which will be discussed briefly in the next chapter. If the wavelength of the incident radiation is of the order of the interatomic distances, scattering or **diffraction** phenomena become important, and these too are modified by the ordered arrangement of crystalline materials.

The techniques of diffraction can be used to study any substance, but the information obtained about those devoid of long-range order is very limited; one may perhaps deduce the coordination number of some of the atoms and the average distance between neighbours, but very little more. Such studies can hardly be termed crystallography and will not be dealt with here. Provided that the material is even partially ordered, diffraction studies become much more powerful; the particles do not scatter the radiation independently, and interference effects arise. These may be interpreted to give detailed information about the structure of the material being examined.

Diffraction studies on crystals most often use X-rays as the incident radiation, although beams of neutrons or electrons of suitable wavelength may also be used. Most of this book will be concerned with the practical details of such studies and the interpretation of the results. However, a proper understanding of both diffraction effects and optical crystallography requires some familiarity with the basic concepts of pattern and symmetry; a concise account of these follows.

1.2   Concepts of pattern

Since patterns or arrays are so basic to crystallography, it is convenient to devise shorthand ways of describing them. To begin with, let us consider the two-dimensional patterns in Fig. 1.2.

Figure 1.2(a) shows a simple pattern and demonstrates three different ways of defining the pattern repeat or **unit cell**. All three cells have the same size, orientation and shape, although they start and finish in different parts of the pattern; that is they differ only in the choice of origin. Most people would instinctively choose A, but choice C is also good as it emphasizes that only one complete motif is associated with each unit cell (in A, each of the four motifs at the corners is shared between four cells) and that the space between motifs is as much a part of the pattern as is the motif itself. Choice B has little to commend it aesthetically, and there are also sound intellectual reasons for rejecting it; these will emerge later.

For many purposes, the pattern may be represented by an array of points, one for each repeat unit, as on the right-hand side of the diagram. The arrangement of these points reproduces the size, orientation and shape of the unit cell. The array formed is called a **lattice**, and the points **lattice points**. The arrangement shown in Fig. 1.2(a), with only one repeat unit or lattice point associated with each unit cell, is called **primitive**.

The choice of unit cell for the pattern shown in Fig. 1.2(b) is trickier. Leaving aside the question of origin, cells can be chosen that differ in shape and size. Both A and B

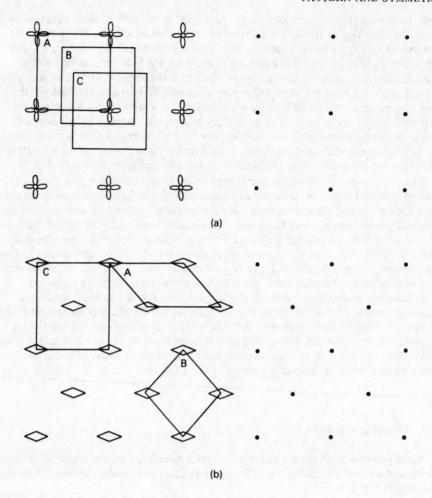

(a)

(b)

Fig. 1.2   Two-dimensional patterns (left) and their associated lattices. (a) A primitive pattern; the pattern unit may be chosen with its origin in different parts of the pattern, but its size, orientation and shape are unchanged. (b) A centred pattern; the primitive pattern unit (A or B) is an inconvenient shape and moreover has the wrong

look wrong, although each contains the smallest area of pattern that if repeated will reproduce the whole. Choice C is preferable; it is a more convenient shape and also reflects the **symmetry** of the pattern, a point that is discussed in detail below. In this case more than one pattern unit or lattice point is associated with each unit cell, and such an arrangement is called **non-primitive** or **centred**.

The *orientation* of the motifs must be considered when the repeat unit of the pattern is being determined. Although each unit cell of the patterns shown in Fig. 1.2(c) and (d) has two motifs associated with it, the arrangements are nevertheless primitive: no smaller area of pattern can be found that will, by a simple repeat, reproduce the whole. Comparison of Fig. 1.2(b) and (d) should make the distinction clear.

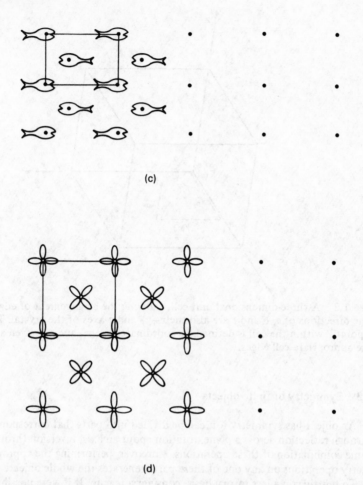

(c)

(d)

symmetry; the proper choice (C) has two lattice points per cell. (c) The orientation of the motif must be considered when determining the pattern repeat; although the unit cell here contains two motifs, it is nevertheless primitive. (d) Another example showing the importance of the orientation of the motifs: compare with (b).

The study of two-dimensional patterns is excellent training for the beginner crystallographer, and has the advantage of providing intellectual stimulation in unlikely situations: many a bus or tube journey has been beguiled by a detailed study of the upholstery on the seats.

In crystals, everything is a bit more difficult because the pattern and lattice are three-dimensional. In general, the unit cell is a parallelepiped (Fig. 1.3) whose edges a, b and c are unequal, as are the angles between them (α, β, γ). Very often, however, as with two-dimensional patterns, symmetry requires that the unit cell be less general than this. A fuller discussion of this point will be deferred until after the next section, in which symmetry concepts will be considered in some detail.

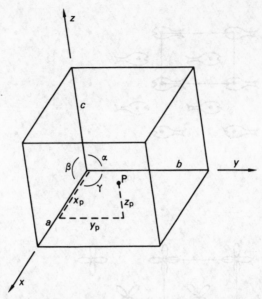

Fig. 1.3   A three-dimensional unit cell, showing the arrangement of edges and angles. The directions of a, b and c are also the x-, y- and z-axes of the crystal. The position of a point P within the cell is defined by coordinates x_p, y_p and z_p, given as fractions of the appropriate cell edges.

1.3   Symmetry of finite objects

An object has symmetry if it can be divided into parts that correspond exactly through reflection across a plane, rotation about an axis, inversion through a point, or some combination of these operations. Moreover, performing the appropriate symmetry operations on any one of these parts generates the whole object.

To put this on a less formal basis, consider a teacup. If it were possible to slice it in half through the handle, as in Fig. 1.4(a), each half would be the mirror image of the other; holding either half with its cut edge against a mirror would reproduce the appearance of the whole. The molecule of monochloramine (Fig. 1.4(b)) shows the same type of symmetry. For obvious reasons this is called a **mirror plane**; in the Hermann–Mauguin notation usually used in crystallography it is given the symbol m. In the older Schoenflies notation used in spectroscopy it may have the symbol h, v or d according to its orientation (*h*orizontal, *v*ertical or *d*iagonal, with respect to the principal axes).

Figure 1.5 shows the standard diagrammatic representation used in crystallography for vertical and horizontal mirror planes and also serves to introduce some of the other conventions used. Crystallographic diagrams are conventionally referred to x-, y- and z-axes; the unit-cell edges a, b and c are the repeat distances in these directions. Normally, in projections, x and y lie in the plane of the paper; y is horizontal with its positive direction to the right and the positive direction of x points down the page, although not necessarily at right angles to y. The positive direction of z points upwards from the paper but again need not be perpendicular to the xy plane. Unless otherwise stated, diagrams in this book conform to this convention.

The asymmetric unit—any one of the 'parts' referred to in the opening paragraph of

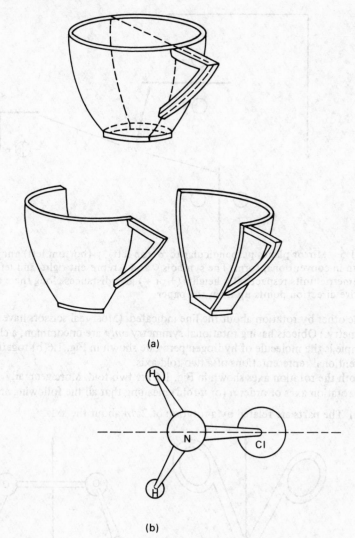

(a)

(b)

Fig. 1.4 (a) A teacup, showing its mirror plane of symmetry. (b) The molecule of monochloramine.

this section—is represented by an open circle, and a circle with a comma in it is its mirror image or **enantiomorph**; these are often called 'right handed' and 'left handed'. In the present context these may represent any object or part of an object (half a teacup, for example!). In a molecule or crystal they will represent an atom or group of atoms; we shall see later how molecular and crystal symmetry interact.

Where right- and left-handed units are superimposed in projection, a divided circle is used with a comma in one half. Heights are represented by '+' and '−' signs meaning respectively '+z' and '−z' from the plane of the paper. If this is not clear, try converting Fig. 1.5 into three dimensions by using your hands as asymmetric units.

The pair of scissors shown in Fig. 1.6(a) has a **rotation axis**, one half being related

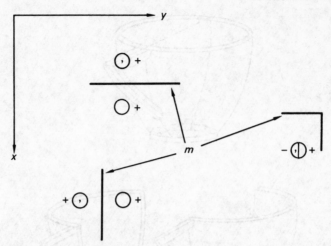

Fig. 1.5   Mirror planes perpendicular to x (top left), y (bottom left) and z (right), shown in conventional form. The symbols ○ and ⊙ represent right- and left-handed asymmetric units respectively; heights (+ or −) give distances along the z axis, whose positive direction points up from the paper.

to the other by rotation about the line indicated. (Most real scissors have only pseudo-symmetry.) Objects having rotational symmetry *only* are uncommon; a chemical example is the molecule of hydrogen peroxide shown in Fig. 1.6(b) together with the conventional representations of a two-fold axis.

Both the rotation axes shown in Fig. 1.6 are two-fold. More generally, objects may have rotation axes of order n (or n-fold) meaning that all the following are true:

(a) The parts are related by a rotation of $2\pi/n$ about the axis.

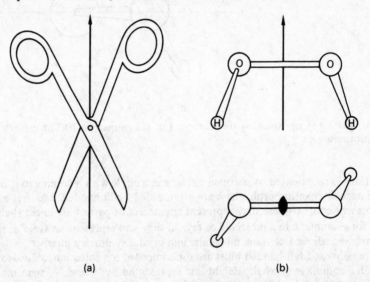

Fig. 1.6   Two-fold rotation axes: (a) in a pair of scissors, (b) in the molecule of hydrogen peroxide; two views, showing the conventional symbol for a two-fold axis in the plane of the paper (top) and perpendicular to it (bottom).

(b) Performing the operation n times will generate the whole from one of its parts and bring the original part back to where it started.

(c) In the course of one complete revolution of the object about its symmetry axis, there will be n positions in which it presents an identical appearance.

For an isolated object, n may take any value including infinity (consider a wine bottle), but crystal lattices can have only those axes that are compatible with a space-filling array. For example, individual molecules can have a five-fold rotation axis (cyclopentane) but they cannot be fitted together in an array which retains this symmetry; Fig. 1.7 shows the results of trying. This means that in crystallography n can have only the values 2, 3, 4 and 6, which simplifies things considerably.

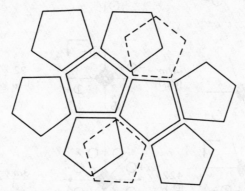

Fig. 1.7   An attempt to construct an infinite array based on five-fold symmetry.

In crystallographic notation a rotation axis is represented simply by its order, n; the equivalent spectroscopic notation is C_n. A 'one-fold' axis is equivalent to no symmetry at all, and the corresponding symbols (1 or C_1) are used for a totally asymmetric object. Conventional representations of all these axes are to be found in Fig. 1.9; note that axes of order greater than two are taken perpendicular to the plane of the paper if

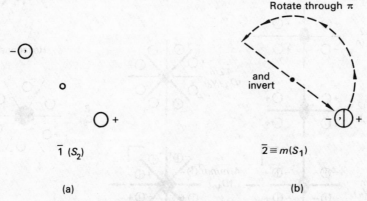

Fig. 1.8   (a) A centre of symmetry (small open circle) relating an enantiomorphous pair of objects. (b) A two-fold inversion axis passing vertically through the black dot is equivalent to a mirror plane in the plane of the paper.

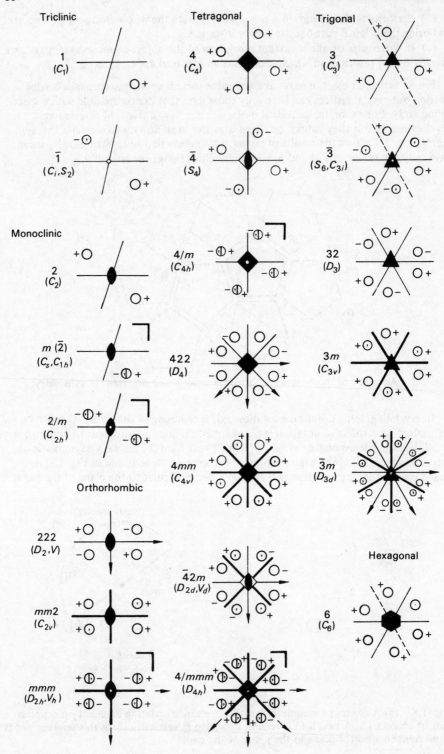

Hexagonal (cont)

Cubic

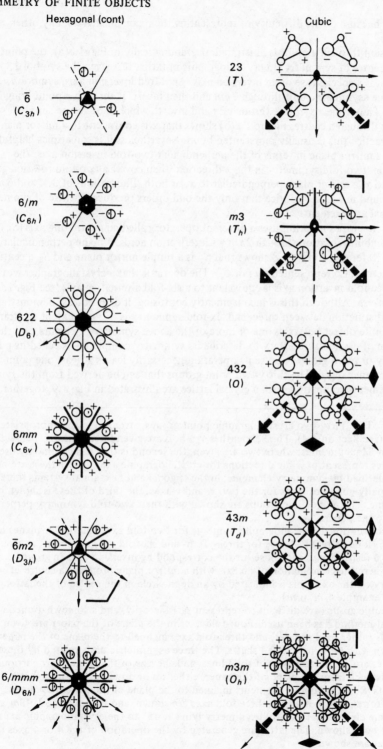

$\bar{6}$
(C_{3h})

6/m
(C_{6h})

622
(D_6)

6mm
(C_{6v})

$\bar{6}m2$
(D_{3h})

6/mmm
(D_{6h})

23
(T)

m3
(T_h)

432
(O)

$\bar{4}3m$
(T_d)

m3m
(O_h)

Fig. 1.9   (see caption overleaf)

possible, because of the difficulty of representing them convincingly in any other direction.

Inversion through a point is illustrated diagrammatically in Fig. 1.8(a); the point is called a **centre of symmetry**. In crystallographic notation it is given the symbol $\bar{1}$, because it is a special case of an **inversion axis**. An n-fold inversion axis, symbol $\bar{n}$, rotates the asymmetric unit through $2\pi/n$ and then inverts it through a point lying in the axis. Thus $\bar{1}$ means 'rotate through 2π and invert', which is of course simply inverting through a centre. Figure 1.8(b) shows that $\bar{2}$ is equivalent to a mirror plane, and in practice this is usually represented by m. Nevertheless it is sometimes helpful to think of a mirror plane in terms of the perpendicular two-fold inversion axis: the expression 'two-fold symmetry in the x-direction' then covers a two-fold rotation axis parallel to x, a mirror plane perpendicular to x, or both. Illustrations of $\bar{3}, \bar{4}$ and $\bar{6}$ axes can be found in Fig. 1.9; notice that only the odd orders produce a centre of symmetry in the final arrangement.

The Schoenflies notation uses a different operator called an **alternating axis** (S_n), which combines rotation through $2\pi/n$ with reflection across a plane perpendicular to the axis. Reference to Fig. 1.8 shows that S_1 is a simple mirror plane and S_2 a centre of symmetry (also represented by i or C_i). The operator that a crystallographer would call a three-fold inversion axis is equivalent to a six-fold alternating axis (see Fig. 1.9) and *vice versa*. Although this is inconveniently confusing, it does at least demonstrate that the distinction between three- and six-fold symmetry is to some extent arbitrary.

Any finite object possesses one or more of the above symmetry elements, and the collection of elements necessary to describe its symmetry completely is called its **point symmetry** or **point group** because its operation necessarily leaves at least one point in the object unchanged. The thirty-two point groups that can be derived from the symmetry elements compatible with a crystal lattice are illustrated in Fig. 1.9, together

---

Fig. 1.9 The thirty-two crystallographic point groups, arranged in the appropriate systems (see Section 1.4). The Schoenflies symbols are given in parentheses below the Hermann–Mauguin ones; where two are given, the second is that less commonly used. Faint lines represent possible directions for crystallographic axes, where these are not already defined by symmetry elements; in the trigonal and hexagonal systems there are three equally good positions for the two x- and y-axes; the third of these is shown by a dotted line. The monoclinic groups are shown with their two-fold symmetry perpendicular to the paper.

The conventional crystallographic symbols for two-fold axes and mirror planes have been mentioned already. Those for three-, four- and six-fold axes are shown in groups 3, 4 and 6 respectively, and those for the corresponding inversion axes in groups $\bar{3}, \bar{4}$ and $\bar{6}$. Where the combination of an axis with a mirror plane produces a centre of symmetry on the axis, this is indicated by an open circle in the centre of the latter (see, for example $4/m, 6/m$).

The cubic groups are difficult to represent satisfactorily, and a somewhat unconventional method has been used. Four-fold axes in the plane of the paper are given diamonds rather than squares, and three-fold axes inclined to the plane of the paper are shown with tapering, dashed shafts. The three asymmetric units related by these latter axes are connected by light solid lines, and the size of the circle is proportional to the distance from the plane of the paper, either up or down, of the unit that it represents. Some symmetry elements inclined to the plane of the paper have been omitted for clarity: not all the three-fold axes are shown, and in groups 432, $\bar{4}3m$ and $m3m$ some elements of two-fold symmetry lying at $45°$ to the crystallographic axes have not been shown. The latter are generated by the operation of the 4 or $\bar{4}$ axes upon those that are shown.

with the crystallographic and equivalent Schoenflies symbols. The latter are given to provide concordance for those familiar with them, but are not explained further since they will not be used here. Details of the crystallographic nomenclature that are not self-evident, and the reasons for classifying the groups as triclinic, monoclinic, etc., will be explained in Section 1.4.

Full appreciation of symmetry comes only with using the concepts. Determining the symmetry of everyday objects (ashtrays and vases are particularly rewarding) is splendid practice and an additional source of intellectual stimulation for life's duller moments; you can ponder over the reasons why the symmetries m and $mm2$ are found so frequently in man-made objects. It is also instructive to investigate some of the 'missing' groups: why, for example, is there no group with symmetry $m22$ or $\bar{4}/m$?

A crystal is a finite object, and, if perfectly developed, its external shape or **morphology** reflects its internal symmetry and enables it to be assigned to the appropriate point group, which is then referred to as its **crystal class**. For example, common salt normally crystallizes as cubes, but can be made to crystallize as octahedra; both shapes have symmetry $m3m$, and this is the crystal class of NaCl. Uneven development of faces frequently obscures the true symmetry, which can however be revealed by measurements of the angular relationships between faces. Such **goniometric** measurements, although not inherently difficult, are seldom made, except by mineralogists, probably because few laboratories possess the necessary goniometer. Occasionally, however, they give information not readily obtainable by other means, and then they should certainly be considered. More information will be found in some of the texts suggested for further reading; a mineralogical laboratory should be able to help with both instrument and know-how. At least you should consult the literature to see whether someone else has already made the measurements for you, particularly if you are repeating a preparation first made before the development of X-ray diffraction, for then the study of the morphology of crystals was often an important part of the characterization of a compound.

Even if complete goniometric measurements are not possible, it is useful to note the shape of the crystal, since the faces that develop usually bear simple relations to the crystal axes. In the example of common salt just quoted, the formation of cubes means that the faces developed are those perpendicular to the crystal axes; octahedra are formed if the faces that develop are those perpendicular to the body diagonals of the unit cell.

If crystals grow as prisms or needles, the needle or prism axis is usually also a crystal axis; if the prism faces are well developed, other axes may be perpendicular to them or bisect the angle between them. Plate-like crystals often have a principal axis perpendicular to the plate, or nearly so; the outline of the plate may indicate the possible symmetry of the crystal and the positions of the other axes. The relation of morphology to crystal axes will be discussed further in the next chapter.

1.4 Systems and lattices

The crystal classes fall into seven crystal **systems**, according to the way in which their symmetry elements restrict the shape of the unit cell. This is explained in the following brief notes, which should be studied in conjunction with Table 1.1 and Fig. 1.9.

If a crystal has no symmetry (point group 1), or a centre of symmetry only ($\bar{1}$), there are no restrictions on the shape of the unit cell; all three angles, α, β, and γ have

TABLE 1.1
Crystal systems and space lattices

Crystal system	Essential symmetry elements	Associated lattice types	Unit cell shape[1]
Triclinic	None	P	$a \neq b \neq c$ $\alpha \neq \beta \neq \gamma \neq 90°$
Monoclinic	One 2 or $m(\equiv \bar{2})$	P, C (or A)[2,3]	$a \neq b \neq c$ $\alpha = \gamma = 90° \neq \beta$
Orthorhombic	Three 2 or m (mutually perpendicular)	P, I, F $A(B$ or $C)$[2]	$a \neq b \neq c$ $\alpha = \beta = \gamma = 90°$
Tetragonal	One 4 or $\bar{4}$[2]	P, I	$a = b \neq c$ $\alpha = \beta = \gamma = 90°$
Trigonal	One 3 or $\bar{3}$	(R) $\left\{ \begin{array}{l} R \\[1ex] P \end{array} \right.$	(R) $a = b \neq c$ $\alpha = \beta = \gamma \neq 90°$[4]
			(P) $a = b \neq c$ $\alpha = \beta = 90°; \gamma = 120°$
Hexagonal	One 6 or $\bar{6}$	P	
Cubic	Four 3 or $\bar{3}$ (parallel to cube diagonals)	P, I, F	$a = b = c$ $\alpha = \beta = \gamma = 90°$

(1) The conditions given are minimum ones; $\neq$ should be read as 'not necessarily equal to'.
(2) Depending on choice of axes.
(3) Using the setting with b as unique axis.
(4) Referred to the smallest, primitive cell; the centred cell with three times the volume has $a = b \neq c$, $\alpha = \beta = 90°$
$\gamma = 120°$ (see text).

to be specified and the system is hence called **triclinic** or occasionally **anorthic** (that is, non-orthogonal). A **monoclinic** crystal has two-fold symmetry in one direction only $(2, m(\equiv\bar{2})$ or $2/m$; the last means 'a two-fold rotation axis with a mirror plane perpendicular to it'). One crystallographic axis is taken parallel to the direction of two-fold symmetry, and the other two axes must therefore be perpendicular to it. The choice of cell is thus restricted to a parallelepiped having two right angles; one angle has to be specified, hence the name monoclinic.

An **orthorhombic** crystal has two-fold symmetry in three mutually perpendicular directions; the crystallographic axes are taken parallel to the symmetry directions, so the unit cell is orthogonal. The point groups $(222, mm2, mmm)$ give the symmetry of each crystallographic axis in turn (that is, $mm2$ has $\bar{2}$ parallel to x and y, and 2 parallel to z). Note that here, as in many other more symmetrical groups, redundant symmetry elements may be omitted. The full symbol for mmm is $2/m\ 2/m\ 2/m$, but the three mirror planes generate the two-fold rotation axes, which are therefore omitted from the symbol.

Higher symmetry, involving axes of order greater than two, imposes more stringent restrictions on the shape of the unit cell. The **trigonal**, **tetragonal** or **hexagonal** systems are characterized by a single three-, four- or six-fold axis respectively. One crystallographic axis, always designated c, is taken parallel to this unique axis (except for primitive setting of rhombohedral cells: see p. 16), the other two must be perpendicular to it and equal to each other. The point group symbol begins by stating the nature of the unique axis; any mirror plane perpendicular to it is denoted by $/m$, as above. One or more symbols follow, representing the symmetry in various directions perpendicular to the unique axis. An example may make this clearer. The symbol $\bar{4}2m$ means a four-fold inversion axis with two-fold rotation axes perpendicular to it, the angle between the latter being bisected by mirror planes (see Fig. 1.9). The final m is strictly speaking redundant, since it is generated by the combined action of the other two elements; retaining it is convenient because the symmetry in all principal directions is then specified.

The highest symmetry of all is that of the **cubic** system. The three crystallographic axes are orthogonal and equivalent, being related by secondary three-fold axes running parallel to the body diagonals of the unit-cell cube. Rather unexpectedly, the cubic system is defined not by the symmetry of its crystallographic axes, but by the possession of these secondary three-fold axes. The point group symbols give first the symmetry of the crystallographic axes, *then* the essential three-fold axes, and finally any symmetry parallel to the face diagonals of the unit cell.

There is an unfortunate inconsistency in the convention for naming the axis parallel to a unique symmetry direction. In the monoclinic system this has historically been called crystallographic b, whereas in systems where the unique axis is of higher than two-fold symmetry it is called c. Some years ago an attempt was made to bring the monoclinic system into line with the others; it turned out to be one of those reforms to which nearly everyone assents in theory but which hardly anyone adopts in practice. The current edition of *International Tables for X-ray Crystallography* Vol. I [1] which is the standard work of reference on the subject, gives both settings for monoclinic crystals; it is thus permissible to use either, and it is as well to be aware of this potential source of confusion. This book will follow the almost universal practice of calling the unique axis b (thereby providing a fine example of the attitude that prevented the adoption of the reform).

It must be emphasized that it is the symmetry of the atomic pattern of the crystal that determines the shape of the unit cell and not *vice versa*. It is unwise to deduce the

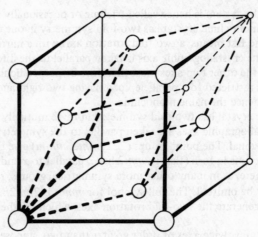

Fig. 1.10   A face-centred cubic unit cell; the dashed lines show an alternative choice of cell. Being primitive, this is smaller, but its shape is inconvenient and it does not exhibit the full symmetry of the cubic system.

crystal system from the shape of the unit cell alone, because the latter may fortuitously be more regular than that demanded by symmetry. For example, monoclinic crystals are known with $\beta = 90°$; this makes the unit cell orthogonal, but does not make the crystal orthorhombic.

The reasons for sometimes choosing non-primitive unit cells should now be obvious (refer back to Fig. 1.2). It is always *possible* to define a primitive unit cell, but one should not normally do this if it makes the cell an inappropriate shape. Figure 1.10 illustrates this point for a cubic unit cell.

Table 1.1 lists the lattice types that occur in the various crystal systems. The R lattice is unique to the trigonal system and is dealt with below; the other possible types are shown, for the orthorhombic system, in Fig. 1.11. They are symbolized by capital letters: P for *P*rimitives, I for body-centred (*I*nner-centred, or strictly from the German *i*nnenzentrierte), F for all-*F*ace-centred, and A, B, or C for centred on one face only, the letter indicating the crystallographic axis opposite to the face concerned (for example, an A-centred lattice is centred on the bc face). A, B and C lattices are not normally distinct, since they differ only in the choice of labels for the axes.

Not all systems give rise to all these types; for example, a cubic cell cannot be centred on one face only (wrong symmetry) and a C-centred tetragonal cell can be reduced to a smaller, primitive cell which still has the correct shape. All told, there are fourteen distinct combinations of crystal system and lattice type, and the resulting arrays are known as the **Bravais space lattices**, after the nineteenth century French crystallographer who worked them out [2].

The R or *R*hombohedral lattice deserves special mention, as it is a first-rate source of confusion. It is shown in Fig. 1.12. Although the primitive unit cell shown there and listed in Table 1.1 has the proper trigonal symmetry, it is usually more convenient to work in terms of the larger, non-primitive cell with $a = b \neq c$ and $\alpha = \beta = 90°$, $\gamma = 120°$. This cell has three times the volume of the primitive cell, with lattice points at 2/3, 1/3, 1/3 (that is $2a/3, b/3, c/3$) and 1/3, 2/3, 2/3, in addition to those at the

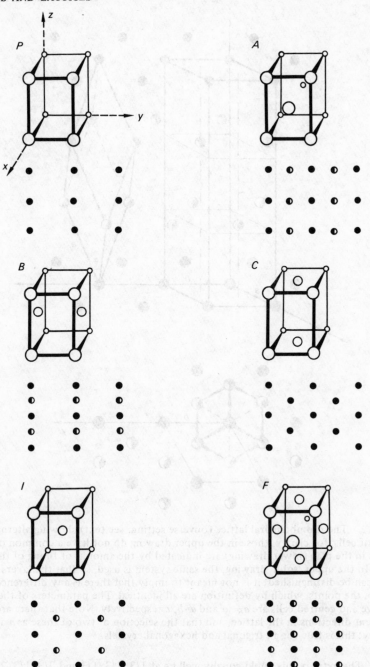

Fig. 1.11   Possible lattices of the orthorhombic system, shown 'solid' (axes at top left) and in plan (looking down z). In the plans, solid circles represent lattice points at heights 0 and c (and by implication at 2c, 3c, etc., since the array is infinite). Half-filled circles represent points at c/2 (and 3c/2, etc.). Note that there is no fundamental difference between the A, B and C arrangements.

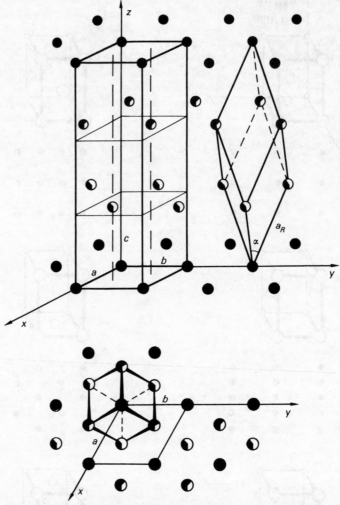

Fig. 1.12   The rhombohedral lattice (obverse setting: see text) showing alternative
choice of cells; for clarity, those in the upper drawing do not have a common origin.
Heights in the plan (lower drawing) are indicated by the amount of filling of the
circles. In the upper 'solid' drawing, the same system is used, so that the layers of
points can be distinguished; it is not meant to imply that there is any difference
between the points, which by definition are all identical. The parameters of the
primitive and centred cells are a_R, α and a, b, c respectively. Note that there are three
equivalent directions in the lattice, and that the selection of two of these as a and b is
arbitrary; this is true for all trigonal and hexagonal crystals.

corners. The extra points could equally well be at $\bar{1}/3$, 2/3, 1/3 and 2/3, 1/3, 2/3,
producing an enantiomorphous relationship between the small and large cells; the two
settings are usually distinguished as 'obverse' and 'reverse' respectively.

The term 'rhombohedral' thus defines a lattice type in the trigonal system; it is not
correct to use it for a crystal system, and although some systems of nomenclature
based on morphology use it to describe crystal class $\bar{3}$, this use is better avoided as it is

liable to lead to confusion: crystals in class $\bar{3}$ need not have rhombohedral lattices, nor is the occurrence of the latter restricted to crystals of this class. The terms 'trigonal' and 'rhombohedral' are not synonymous, as is sometimes stated or implied; the relationship is rather that of 'dogs' to 'terriers'.

Because (regardless of lattice type) so many people have difficulty at first in figuring how many lattice points are associated with each unit cell, it is worthwhile to repeat and amplify a point made earlier. Although a primitive cell has a lattice point at each corner, each of these eight points is shared by eight cells, so that the net result is one point per cell. The same conclusion may be reached by mentally displacing the origin of the cell so as totally to include one lattice point; the other seven will then automatically be excluded (cf. Fig. 1.2(a)). Or you can use the following rule: a point does not count if it is related by simple unit cell translations to one already counted. Applying this to the primitive cell, the point at the first corner counts as one; the points at the other corners are derived from it by translations along one or more of the unit cell edges and therefore do not count: each must be associated with an adjoining cell.

It is important to be clear about this; the same principle applies to atomic coordinates, and failure to appreciate it has led many a student to claim that the unit cell of sodium chloride contains $Na_{13}Cl_{14}$. A useful check on your understanding is to count up the number of points per cell in the various centred lattices; you should find that A, B, C and I lattices give two points per cell, F gives four, and R, referred to the non-primitive cell, gives three.

1.5 Translational symmetry elements

In an extended array, such as the atomic pattern of a crystal, symmetry elements may occur that involve translation as well as rotation or reflection. The imaginary climbing plant in Fig. 1.13 illustrates such a symmetry element. An axis of symmetry lies in the pole up which the plant climbs; each flower is related to the next by rotation through $2\pi/4$ about this axis, combined with translation along it. Repeating this operation four times brings the original flower into coincidence with a flower immediately above or below it, whereas an ordinary four-fold rotation axis would bring it into coincidence with itself. The plant has a **screw axis** whose formal symbol would be 4_1, meaning that each rotation of $2\pi/4$ in an anti-clockwise direction about the axis is accompanied by a translation of one quarter of the pattern repeat in the positive direction. Figure 1.14 shows a representative selection of screw axes, and the results of operating with them on an asymmetric unit.

Similarly, combining reflection and translation produces a **glide plane**, illustrated in Fig. 1.15 by an aerial view of a car park containing an array of externally identical parked cars. The glide plane, indicated by the dashed line, relates each car to the one at right angles to it and incidentally converts right-hand-drive cars into left-hand-drive ones and *vice versa*. Formal representations of some glide planes and their effects on asymmetric units are shown in Fig. 1.16. They are shown in the context of the unit cell repeat, and it can be seen that placing one glide plane in a cell automatically creates another (this is clearly seen in Fig. 1.16(d), (e) and (f)). Thus glide planes occur in sets; in the examples illustrated they are separated by one half of the perpendicular cell edge. Similar effects are found with other symmetry elements when they are applied to infinite arrays; some examples are shown in Fig. 1.17.

Translational symmetry elements are by their nature found only in infinite arrays.

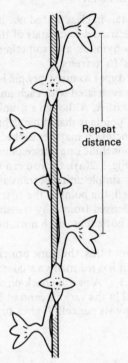

Repeat
distance

Fig. 1.13   *Tetragona scandens*; an imaginary climbing plant illustrating a four-fold screw axis. Each rotation of $2\pi/4$ around the axis is accompanied by a translation along the axis of $1/4$ of the repeat distance.

If they are present in a crystal structure, their non-translational equivalents appear in the point symmetry of the corresponding finite crystal; thus a screw axis becomes a rotation axis and a glide plane a mirror plane. Therefore the crystal class does not distinguish between translational and the equivalent non-translational symmetry elements in the structure of the crystal. Proceeding in the other direction, most crystal classes can give rise to more than one infinite array of symmetry elements. In fact, by systematically adding translation to the symmetry elements of the thirty-two crystallographic point groups, two hundred and thirty different arrays of symmetry elements can be produced, and these are known as **space groups**.

   These were derived in the late nineteenth century [3] as an intellectual exercise, well before the development of X-ray diffraction produced a practical application for the theory. The reader will no doubt be relieved that it is not proposed to repeat the derivation here; for our purposes it is more important to know how to use the results.

   The standard work of reference, *International Tables* Vol. I has already been mentioned. In addition to diagrams for all the space groups, except the cubic ones, and other information about them, it contains a clear and concise account of all the necessary concepts. Let us illustrate some important points using as an example space group number 36, $Cmc2_1$. Its diagrams are reproduced in Fig. 1.18; on the left is the array of asymmetric units, on the right the array of symmetry elements that relates them. From the space-group symbol itself, $Cmc2_1$, by replacing all translational operators with the equivalent non-translational ones, we can derive the crystal class $mm2$, and hence the system—orthorhombic. The initial letter of the symbol, C, gives the lattice

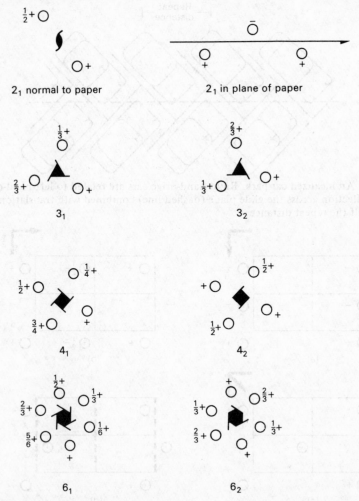

Fig. 1.14 A representative selection of screw axes with their standard symbols. Not illustrated: 4_3, 6_3, 6_4, 6_5.

type, and the subsequent letters the essential symmetry elements in the direction of the three crystallographic axes a, b, c in turn. So the symbol $Cmc2_1$ tells us that the array is C-centred orthorhombic, with a mirror plane perpendicular to a, a c-glide plane perpendicular to b, and a two-fold screw axis parallel to c. Reference to Fig. 1.18 shows that other symmetry elements are present as well; these have been generated through the interaction of the named ones, a phenomenon encountered already in some of the point groups. The two-fold screw axis passing through the origin is in fact produced by the combined operation of m and c; it is the one at 1/4 that produces, or is produced by the C-centreing.

The same principles apply to space groups in all systems. Thus $P2_1/c$ means class $2/m$, system monoclinic, lattice primitive, with a two-fold screw axis parallel to b and a c-glide plane perpendicular to it; $R\bar{3}c$ means class $\bar{3}m$, system trigonal, lattice rhombohedral, with a set of c-glide planes (referred to the centred cell) parallel to the

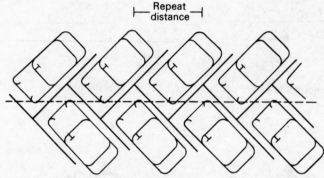

Fig. 1.15 An idealized car park. Right-hand-drive cars are related to left-hand-drive ones by reflection across the glide plane (dashed line) combined with translation through half the repeat distance.

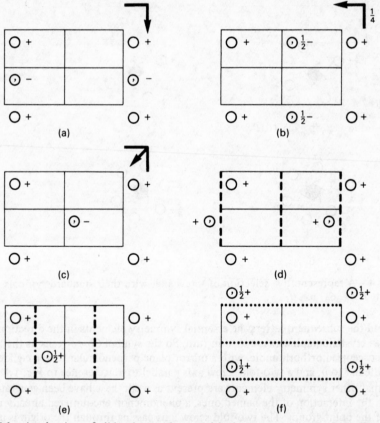

Fig. 1.16 A selection of glide planes, shown with the appropriate symbols. The light solid lines indicate the edges and halves of the unit cells, except where these are defined by symmetry planes. (a) a-glide perpendicular to c, at $z = 0, \frac{1}{2}$. (b) b-glide perpendicular to c, at z 1/4, 3/4. (c) n-glide perpendicular to c, at $z = 0, \frac{1}{2}$. (d) a-glide perpendicular to b, at $y = 0, \frac{1}{2}$. (e) n-glide perpendicular to b, at $y = 1/4, 3/4$. (f) c-glide perpendicular to a, at $x = 0, \frac{1}{2}$. Note that in (b) and (e) the glide plane does not pass through the origin of the cell.

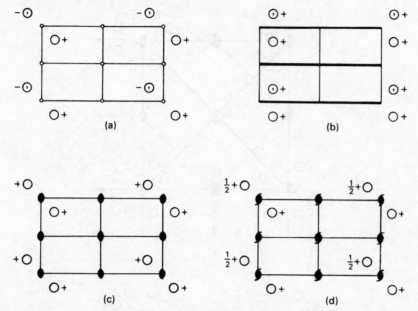

Fig. 1.17 In extended arrays, symmetry elements occur in sets. (a) Centres of symmetry; each position marked in the projection represents *two* centres of symmetry, one at height zero, the other at $c/2$, giving a total of eight in the cell. (b) Mirror planes. (c) Two-fold rotation axes. (d) Two-fold screw axes.

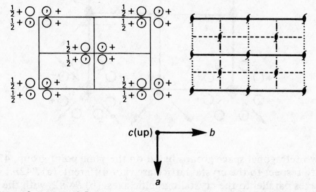

Fig. 1.18 Part of a page of *International Tables*, showing the system used for representing space groups. The one shown is number 36, $Cmc2_1$. The equivalent positions are shown on the left, the symmetry elements that relate them on the right. Note the symmetry elements not mentioned in the space group symbol. The conventional orientations of a, b and c have been added to the diagram. [Reproduced by courtesy of the International Union of Crystallography.]

three-fold inversion axis. Space groups $P\bar{4}2m$ and $P\bar{4}m2$, illustrated in Fig. 1.19, both belong to tetragonal class $\bar{4}2m$; comparison with Fig. 1.9 shows that they differ in the orientation of the symmetry elements of the point group relative to the crystallographic axes. As inspection of Fig. 1.19 shows, this produces profound differences between the resultant space groups. It was noted earlier that the final m of the point-

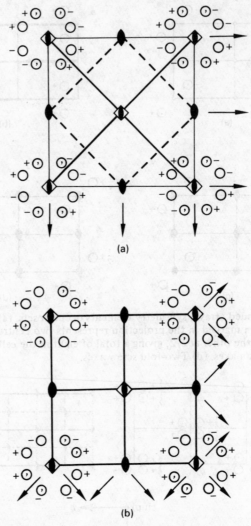

Fig. 1.19 Two tetragonal space groups based on the same point group, $\overline{4}2m$, oriented differently with respect to the crystal lattice are very different. (a) $P\overline{4}2m$, with the two-fold rotation axes parallel to the crystallographic axes. (b) $P\overline{4}m2$, with the mirror planes perpendicular to the crystallographic axes.

group symbol is redundant; so is the final character of each space-group symbol, but retaining it makes the relationship between them clearer. Similar devices are adopted in other cases in which a point group can relate to a lattice in more than one way.

Finally, a word about cubic space-group diagrams. It is probably obvious from Fig. 1.9 that representing cubic symmetry in two dimensions presents formidable problems. Because of this, and because for most purposes one can get along perfectly well without them, the diagrams for the cubic space groups are omitted from the current edition of *International Tables*. However, should you require them for any reason, such diagrams can be found in an earlier German edition [4].

References

[1] *International Tables for X-ray Crystallography* Vol. I, International Union of Crystallography (1965).

[2] Bravais, A., *Journ. de l'École Polytech.* **19** (No. 33), 1–128 (1850).

[3] Schoenflies, A., *Kristallsystems und Kristallstruktur*, B. G. Teubner, Leipzig (1891).
Federov, E. S., *Z. Kristallogr.* **23**, 99–113 (1894); **24**, 209–252 (1895); **26**, 332 (1896).
Barlow, W., *Z. Kristallogr.* **23**, 1–63 (1894).

[4] *Internationale Tabellen zur Bestimmung von Kristallstrukturen*, Berlin (1935).

CHAPTER 2

Elementary optical crystallography

2.1 Light waves and crystals

The optical properties that concern us are those of transparent crystals viewed in transmitted light; opaque crystals such as metals can be studied only in reflected light, a more specialized technique which will not be covered here. Nevertheless, a surprising number of materials *are* transparent if viewed in sufficiently thin sections: a fact constantly made use of by biologists. Rocks, rust and rubber are just three examples of apparently unpromising materials that can be examined in transmitted light.

The wavelength of visible light (4000–7000 Å, depending on its colour; or roughly half a micrometre) is much greater than the interatomic distances in crystals, and we can therefore neglect diffraction effects when considering the interaction of light with matter on the atomic scale. Even so, a full analysis of the transmission of light through crystals is complicated, and in the following simplified account some apparently improbable results are taken for granted; the sceptic should consult an advanced text on crystal physics.

We must begin with some definitions. A light wave, being a form of electromagnetic radiation, is accompanied by periodic variations in the strengths of electric and magnetic fields perpendicular to its direction of travel. Only the electric field need be considered here, and the direction in which it oscillates will be called the **vibration direction** of the light. A beam of light coming directly from a radiant source such as an electric lamp contains waves vibrating in all directions perpendicular to its direction of travel; these are represented in Fig. 2.1(a) by vectors. Such a ray is said to be **unpolarized**. Light in which all the waves are vibrating in the same plane (Fig. 2.1(b)), is said to be **plane polarized**. It can be produced by passing unpolarized light through some device that will transmit only light waves vibrating in one particular direction. Nicol prisms and Polaroid sheets are examples of such devices; we will refer to them collectively as **polars**, and not worry about how they work.

Because the electric field interacts with the electron clouds of atoms, light waves travel more slowly in matter than in a vacuum. The effect is negligible in gases at normal pressures, because the atoms occupy only a tiny fraction of the total volume; in liquids and solids, the atoms are more densely packed and the retarding effect is considerable. It is expressed as the **refractive index**, n, where

$$n = \frac{\text{velocity of light in vacuum}}{\text{velocity of light in medium}}$$

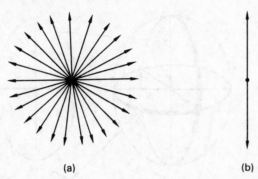

(a)   (b)

Fig. 2.1   Diagrammatic representation of the vibrations of the electric field for a ray
of light travelling perpendicular to the paper. (a) Unpolarized. (b) Plane polarized.

The value of n varies slightly with wavelength, so that different colours of light travel
through matter with slightly different velocities; the splitting of white light by a prism
and the formation of a rainbow are both manifestations of this. For most transparent
solids, n lies between 1.3 and 2.0.

When light passes through an isotropic medium, all vibration directions are equally
affected and, except for the slight variation with wavelength, there is only one value of
the refractive index. In an anisotropic medium, vibrations may interact more strongly
in one direction than in another; the refractive index will then vary with vibration
direction. It is chiefly this effect that is studied in optical crystallography, and it is
usually large compared with the variation of n with wavelength. Most elementary optical studies are therefore made using white light and the effects observed are often
beautiful as well as useful. However, before proceeding to describe them we need a
little more theory.

2.2   The optical indicatrix

The variation of refractive index with vibration direction within a crystal is described by the **optical indicatrix**. This is the surface defined by the end of a roving
vector of fixed origin whose *orientation* gives the vibration direction of the light and
whose *length* is proportional to the appropriate refractive index.

In its most general form, the indicatrix is an ellipsoid (Fig. 2.2). From its mode of
construction, it follows that the length of any radius vector represents the refractive
index for light *vibrating* in that direction (that is *travelling* in some perpendicular
direction). The ellipsoid is defined by its three principal semi-axes, which are the major
and minor semi-axes of three mutually perpendicular ellipses (see Fig. 2.2). The
shortest of these is also the shortest radius vector and is called α, the longest (and
longest radius vector) is γ, and the intermediate one is β. These three values are the
principal refractive indices of the crystal. They may also be written n_α, n_β and n_γ, a
useful notation if there is any possibility of confusion with the interaxial angles of the
unit cell.†

---

† Other notations are sometimes used, including n_X, n_Y, n_Z and n_x, n_y, n_z. The latter
notation in particular should be treated with caution, as it is also used to mean the
refractive indices for light vibrating along the *crystallographic x, y* and *z* axes. Reference to Table 2.1 will show that this is not at all the same thing as n_α, n_β, n_γ.

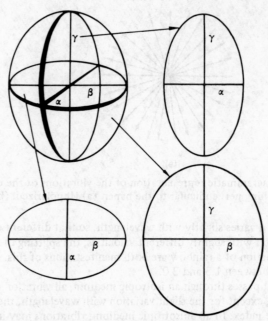

Fig. 2.2 The optical indicatrix. The ellipsoid (top left) is defined by the major and minor axes of the three mutually perpendicular ellipses which are shown projected onto the plane of the paper.

With increasing crystal symmetry, restrictions are imposed on the shape and orientation of the indicatrix (cf. the unit cell). For triclinic, monoclinic and orthorhombic crystals (collectively called **biaxial**, for reasons given below) the shape is the general one described above, but there are increasing restrictions on the orientation as the crystal symmetry increases (Table 2.1); note that there is no restriction as to *which* principal refractive index is parallel to a given crystallographic axis.

TABLE 2.1
Properties of the optical indicatrix

Crystal system	Shape	Orientation
Triclinic	Triaxial ellipsoid	No restrictions
Monoclinic	Triaxial ellipsoid	One principal axis parallel to b
Orthorhombic	Triaxial ellipsoid	All principal axes parallel to crystallographic axes
Tetragonal Trigonal Hexagonal	Ellipsoid of revolution	ϵ parallel to unique axis, ω perpendicular to it
Cubic	Sphere	—

For tetragonal, trigonal and hexagonal crystals, the refractive index for light travelling along the unique axis is the same for all vibration directions, so the indicatrix is an **ellipsoid of revolution** (Fig. 2.3). This needs only two parameters to define it, and such

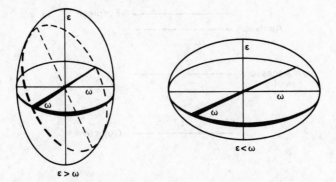

Fig. 2.3   The optical indicatrix for uniaxial crystals. A general section is indicated in the left-hand figure by dotted lines; note that no matter how this is tilted, it must contain ω as one of its semi-axes.

uniaxial crystals have only two principal refractive indices. These are called ϵ and ω, or n_ϵ and n_ω, not (as you may be thinking) from a perverse desire to introduce as many Greek letters as possible, but because of a fundamental difference from α, β and γ. The latter are defined simply in order of increasing magnitude and are never in themselves sufficient to define completely the orientation of the indicatrix with respect to the crystal (see above), but in uniaxial crystals ϵ is reserved for the refractive index for light vibrating parallel to the unique axis and may be either greater or smaller than ω, the radius of the perpendicular circle.

Cubic crystals have a spherical indicatrix whose radius n is the sole refractive index. They are therefore optically isotropic, like fluids and unstrained amorphous solids.

The behaviour of light as it passes through a crystal depends on the shape of the section of the indicatrix perpendicular to its direction of travel. In the general case this is an ellipse, and the light is split into two plane polarized beams whose mutually perpendicular vibration directions are parallel to the axes of the ellipse. The refractive indices for the two vibration directions being different, the two beams travel through the crystal at different speeds. In uniaxial crystals, all such elliptical sections must have ω as one semi-axis (see Fig. 2.3). Light travelling perpendicular to a circular section of the indicatrix is not split in this way; this is the case for light travelling along the unique axis of a uniaxial crystal, along either of *two* special directions in biaxial ones (hence the name), or in any direction in a cubic one.

2.3   Using the polarizing microscope

The optical properties of transparent crystals of the size commonly formed in chemical preparations are conveniently studied with a **polarizing microscope**. In using this, as with any other instrument, practice makes perfect. Even a rudimentary optical examination will be a great help in any subsequent X-ray studies; with practice you will find that you can often identify specimens with the aid of the microscope alone.

A polarizing microscope (Fig. 2.4) has the usual parts of a microscope, as listed on the right of the figure, plus some extra features, of which the ones we shall consider are listed on the left. Most importantly, two polars are provided. One of these, the **polarizer**, is placed below the stage, so that the light entering the specimen is plane

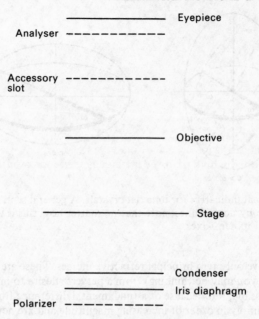

Fig. 2.4   The polarizing microscope (highly diagrammatic). Labels on the right refer to the solid lines, which represent the parts of a conventional microscope. Dashed lines, labelled on the left, represent those additional features of a polarizing microscope that are discussed in the text.

polarized; the other, placed just below (occasionally above) the eyepiece, is called the **analyser**. The latter can readily be removed or inserted; when inserted its vibration plane is usually kept perpendicular to that of the polarizer, so that the field appears dark. Cross-hairs provided in the eyepiece are normally set parallel to the vibration directions of the polars.

By rotating either the polars or the stage (depending on the model) the specimen can be rotated relative to the vibration direction of the incident light. This will be called 'rotating the specimen', even though it may be the polars that actually move. Various **accessory plates**, some of whose functions will be described later, can be inserted into a slot provided somewhere between the objective and the analyser.

There are too many different models of the polarizing microscope for it to be possible to give detailed instructions for their use in a book of this length. The best way of learning how to use one is under the guidance of an experienced user; failing that, study the manufacturer's handbook carefully. There are two golden rules: never use a polarizing microscope without permission and never make an adjustment to it unless you are quite sure you know what you are doing. Neglect of these two simple rules can result in quite extraordinary amounts of ill-will.

The following sections describe some simple studies with the polarizing microscope, using white light. They illustrate the sort of information obtainable by anyone able to focus the microscope and to control the illumination, and who knows how to put the analyser in and out and where the accessory slot is located. At the end of the chapter there is a list of suitable practice materials.

2.4 Sample preparation

Crystals that have formed as isolated individuals of a suitable size 10 μm–1 mm need no further preparation; all that need be done is to sprinkle a *few* on a microscope slide—using large heaps is both wasteful and unhelpful. Very large crystals may be gently crushed between two microscope slides or, if they are very hard, with a pestle and mortar. Unfortunately crushing usually produces a selection of fragments whose shape is quite unlike the natural form in which the crystals grew, making it very difficult, if not impossible, to interpret observations. In such cases it may be practicable to recrystallize the material, with the aim of producing crystals of a more suitable size. This can be done either in bulk or, if the material is scarce, on a small scale on a microscope slide. If the crystals are all very *small*, and recrystallization is impracticable, the only thing to be done is to try another preparation.

Sometimes the crystals may be intergrown, or twinned (p. 70), or fused together, or embedded in an amorphous matrix; if so the resulting mass should be gently crushed, as described above, with the aim of separating a few individual crystals. Alternatively, scraping the surface with a needle or a knife may produce the desired result. Although preliminary examinations and the selection of single crystals can be done dry, better results are often obtained by adding a drop of **immersion liquid** to the material on the slide to reduce light scatter; the liquid used should not react with or dissolve the material being examined. The correct procedure is to cover the material with a thin glass **coverslip**; a drop of the chosen liquid placed at the edge of this will be drawn in by capillarity and without trapping air bubbles. However, if it is desired to manipulate the crystals in any way, the coverslip must be omitted and the liquid run gently onto the material.

2.5 Examining the specimen

We will now describe the step-by-step examination of an imaginary preparation, digressing as necessary to explain the meaning of our observations in terms of the theory outlined above. Initially, we do not know whether the preparation is homogeneous or not, or even whether it is wholly crystalline. A small sample is prepared for optical examination as described in the preceding section.

The first step is to view the specimen in plane polarized light (that is with the analyser out) at low magnification; the magnification may be increased as necessary. Figure 2.6(a) on p. 35 shows what we see. The shape of the particles suggests that both 'A' and 'B' types are crystalline and of less than cubic symmetry; these conclusions should be checked in other ways, as morphology can be misleading. As the specimen is rotated, particles of type A show no noticeable change in appearance, but those of type B show a marked change in **relief** (the extent to which they stand out from the background of immersion liquid). Change in relief is caused by the variation of *n* with vibration direction, and this observation confirms that particles of type B are neither amorphous nor cubic.

The next step is to view the specimen between crossed polars, that is with the analyser in. Most of the particles show up light or coloured against the dark ground, and as the specimen is rotated all change alternately between bright and dark. When they are dark—every 90°—they are said to **extinguish**; they are at maximum brightness at 45° from the extinction position. The bright appearance of the particles means that light is travelling through them perpendicular to a non-circular section of the indicatrix; this confirms that all are anisotropic, and therefore, as we suspected, crystalline and non-cubic.

The explanation of these phenomena is as follows. When the plane polarized light from the polarizer enters a crystal not in the extinction position it is resolved into two rays p and q, vibrating parallel to the major and minor axes of the relevant section of the indicatrix (Fig. 2.5 (a) and (b)). These travel through the crystal and on reaching

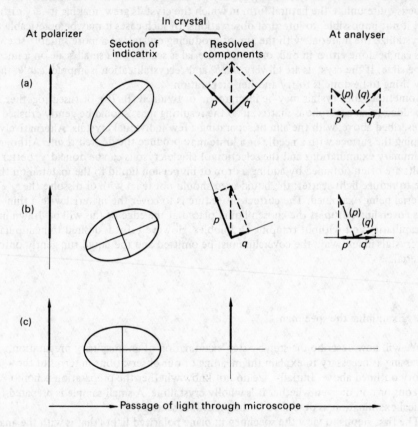

Fig. 2.5   Interaction of light with an anisotropic crystal between crossed polars. Faint lines represent permitted vibration directions in the polars or the crystal. Heavy arrows represent vibration directions of actual rays of light; the length of the shaft is proportional to the amplitude of the ray. Where appropriate, the trace of the ray(s) present at the previous stage of the interaction is shown as an arrow with a dashed shaft. For explanation see text. (a) Crystal in 45° position. (b) Crystal in intermediate position. (c) Crystal in extinction position.

the analyser are resolved yet again into the rays p' and q'. Note that the two successive resolutions effectively introduce a phase shift of π between p' and q' and the amplitudes of p' and q' are equal for all orientations of the indicatrix. If p and q travelled through the crystal at the same speed, p' and q' would therefore cancel and no brightness would be seen. However, because the refractive index in the crystal is different for the vibration directions of p and q, the rays do *not* travel through the crystal at the same speed; since in general the phase difference thus introduced does not equal $2\pi m$ (m is an integer), p' and q' do not cancel, and the crystal appears bright. In the 45° position (Fig. 2.5(a)) this brightness is at a maximum; as the crystal is turned away from this position, the amplitudes of both p' and q' diminish (Fig. 2.5(b)) and less light is transmitted by the crystal. In the limit, when one or other of the axes of the ellipse is parallel to the vibration direction of the polarizer (Fig. 2.5(c)), no component vibrating in the perpendicular direction can pass through the crystal, p' and q' are both zero, and the crystal appears dark. This is the extinction position.

The colour shown by the crystals in the bright position depends on both the difference between the relevant refractive indices or **birefringence** (Δn) and the thickness of the crystal (t); the product $t\Delta n$ is called the retardation. If $t\Delta n$ is a whole number of wavelengths, the phase difference introduced is $2\pi m$. Light of these wavelengths thus interferes destructively at the analyser; the remaining light is often beautifully coloured. The sequence of colours with increasing retardation is shown in Table 2.2; note that white appears twice in the list, at low and at very high values of the retardation. (Anomalous colours may sometimes be observed, for example with crystals which are naturally strongly coloured.)

In our specimen, all the B crystals appear white between crossed polars, as do the smaller of the A crystals, but the larger of the A crystals show colours, usually yellow and orange. Reference to Table 2.2 suggests that the retardation due to the A crystals is small; when t is large, $t\Delta n$ is sufficient to produce low order yellow and orange colours, but when t is small, low white is shown. On the other hand, none of the B crystals shows colour, and it seems likely that they are all showing high white. Unless t is very different for the two types of crystal, this means that the birefringence of the A crystals is very low and that of the B crystals very high. This agrees with the observations made regarding change of relief in plane polarized light (see above).

High and low white are readily distinguished by the use of the accessory plate usually known as the **gypsum plate**, being commonly made of that substance. Its formal name is the **unit retardation plate**, because it has a retardation equal to one wavelength of sodium light (~590 nm). When it is inserted in the microscope between crossed polars, wavelengths from the yellow part of the spectrum cancel and the field appears a uniform magenta (see Table 2.2). When the gypsum plate is introduced, those A crystals that looked white change colour dramatically to blue or yellow, depending on their orientation. Table 2.2 shows why; their low retardations are either adding to or subtracting from that of the gypsum plate thus shifting the observed colour respectively up or down the scale. The colours of the larger A crystals also change. The B crystals, on the other hand, still appear white when the gypsum plate is inserted; reference to Table 2.2 shows that at large values of $t\Delta n$ the effect of the additional retardation introduced by inserting the gypsum plate is negligible. This confirms that the B crystals are showing high white.

The position at which the crystals extinguish is studied next. We find that the A crystals are dark when they are in the position shown in Fig. 2.6(b). This is called **parallel extinction**, because extinction occurs when the vibration plane of either polar (shown by the cross-hairs) is parallel to a principal edge of the crystal. The axes of the elliptical section of the indicatrix being viewed must therefore also lie along these directions. With only rare exceptions, at least one of these will be a principal refractive index direction parallel to a crystallographic axis, and it follows that the A crystals are probably at least of monoclinic, and possibly of higher, symmetry. Their shape accords well with these conclusions.

The B crystals behave differently; they show **inclined extinction** (Fig. 2.6(c)), in

TABLE 2.2[1]

*Normal interference colours shown by anisotropic
materials between crossed polars*

Retardation ($t\Delta n$, nm)	Colour
0	black
	grey
	white ('low' white)
	yellow — gypsum plate – low white
	orange
500	magenta — gypsum plate
	purple
	blue — gypsum plate + low white
	green
	yellow
1000	orange
	red
	purple
	blue
	green
1500	yellow
	pink
	green
	pink ⎫ repeated,
	green ⎭ becoming paler
	,,
	,,
	,,
	,,
	,,
	,,
2500+	white ('high' white)

[1] This table can give only an approximate idea of the colour sequence; for advanced work a coloured chart should be consulted.

which the extinction directions, and hence the axes of the elliptical section of the indicatrix being viewed, bear no simple relation to a principal edge of the crystal. This type of extinction behaviour is characteristic of triclinic crystals or of monoclinic crystals when *b* is not lying in the plane of the microscope slide.

One explanation of the above observations, taking into account the shapes of A and B, is that the specimen is homogeneous and consists of monoclinic crystals lying on the slide in two perpendicular orientations. If this is so, *b* must be parallel to one of the principle vibration directions, probably one of those shown in Fig. 2.6(b). The inclined extinction shown by the crystal in Fig. 2.6(c) shows that *b* cannot be parallel to the length of the crystal; it must therefore lie across the crystal shown in (b) and is probably perpendicular to the section shown in (c). This knowledge will be very helpful if a crystal is to be mounted for examination by X-ray diffraction.

There is of course another possible explanation of the observations, which a wise

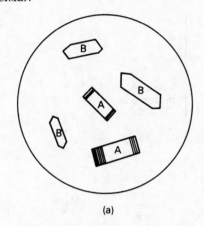

(a)

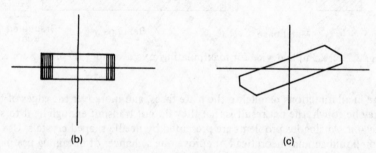

(b)   (c)

Fig. 2.6   Crystals under the polarizing microscope. (a) General view. (b) Enlarged
view of an 'A' crystal, showing position of cross-hairs at extinction. (c) Enlarged view
of 'B' in the extinction position.

chemist will not discount: the preparation may contain two different sorts of crystals.
There are several ways of checking this. In the present example, the simplest way is the
obvious one; turning one of the crystals over with a microscope needle shows that A
and B represent perpendicular orientations of the same sort of crystal.

Unfortunately, in practice, crystals are not usually so obliging as to arrange themselves thus, in two perpendicular orientations. They frequently grow as laths or plates,
which obstinately refuse to sit on their narrow edges. If they cannot be persuaded to
do so by lifting them with a microscope needle, it may be possible to turn them by
sticking them to a fine glass fibre, itself attached to the tip of a microscope needle with
a small piece of modelling clay or plasticene. The tip of the fibre is coated with a suitable adhesive and applied to the crystal. If the latter is small, this must be done under
the microscope—an operation requiring a steady hand and lots of practice. It is nevertheless an essential skill for anyone intending to proceed to single crystal diffraction studies.

A more refined technique is to attach the mounted crystal to some form of
'twiddler' (Fig. 2.7), which can readily be home-made. This allows much better control
than a hand-held microscope needle, and the graduated drum can be used to measure
the angle through which the crystal has been turned.

Whichever technique is used, snags can arise. Many plate-like crystals are relatively

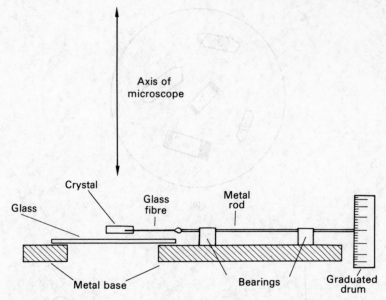

Fig. 2.7   A simple device for manipulating crystals under the microscope.

very large in all directions parallel to the plate faces, and moreover the edges of the plates may be rough; the net result is that they do not transmit enough light to study them edge-on. Analogous problems are presented by needle-shaped crystals. Use of an immersion liquid should theoretically improve one's chances of obtaining useful information, but in practice the surface tension effects introduced tend to hold the crystal with its largest dimensions parallel to the slide, sometimes with sufficient force to pull it off its mounting or to twist the fibre. In such cases one has to make do with the information obtainable from the orientations that are possible.

2.6   Some further examples

When the specimen shown in Fig. 2.8(a) is viewed between crossed polars, the crystals appear uniformly dark in all positions. The light is therefore passing through them perpendicular to a circular section of the indicatrix; no splitting of the incident light occurs, and no interference colours or extinction effects are seen. This almost certainly means that the crystals are either

(a) cubic, and therefore isotropic, or

(b) uniaxial, with the unique axis vertical (Fig 2.8(b)). In view of their shape they are more likely to be tetragonal than trigonal or hexagonal.

The two cases can be distinguished by tilting one of the crystals. Cubic crystals, being isotropic, will remain dark whatever the direction of the incident light; tetragonal ones will show interference colours and extinction effects because the relevant section of the indicatrix becomes elliptical (Fig. 2.8(c)). The effect may be quite weak if the angle of tilt is small, but the transmission of any light, however faint, eliminates cubic symmetry. In practice, crystals rarely lie so neatly upon the slide as in the dia-

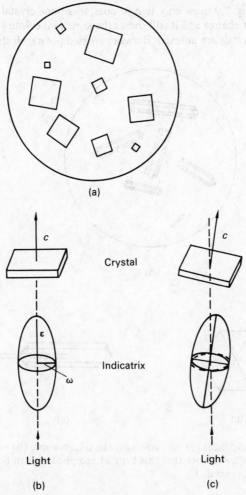

Fig. 2.8 Tetragonal crystals (a) under the polarizing microscope, (b) with the light travelling parallel to *c*, and (c) with the *c*-axis slightly tilted from the axis of the microscope.

gram; usually some will be lying partly on top of others, or may have small crystals adhering to them, or be malformed in some way, with the result that any anisotropy is revealed.

The crystals shown in Fig. 2.9 are coloured. When they are viewed in plane polarized light (analyser out), they change colour as they are rotated, from blue when their length is parallel to one of the cross-hairs to brown when it is parallel to the other. This means that some frequencies of light are being absorbed more strongly in one vibration direction than another. This change of colour or tint with vibration direction shown by some (not all) coloured crystals is called **pleochroism**; it can give information about the distortion of ions in inorganic crystals, or the position of double bonds in organic ones. Biaxial crystals may show up to three different colours (or, more precisely, extremes of colour), uniaxial ones only two; the latter are said to be **dichroic**.

The crystals in Fig. 2.9 show only two colours; when one crystal is rolled over its appearance does not change and it still shows the same two colours. This strongly suggests that the crystals are uniaxial. Between crossed polars, all show parallel extinc-

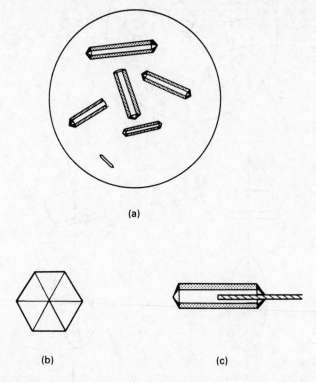

(a)

(b)   (c)

Fig. 2.9   Hexagonal prisms (a) viewed under the microscope, (b) viewed end-on, (c) mounted on a 'twiddler'. (Note that this type of morphology can be shown by trigonal as well as hexagonal crystals.)

tion, and again no change in behaviour is observed on turning one over. The extinction behaviour could be shown by orthorhombic crystals or by monoclinic ones with b lying along the needle axis, but the similar appearance of the crystals when turned over and the observations in plane polarized light both suggest a higher symmetry. There are several ways of confirming this. The most direct is to manipulate one of the crystals so as to view it end-on; Fig. 2.9(b) shows its appearance, which strongly suggests trigonal or hexagonal symmetry. Theoretically, the crystal should now appear isotropic, but in practice its thickness and the difficulty of aligning it vertically will probably prevent this from being established with certainty. Alternatively, it may be mounted on a 'twiddler' as in Fig. 2.9(c), and an attempt made to measure the angles between its faces by turning it in the horizontal plane; at the same time its refractive indices may be checked as described in the next section.

Occasionally, crystals extinguish when the vibration direction bisects the angle between the crystal edges (Fig. 2.10) and this is called **symmetrical extinction**. Figure 2.10(a) shows how this arises for a trigonal crystal lying on one face of a rhomb; the unique axis (and ϵ) runs from A to A', so the section of the indicatrix normal to the incident light is an ellipse with one axis parallel to the projection of AA′, along the long diagonal of the upper face. Figure 2.10(b) shows how it may arise for an ortho-rhombic crystal with one crystallographic axis vertical; the faces parallel to it have developed obliquely but symmetrically with respect to the other two axes, which lie along the lines indicating the extinction directions.

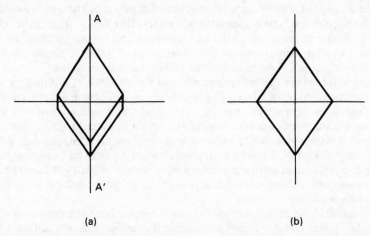

(a)   (b)

Fig. 2.10   Crystals showing symmetrical extinction in the directions indicated by the horizontal and vertical light lines. (a) In a trigonal crystal lying on one face of a rhomb. (b) In an orthorhombic crystal with one crystallographic axis perpendicular to the plane of the drawing; the other two coincide with the extinction directions.

Space does not permit the discussion of further examples; hopefully enough have been given for you to grasp the essentials of the technique, and, equally important, to encourage you to try it out for yourself. Enthusiasts can pursue the matter further with the help of the more advanced texts listed in the Bibliography.

2.7   The measurement of refractive indices

Refractive index measurements can serve to identify compounds, to check deduc-tions regarding symmetry, or to give information about composition. With the polariz-ing microscope, the several refractive indices of anisotropic crystals can be indepen-dently determined. However, measurements on isotropic substances will be considered first; they are simpler to describe, because there is only one value of n to be deter-mined.

The method is to immerse the test substance in one of a series of standard liquids of known refractive index. If substance and liquid are of widely different n, the outlines of the former stand out clearly, that is, it shows strong relief. If a liquid is selected whose n more nearly matches that of the test substance, the relief becomes weaker, and when an exact match is found the outlines of a colourless substance should virtually disappear. Plainly one could proceed by trial and error, although with a set of standards containing up to forty liquids (depending on the range covered and the interval between refractive indices) this would be rather tedious even if only one index had to be determined.

The method can be systematized as follows. Using a medium power objective and a reduced intensity of illumination, the microscope is slowly moved through the focused position; a bright line will be seen to move across the boundaries of the particles. This is the **Becke line**, and it moves into the medium of *higher n* as distance between the stage and objective lens is *increased* (and *vice versa*). This shows whether the selected liquid has a higher or lower *n* than the test substance, and hence speeds up the search for a match. In white light, *n* can usually be measured to 0.005; if greater accuracy is needed, monochromatic light must be used and its wavelength stated.

The intervals between the refractive indices of the standard liquids may be too great for an exact match to be obtained. This is usually overcome by making an *ad hoc* mixture from a few drops of the two adjacent liquids; a 'dimple' slide or very small watch glass is a suitable container. As soon as a match is found, the refractive index of the mixture is measured with a refractometer. Even if the set of standards is sufficiently finely graded, it is still a useful precaution to check them from time to time; since the standards are in general mixtures whose components do not have the same vapour pressure, their compositions, and hence their refractive indices, are liable to change slowly with time.

In the course of the determination, the test substance has to be compared with a number of different liquids. If plenty of sample is available, it is best to take a fresh supply for each liquid tried; if the available amount is limited, it is possible to draw off the liquid with a piece of filter paper, wash the sample with a suitable solvent, dry with more filter paper and add the next liquid.

Measurements on anisotropic crystals are complicated by the need to measure more than one refractive index. One procedure can be illustrated by considering the case of the monoclinic crystals discussed in Section 2.5. To determine the refractive index parallel to *b*, the specimen is rotated so that light from the polarizer is vibrating across one of the A crystals (Fig. 2.6). (The plane of vibration of the polarizer must of course be known; this is usually stated by the manufacturer, but if not can be readily determined with the aid of a crystal of known optics.) The other two refractive indices can be determined from B crystals, rotated so that they lie in each of their extinction positions in turn.

These results should be checked to see that they are consistent with the birefringence already observed, making due allowance for crystal size. For example, the A crystals showed low order colours; if they were about 0.1 mm thick, the two refractive indices might reasonably differ by up to 0.01, but not by as much as 0.1 ($t\Delta n < 500$ nm).

At this point some additional jargon may usefully be introduced. Prismatic or lath-like crystals showing parallel (or sub-parallel) extinction with the higher refractive index parallel to their longer dimension are described as **'length slow'** or as having **'positive elongation'**; conversely, if the lower refractive index is parallel to their length they are said to be **'length fast'** or to have **'negative elongation'**. Crystals with β parallel to their length may appear either length slow or length fast according to their orientation on the slide, a situation known as '± elongation'.

The elongation shown by crystals can often be determined by using one of the accessory plates, and gives a useful additional check on the measured refractive indices, which should, of course, be consistent with the elongation. In Section 2.5 it was explained that when the gypsum plate is inserted, crystals showing low white appear blue

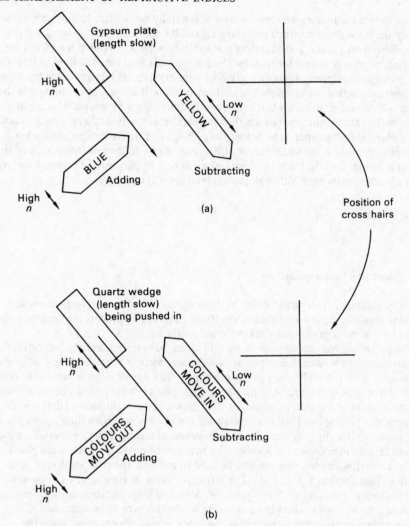

Fig. 2.11   The effect of introducing accessory plates. (a) The gypsum plate. (b) The quartz wedge. In both (a) and (b) the crystals are length fast (negative elongation), while the accessory plate is length slow.

or yellow according to whether the retardations are adding or subtracting (Table 2.2). Figure 2.11(a) shows how the observed colours can be used to compare the elongation of the crystals with that of the gypsum plate (whose vibration directions are usually labelled). For a gypsum plate cut with the opposite elongation, the colours would of course be reversed.

If the crystals are showing colours rather than low white, their elongation can be checked with another accessory plate, the **quartz wedge**; Fig. 2.11(b) shows how. The wedge is cut to have steadily increasing retardation; since crystals are usually thinner at the edges, if their retardation is adding to that of the quartz wedge, their bands of colour will move outwards as the quartz wedge is pushed in, and *mutatis mutandis*.

The simple techniques described here will generally not suffice to determine completely the optical constants of any given crystalline specimen. The examples given have all been imaginary, and therefore not subject to the well-known law governing the contrary behaviour of real substances. More often than not, you will have to be satisfied with examining only one orientation of your crystals, and determining the higher and lower refractive indices shown in that orientation. It is *not* correct to equate these values with α and γ, although this is frequently done, often by people who ought to know better. Unless the crystals are showing parallel extinction, there is no guarantee that *either* value corresponds to *any* of the principal refractive indices; even when parallel extinction is shown, there are still a great many unknowns (refer back to the example in Fig. 2.6). In these circumstances it is best to play safe and merely record your observations which, although incomplete, are still useful.

2.8   Some practical applications

Many substances can be identified by their optics alone; some reference works useful in this connection are listed in the Bibliography. The process is of course easier if you have some idea of what the compound might be.

The polarizing microscope can be used to check both purity and reproducibility of preparations. If a preparation contains two or more sorts of crystals of very different appearance, you should be alert to the possibility that it may contain more than one phase. Alternatively, of course, it may be a single phase whose crystals lie in different orientations (as in our first example) or have grown in different **habits** (that is with different morphologies). If all the crystals *are* the same phase, then their optics must be consistent with this; for example, if both values of n shown by one crystal are lower than either of those shown by another, the two cannot possibly be the same phase.

The polarizing microscope can also be used to estimate the composition of solid solutions (see Section 5.3, p. 114). The refractive index of structurally similar substances changes regularly with composition. A plot of n against composition for some standard preparations enables the composition of unknowns to be estimated.

It is sometimes possible to use refractive index measurements to estimate the density (d) of a compound, if for some reason the latter is difficult to measure directly. Various equations have been derived that relate n and d; the most useful one for solids is that due to Lorentz and Lorenz:

$$\frac{n^2 - 1}{n^2 + 2} \cdot \frac{1}{d} = \frac{R}{M}$$

where n is the mean refractive index, M is the formula weight and R the molecular refractivity, a quantity which to a good approximation is given by

$$R = p_1 r_1 + p_2 r_2 + \cdots$$

where p_1, etc. represents the number of each kind of atom in the formula of weight M, and r_1, etc. their respective contributions to the refractivity. Values for r_1, etc. must be obtained empirically from the measured values of n and d of other compounds containing the same elements as the unknown. The value of r for an element varies somewhat from compound to compound, particularly if the coordination number of its atoms changes. Because of this, and the difficulty of deciding the appropriate value of n for anisotropic crystals, the relationship is not exact but it holds sufficiently often to be useful in practice.

Finally, the microscope is invaluable for the selecting and mounting of crystals for single crystal X-ray diffraction studies. This will be discussed in more detail in Chapter 4.

2.9 Suitable practice materials

Unfortunately, since manufacturers of chemicals are not usually concerned with the suitability of their products for optical examination, few materials can be examined directly as they come from the bottle. If you find that the crystals are too small, or too large, or too ill-formed, you will need to recrystallize them from a suitable solvent. In many of the examples that follow this can be done quite simply by taking a few milligrams on a 'dimple' microscope slide. Add a drop of hot water, stir with a microscope needle, and then leave the slide in a warm place until crystals form.

To practise measuring refractive indices, it is best to begin with an isotropic material. Any of the common alkali halides are suitable, and these usually *can* be used straight from the bottle.

A good example of uniaxial crystals that lie with their unique axes perpendicular to the slide (cf. Fig. 2.8) is given by lead iodide 'spangles' (precipitated PbI_2 recrystallized from hot water: this is best done in a test-tube). Well-crystallized iodoform crystals show a similar habit. $NH_4H_2PO_4$ (or KH_2PO_4) crystals are also uniaxial, but form prisms and lie with their unique axes in the plane of the slide (cf. Fig. 2.9). Try to decide to which crystal system these materials belong.

$NaNO_3$ is also uniaxial, and if this is recrystallized on a slide it forms birefringent rhombs showing symmetrical extinction (cf. Fig. 2.10). The birefringence is very high ($\epsilon \sim 1.336$, $\omega \sim 1.587$); if the crystals are immersed in a liquid of refractive index 1.58–1.59, pronounced change in the relief will be observed as the plane of polarized light is rotated. (Remember that all sections through the indicatrix of uniaxial crystals contain ω; see Fig. 2.3.)

Crystals of $FeSO_4 \cdot 7H_2O$ or of phthalic acid are monoclinic and show effects similar to those given by the hypothetical crystals in Fig. 2.6. $FeSO_4 \cdot 7H_2O$ forms more or less equant grains, phthalic acid short tablets, and a search through a number of crystals of either will show that some have parallel and others inclined extinction. Being real crystals rather than an idealized example they behave rather less perfectly than the crystals in Fig. 2.6!

Crystals that form needles or tablets with parallel extinction are very common. Examples are oxalic acid (monoclinic, $b//$needle axis) and potassium sulphate (orthorhombic).

Good examples of pleochroic materials are to be found among transition-metal complexes, and these you will have to prepare yourself. An easy one to prepare is potassium trioxalatochromate (III)trihydrate, $K_3[Cr(C_2O_4)_3] \cdot 3H_2O$. Dissolve 9 g oxalic acid dihydrate in 20 ml of water and *cautiously* add 3 g potassium dichromate. a little at a time, to the warm solution. When the reaction has subsided, heat the solution to boiling and dissolve 3.5 g of potassium oxalate monohydrate in the hot solution; leave to cool. Addition of a few millilitres of ethyl alcohol to the cold solution will precipitate the product, which can be filtered at the pump and washed with a 50/50 alcohol–water mixture. The crystals are blue-green and fibrous; in plane polarized light they appear blue when the light is vibrating parallel to the length of the fibre and brown when it is vibrating across the fibre.

CHAPTER 3

The diffraction of X-rays

3.1   The production of X-rays

At the beginning of the century, Moseley studied the X-ray spectra emitted by atoms that are being bombarded with high-energy electrons. He found that the frequencies of the lines in these spectra were characteristic of the target element, and was thus able to make direct measurements of atomic numbers. These **characteristic X-rays** are used in diffraction experiments, for which it is a great convenience to have monochromatic radiation.

X-rays, like visible light, are a form of electromagnetic radiation; they differ from visible light in having much shorter wavelengths, typically of the order of 1 Å (10^{-1} nm), that is they represent a relatively high-energy form of radiation. The highest energy (highest frequency, shortest wavelength) characteristic X-rays result from the displacement of electrons from the innermost shell, or K-shell, of the target atoms; these are then replaced by electrons from the outer shells, which emit their excess energy as X-rays. Most often they are replaced by electrons from the next shell, resulting in the Kα line (Fig. 3.2). Although for many purposes this can be treated as monochromatic, it is actually a very close doublet, because of the slight energy differences between the 2s and 2p levels; the slightly higher Kα_1 frequency (2p → 1s) predominates over Kα_2 (2s → 1s). A still higher frequency line, Kβ, results from their replacement by electrons from the third shell, but this is a less probable transition and the line is correspondingly much weaker. The K-radiations from elements of intermediate atomic weight have wavelengths comparable to interatomic dimensions and thus are suitable for crystal diffraction experiments.

The essential parts of an X-ray tube are set out in Fig. 3.1. The heated tungsten filament provides a source of electrons, and, if it is maintained at a large negative voltage relative to the target or anode, the electrons are accelerated towards the latter, where they excite X-rays. About 30–50 kV is required to provide sufficient energy to excite reasonable amounts of K-radiation; to prevent the electrons from losing their energy by colliding with gas molecules before they reach the target, the intervening space is evacuated. This arrangement is effectively a diode valve, and if supplied from a high-tension a.c. source will be self-rectifying; many sets are built this way. More sophisticated versions supply rectified, or (better) rectified and smoothed current, and this improves output and tube life.

The negatively charged screen surrounding the tungsten filament serves to focus the electron beam onto the target. The X-rays produced pass out of the tube through windows usually made of beryllium, which when not in use are covered by shutters

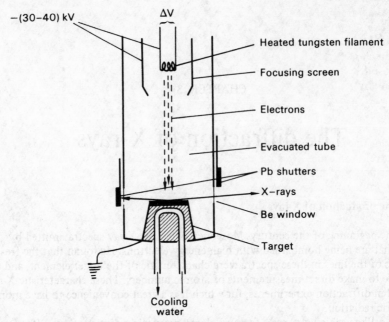

Fig. 3.1 The principles of an X-ray tube (highly diagrammatic). The cathode is
maintained at a high negative voltage relative to the anode or target which is earthed.
A small fraction ΔV, of this high voltage is used to generate a heavy current (of the
order of several amps) in the tungsten filament. The emitted electrons are directed
towards the target by the negatively charged focusing screen.

made of lead. These materials are chosen because they have respectively low and high
absorption coefficients for X-rays, absorption increasing in a general way with atomic
number.

The current carried by the electrons (the **tube current**) is about 20 mA; multiplying
this by the tube voltage shows that the tube consumes about 1 kW. Because the production of X-rays is a very inefficient process, most of this energy appears as heat.
Since for X-ray diffraction experiments the tube must be run for long periods (hours
or days), the target gets hot and must be water-cooled. The X-ray set should have some
sort of safety switch to shut off the power if the water supply becomes inadequate,
'adequate' usually being about 5 l min⁻¹. One of the commonest causes of failure in
X-ray sets is reduction of the water supply by clogged filters; the remedy is to clean
the filters. The trouble may result from connecting the set to the mains with transparent plastic hose; the light admitted through this often results in a splendid growth
of algae. Hoses and their clips should be inspected regularly for signs of deterioration,
if only out of consideration for anyone occupying the rooms below.

The choice of target material depends on several factors. From the engineering
point of view, it should be a good conductor of heat (so that it can be efficiently
cooled) and of electricity (because it has to function as an electrode), which in practice means a metal; it should also have a reasonably high melting point. From the
crystallographer's viewpoint, it should emit X-rays of a convenient wavelength
(0.5–2.0 Å). This limits the choice to the first- and second-row transition metals. The
most widely used material is copper ($\lambda_{K\alpha}$=1.542 Å), which fulfils the above conditions

well. Its chief drawback is that materials containing a high proportion of iron or manganese fluoresce in copper Kα radiation, often producing an unacceptably high level of background 'noise'; in such cases iron, chromium or cobalt radiation can be used. Molybdenum or silver are suitable targets if a short wavelength radiation is required. Since most other metals are poor conductors of heat compared with copper, cooling the target is more difficult. For this reason, the bulk of the target is usually made of copper, with the required metal merely forming a thin surface layer; even so, the output from such a tube is reduced and the beam intensity correspondingly weakened.

It is important not to exceed the power rating of the tube, which is limited by the rate at which heat can be removed from the target; recklessly increasing the tube voltage or current can cause premature failure. Recently, efforts have been made to increase the power of tubes; one method has been to use a rotating anode. Since this is constantly moving, the heat produced by the electron beam is spread over a larger area, and the power input can be correspondingly increased.

X-ray tubes may be permanently sealed after evacuation, or may be **demountable**, with the vacuum maintained by continuous pumping. In the first type, there is no possibility of changing any of the components or of rotating the anode; when the target or windows become coated with tungsten evaporated from the filament (as happens gradually in use) the whole tube has to be replaced. Moreover a different tube is needed for each type of radiation.

However, against the apparent advantages of demountable tubes must be set the extra maintenance required. Most crystallographers use permanently sealed tubes, which are relatively robust and are available for use immediately after switching on. A tube life of several thousand hours can be expected, and can be increased if the tube is not run at the limits of its performance.

The relevant part of the spectrum emitted from an X-ray tube operating under normal conditions is shown in Fig. 3.2. The characteristic lines are superimposed on a continuous background of 'white' radiation emitted by the exciting electrons themselves as they are decelerated at the target; the short wavelength cut-off corresponds to the maximum energy of these electrons, and this varies with the tube voltage. The dotted line represents the absorption curve of an element suitable for use as a β-filter with the given radiation; the vertical portion, or **absorption edge**, corresponds to the energy required to eject K electrons from the filter element. If the atomic number of the filter element is one or two less than that of the target element, the absorption edge lies between the Kα and Kβ wavelengths of the radiation to be filtered. After passing through such a filter, the intensity of the Kβ radiation will be greatly diminished relative to the Kα, and the resulting beam, while not strictly monochromatic, is quite suitable for many diffraction experiments. More sophisticated methods of producing monochromatic beams are sometimes needed, and will be described along with their applications.

X-rays are dangerous. Exposure of small areas of the body to a direct beam can result in nasty burns, while lower levels of radiation absorbed by the whole body can cause genetic mutations and sterility. The former can be avoided by never allowing the direct beam to escape into the room, and the latter by reducing incidental scatter to a minimum. Many sets are provided with safety shutters that interlock with the equipment in use at the windows they protect. These then close automatically whenever operations are in progress that might allow the escape of X-rays. Such devices can be made foolproof but they can seldom be idiot-proof: the maxim should be CARE, always. Anyone who is responsible for X-ray diffraction equipment should be familiar with the local regulations covering hazardous radiations, and should ensure that these are complied with.

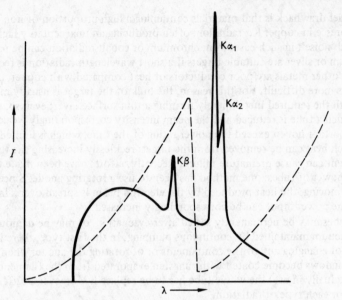

Fig. 3.2   The X-ray spectrum emitted by a typical tube, showing intensity, I, plotted against wavelength, λ. The solid line shows the characteristic radiation bands super-imposed on a background of 'white' radiation. The dotted line shows the absorption characteristics of a material suitable for use as a β-filter, to give approximately mono-chromatic radiation.

3.2   Diffraction of X-rays

The electric fields of X-rays, like those of visible light waves, interact with the electron clouds of atoms. Because of their shorter wavelength, X-rays scattered by adjacent atoms in crystals can interfere and diffraction effects become important. In crystal optics, we were concerned with the effect of the crystal on the direct beam; in X-ray diffraction we are interested not in the direct beam, but in the scattered radiation. The diffraction pattern which the latter produces can tell us much about the internal arrangement of the crystal.

Corresponding to the three-dimensional atomic pattern of the crystal, there is a three-dimensional pattern of electron density, all of which takes part in the scattering of the X-rays. Although at first sight the task of interpreting the resulting diffraction effects appears rather daunting, the problem is greatly simplified by tackling it in two stages. The first considers the geometry of the interaction of X-rays with a simple periodic arrangement consisting of a primitive lattice with a single electron (considered in this context to be a particle) at each point (Fig. 3.3(a)); the second modifies the conclusions drawn from this highly artificial model to take account of the arrangement of electron density within each pattern unit of the real crystal.

When a beam of X-rays strikes an array of electrons such as that shown in Fig. 3.3(a), each electron scatters some of the radiation in all directions. In general, the radiation scattered by adjacent electrons is not in phase; only when it is will reinforce-

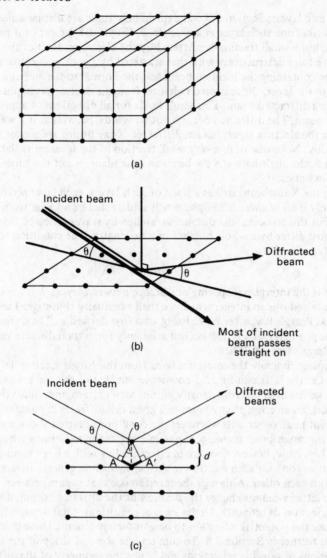

Fig. 3.3   The diffraction of X-rays. (a) a 'single electron lattice'. Each dot represents an electron; points behind the surface layers are omitted for clarity. (b) The inter-action of an X-ray beam with the top layer of the lattice. (c) The interaction of the beam with subsequent layers in the stack; d is the distance between successive layers. The thickened line AA' represents the path difference between beams reflected from adjacent layers. Reinforcement will occur only when this is a whole number of wave-lengths ($n\lambda$).

ment occur and a diffracted beam be observed. It is not too difficult to work out the conditions for this; the following derivation is pictorial rather than rigorous, but leads to the right result.

The array shown in Fig. 3.3(a) can be regarded as a stack of parallel layers each like that shown in Fig. 3.3(b). (There are of course other ways in which the stack could be

divided into layers; Section 3.3 will explain how these are distinguished.) If a beam of
X-rays strikes one such layer at any angle, θ, (Fig. 3.3(b)) most of it passes straight
through, but a small fraction is scattered by the electrons. Most of the scattered radiation interferes destructively with that scattered by the other electrons. However, in
the plane containing the incident beam and the normal to the electron layer, and at an
angle θ to the layer, the scattered radiation from all electrons is in phase, and hence
produces a diffracted beam. This result holds for all directions of approach by the
incident beam. The diffracted beam, in other words, behaves as if it were being *reflected* from the electron layer; in fact, diffracted X-ray beams are almost invariably called
'reflections'. Note that only a very small fraction of the incident radiation is reflected
and that θ, the angle between the beam and the plane, is not the 'angle of incidence' as
defined in optics.

When the X-ray beam strikes a stack of such layers, each layer produces a reflected
beam; only if all of *these* are in phase will a diffracted beam arise from the stack as a
whole. For this to occur, the distances travelled by waves reflected from successive
layers must differ by a whole number of wavelengths. The condition for this is shown in
Fig. 3.3(c); it is that

$$2d \sin \theta = n\lambda$$

where d is the **interplanar spacing** or distance between layers, λ is the wavelength of
the X-rays and n is an integer which we shall eventually eliminate. This relationship is
known as Bragg's law, after W. L. Bragg who first derived it. The diffracted beams thus
fulfil the geometry of a reflection but arise only for certain discrete values of θ for
which Bragg's law is fulfilled.

It remains to apply the result obtained from this 'single electron lattice' to a real
crystal. Let the lattice in Fig. 3.3 now represent that of the real crystal with a continuous variation of electron density within each pattern unit. Since this arrangement
is periodic, an electron at any point in a given cell diffracts in phase with those at the
same point in all other cells whenever the conditions derived above are fulfilled. In this
respect the situation is unchanged: possible angles for reflections are still predicted by
Bragg's law. Now, however, we are in effect dealing with a large number of single electron lattices (one for each electron in the cell) which in general do *not* all diffract in
phase with each other. Although the interference that occurs between the different
electron lattices cannot change the *position* of the diffracted beam, it will have a profound effect on its *intensity*. Under certain conditions, total destructive interference
may cause the potential reflection to be completely absent. These points will be
explored further in Section 3.4. To sum up, the size and shape of the unit cell control
the positions of possible reflections and hence the geometry of the diffraction pattern;
the intensity of the individual reflections is controlled by the distribution of electron
density within the cell.

The diffraction pattern is usually recorded either by allowing the diffracted beams
to strike and blacken photographic film (Figs. 4.4, 4.11 and 6.8 show some typical
patterns recorded in this way), or by measuring the diffracted radiation with some
form of counter. The relative merits of the two methods will be considered in the
appropriate places.

3.3 Indices

In the last section, we derived the conditions for diffraction from a set of layers or
planes within a crystal lattice without specifying which set was being discussed. Plainly

this will not do; we need a way of labelling the planes, and this is done with three integers called **indices**. A set of planes whose indices are h, k and l intercepts the x, y and z-axes at intervals of a/h, b/k and c/l respectively.

This is illustrated in Fig. 3.4, using a two-dimensional lattice for the sake of clarity; only two of the three indices are then needed, and the planes become lines. The set of

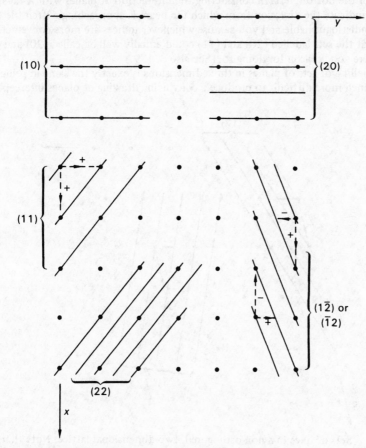

Fig. 3.4   Indices of sets of lines in a two-dimensional lattice.

lines at the top left of the diagram intercepts the x-axis at intervals of a, or one whole cell edge, so $h = 1$; the lines are parallel to the y-axis, which means that they intercept it at infinity, so $k = 0$. The indices for this set of lines are thus (10) (we say 'one-oh', not ten). To the right is shown a parallel set of lines at half the spacing; these cut the x-axis at intervals of $a/2$, and are thus the (20) lines. At the lower left, the (11) and (22) sets of lines intercept the x- and y-axes at intervals of a, b, and $a/2$, $b/2$, respectively.

The remaining set of lines (lower right) cuts the x-axis at intervals of a and the y-axis at $b/2$; to get from one line to the next, however, if we count the x intercept in the positive direction, then the y intercept will be in the negative one and *vice versa* (compare the directions of the dotted arrows with those in the (11) lines). This is expressed by making one of the indices negative, that is by writing $(1\bar{2})$ or $(\bar{1}2)$. In the orthogonal array in Fig. 3.4, the spacing between lines is the same as it would be for the (12) set, but this will not always be true as can be seen from Fig. 3.5.

The question now arises as to which is correct—$(1\bar{2})$ or $(\bar{1}2)$? Reference to Fig. 3.4 suggests that the correct choice depends on whether the lines are approached from the top right or the bottom left. In considering the interaction of planes with X-rays, the signs thus indicate the direction from which the beam is approaching. Often the two cases are indistinguishable and you can use whichever indices are more convenient. It follows that the sets labelled (20) and (11) could equally well be called $(\bar{2}0)$ and $(\bar{1}\bar{1})$ if there were good reason for doing so. (See also p. 179.)

The labelling of sets of planes in three dimensions is exactly the same in principle, but it is much more difficult to produce a convincing drawing of planes intercepting

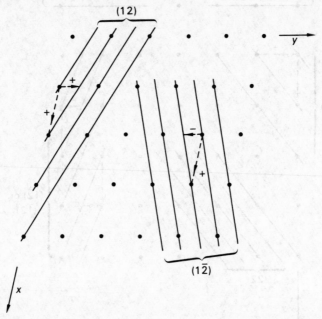

Fig. 3.5   Sets of lines in a non-orthogonal, two-dimensional lattice. Note that the spacing of the (12) lines differs from that of the $(1\bar{2})$ lines.

three axes than of lines intercepting two. Figure 3.6 shows two attempts. Figure 3.6(a) shows a set of (020) planes in relation to a lattice; Fig. 3.6(b) shows the (213) planes of the same lattice in terms of their intercepts on the axes.†

We can now reconsider the integer n in the Bragg equation. Figure 3.7(a) shows the formation of the first-order reflection ($n = 1$) from the (100) planes; Fig. 3.7(b) shows the formation of the second-order reflection ($n = 2$) from the same set of planes.

---

† Readers with a knowledge of mineralogy will recognize that these indices are related to the Miller indices used to specify the faces of crystals. The Miller indices, however, never contain a common factor (as in, say, (020) or (222) which would be reduced to (010) and (111) respectively), and when dealing with external form, differentiation between (hkl) and $(\bar{h}\bar{k}\bar{l})$ may be more important.

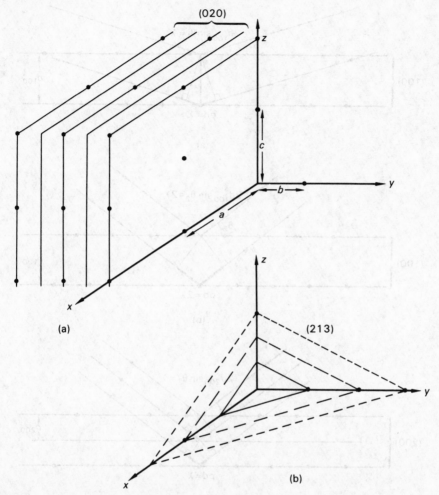

Fig. 3.6 Sets of planes in a three-dimensional lattice. (a) The (020) planes drawn in relation to the lattice; lattice points behind the surface are omitted for clarity. (b) The (213) planes of the same lattice shown in terms of their intercepts on the axes.

Figure 3.7(c) shows that the latter is geometrically equivalent to the first-order reflection from a set of parallel planes with half the spacing, that is the (200) planes. In other words, the *n* can be absorbed in the indices; we speak not of 'the second-order 100 reflection' but of 'the 200 reflection' and so on. Note the omission of the brackets from the indices of a reflection; the set of (*hkl*) planes gives rise to the *hkl* reflection.

The remarks made regarding the choice of signs of indices in two dimensions apply equally in three. The (*hkl*) and ($\overline{hkl}$) planes are indistinguishable if the crystal is centrosymmetric. Even if it is not, the *hkl* and $\overline{hkl}$ reflections are normally identical in intensity; crystals for which this is true are said to obey **Friedel's law**. Crudely expressed, this means that, so long as the Bragg condition is fulfilled, it usually does not matter from which side of a given set of planes the X-ray beam approaches; for

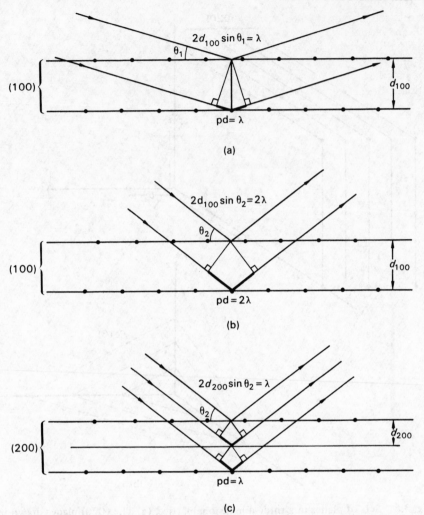

Fig. 3.7   Formation of (a) the first-order reflection from the (100) planes, (b) the second-order reflection from the (100) planes and (c) the first-order reflection from the (200) planes; pd = path difference. Note that (b) and (c) are merely different ways of describing the same reflection. The dots represent lattice points.

example in Fig. 3.7 the beam could equally well have been shown approaching from the bottom of the page. We shall assume that Friedel's law is obeyed, unless otherwise stated. Exceptions are discussed on p. 179.

3.4   Information received

The practical process of obtaining information about a crystal structure from a study of its diffraction pattern falls roughly into two stages, corresponding to the two stages in the argument used in Section 3.2. The first step is to study the positions of the diffracted beams, with the object of determining the size and shape of the unit cell. The second is to study the intensity of the beams, with the object of deducing details of the atomic arrangement within the cell. Both these processes will be described in some detail in the following chapters; meanwhile to get a general picture of the way in which the atomic arrangement affects the intensities of diffracted beams, let us consider diffraction from two simple crystalline substances.

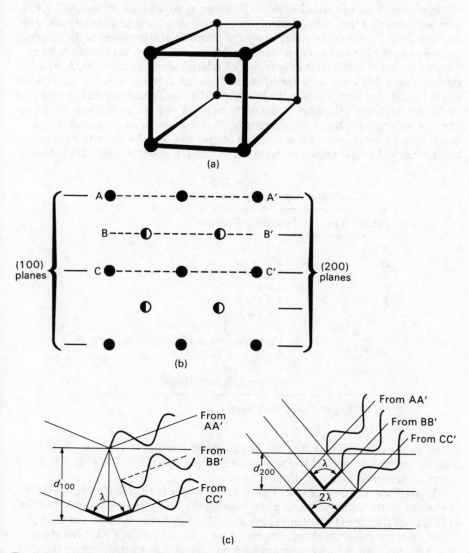

Fig. 3.8   (a) The body-centred structure of α-Fe, shown in perspective. (b) The structure of α-Fe projected down c. Full circles represent Fe atoms at 0, c, $2c$, etc; half-filled circles represent Fe atoms at $c/2$, $3c/2$, etc. The (100) and (200) planes are indicated. (c) The Bragg condition for the formation of the 100 and 200 reflections. In the former, waves from the centreing (BB') exactly cancel those from the corner atoms, and the reflection has zero intensity.

The first, α-Fe, has a body-centred cubic lattice, with an Fe atom at each lattice point (Fig. 3.8(a)). The atoms are finite in size and vibrating about their mean positions; both these facts can be allowed for, but it will not affect the present argument if, for convenience, we treat the atoms as stationary points. The condition given by the Bragg equation for the formation of the 100 reflection is that waves reflected from successive (100) planes (Fig. 3.8(b), left-hand side) have a path difference of one wavelength. This means that the waves scattered by the atoms (strictly, by their electrons) at the corners of the cell are all in phase. However, as pointed out in Section 3.2, this does not mean that they will necessarily be in phase with those scattered by the other atoms in the cell. In α-Fe, an equal number of atoms lie at the centres of the cells, and these also scatter in phase with one another. What is more, they are exactly halfway between the set of (100) planes illustrated, on which the corner atoms lie. A little thought shows that when the wave diffracted from the atoms in layer CC' is one wavelength behind that from atoms in the layer AA' (the Bragg condition for the formation of the 100 reflection), the wave from the atoms in BB' will be one half-wavelength out of phase with either (Fig. 3.8(c)). The net result is that the waves diffracted by the corner atoms exactly cancel those from the centre ones, and the 100 reflection has zero intensity. The 200 reflection, on the other hand, is strong; for the (200) planes,

TABLE 3.1

Conditions imposed by various types of centreing

Lattice type	Possible reflections
A	$k + l = 2n$
B	$h + l = 2n$
C	$h + k = 2n$
I	$h + k + l = 2n$
F	$\left.\begin{array}{l} h + k = 2n \\ k + l = 2n \\ h + l = 2n \end{array}\right\}$
	(h, k and l are either all odd or all even)
$R^{(1)}$	or $\left.\begin{array}{l} h - k + l = 3n \\ h - k - l = 3n \end{array}\right\}$
	(depending on setting)

[1] On trigonal axes; see Chapter 1.

shown on the right of Fig. 3.8(b), the Bragg condition is that waves from BB' and CC' shall be respectively one and two wavelengths behind those from AA' (Fig. 3.8(c)); all atoms consequently scatter in phase.

The argument can be extended. Figure 3.9 shows the (110) and (120) planes; for the former all the atoms scatter in phase, making the 110 reflection strong, while the (120) planes (like the (100) planes) have atoms halfway between them, and the 120 reflection is consequently absent. In general, all reflections with ($h + k + l$) odd are absent for this reason. This can be proved more formally, as we shall see; for the present the important thing is that the idea be grasped in a qualitative way.

Any crystal with a centred lattice shows **systematic absences** of this kind; indeed this is how centreing is detected. The rules for lattice absences are summarized in Table 3.1; if you have followed the argument so far, you should be able to work out the reasons for them (except perhaps for rhombohedral, which is, as ever, difficult).

Returning to Fig. 3.8, let us now suppose that the atoms at the cell corners are Cs and those at the centre Cl. The diagram then represents the CsCl structure, with each Cs ion surrounded by eight Cl ions at the corners of a cube, and *vice versa*.

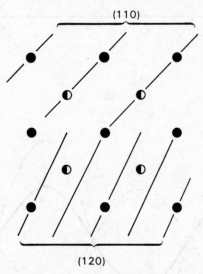

(110)

(120)

Fig. 3.9   The (110) and (120) planes in α-Fe.

Since the atoms at the cell corners are no longer identical with those at the centres, the lattice is primitive, not body-centred. Figure 3.10 shows the effect of this on reflections with $(h + k + l)$ odd. In α-Fe, waves from the atoms at the cell corners are exactly out of phase with *and* exactly equal in amplitude to those from the centreing atoms (Fig. 3.10(a)). In CsCl, waves from the corner (Cs) atoms are still exactly out of phase with those from the centreing (Cl) atoms, but since Cs has more electrons than Cl, the amplitudes are no longer the same. Consequently, the scattered waves do not cancel entirely, though the amplitude of the resultant wave (Fig. 3.10(b)) is reduced relative to those from planes with $(h + k + l)$ even. Reflections with $(h + k + l)$ odd are thus weaker than the others.

These very simple examples show how the cell contents govern the intensities of the diffracted beams. In more complicated structures, it is difficult to use such a qualitative approach and the amplitude of the resultant wave is usually calculated mathematically. Nevertheless, it is important to remember that the mathematical formulae are a convenient way of expressing the physical realities discussed above, and not just an arbitrary collection of symbols.

The general expression for any crystal is complex:

$$F_{hkl} = \sum_{r=1}^{N} f_r \exp 2\pi i (hx_r + ky_r + lz_r)$$

This can be rewritten in the form

$$F_{hkl} = \sum_{r=1}^{N} f_r \{\cos 2\pi(hx_r + ky_r + lz_r) + i \sin 2\pi(hx_r + ky_r + lz_r)\}$$

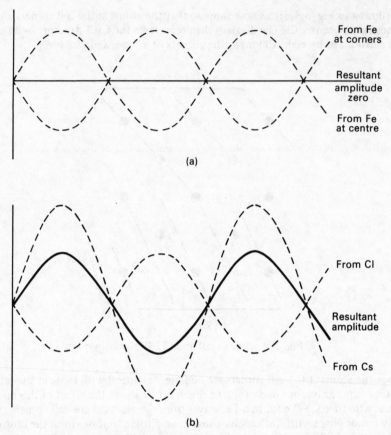

Fig. 3.10   Resultant amplitudes of waves corresponding to reflections with $(h + k + l)$ odd in (a) α-Fe and (b) CsCl.

F_{hkl}, the **structure factor** for the set of planes concerned, is thus obtained by summing the waves diffracted by each of the N atoms in the cell. Each term in the summation represents one such wave; its amplitude is given by f_r, the **scattering factor** (or **form factor**) for the rth atom, and its relative phase by the rest of the term in which x_r, etc., are the fractional coordinates of the rth atom. The value of f_r depends on the number of electrons in the atom concerned, and also (for reasons that will be discussed later) on the angle θ at which the reflection occurs.

If there is a centre of symmetry at the origin of the unit cell, then for every atom with coordinates x_r, y_r, z_r there is an identical atom at $-x_r, -y_r, -z_r$, and since $\sin(-X) = -\sin(X)$, the imaginary part of the expression vanishes, leaving a simplified form involving only the cosine terms:

$$F_{hkl} = \sum_{r=1}^{N} f_r \cos 2\pi(hx_r + ky_r + lz_r)$$

This is the form that will generally be used in the text, in order to keep things relatively simple, but it should be borne in mind that for non-centrosymmetric crystals the complex expression must, in general, be used instead.

If only one of each pair of centrosymmetrically related atoms is included in the summation, the expression may be written:

$$F_{hkl} = 2 \sum_{r=1}^{N/2} f_r \cos 2\pi(hx_r + ky_r + lz_r)$$

provided that there are no atoms situated on the centres of symmetry. The examples that follow are drawn from relatively simple substances that *do* have atoms so situated, so the other form of the expression will be used.

Substituting the coordinates of the two atoms in the cell of α-Fe, we get:

$$F_{hkl} = f_{Fe} \cos 2\pi(h0 + k0 + l0) + f_{Fe} \cos 2\pi(h\tfrac{1}{2} + k\tfrac{1}{2} + l\tfrac{1}{2})$$

$$= f_{Fe}[\cos 0 + \cos(h + k + l)\pi]$$

Since $\cos 0 = 1$, and $\cos(h + k + l)\pi = 1$ if $(h + k + l)$ is even
and $\cos(h + k + l)\pi = -1$ if $(h + k + l)$ is odd

then: F_{hkl} is $2f_{Fe}$ or 0 respectively, which agrees with the result arrived at previously.

Similarly, for CsCl

$$F_{hkl} = f_{Cs} + f_{Cl} \text{ when } (h + k + l) \text{ is even and}$$
$$= f_{Cs} - f_{Cl} \text{ when } (h + k + l) \text{ is odd}$$

again in line with our previous deductions.

3.5   The reciprocal lattice

We are now able to predict the angle that the reflection from a given set of planes will make with the direct beam, and conversely we could calculate d-spacings from a powder pattern (Figs. 6.2 and 6.8), obtained, as its name implies, from a randomly oriented, powdered specimen. The interpretation of **single crystal** photographs (Figs. 4.4, 4.11 and 4.21) is however made much easier by the introduction of a little more theory.

This is best approached by way of analogy with optical diffraction patterns. You may be familiar with the appearance of the pattern produced when a distant street lamp is viewed through fine material, such as a silk umbrella or a fibreglass curtain. Figure 3.11(a) shows such an arrangement of fibres and Fig. 3.11(b) the pattern of diffracted light observed. Successive orders of beams diffracted by the vertical fibres form a horizontal row of points of light, and *vice versa* (cf. Fig. 3.11(c)); if 'x' and 'y' axes are defined in the fabric so that the vertical fibres define the (01) lines in the two-dimensional lattice (cf. Fig. 3.4), the horizontal row of diffracted beams can be indexed as in Fig. 3.11(b). Because the wavelength of light is very short compared with the spacing of the fibres, the angles through which the beams are diffracted are small, so the 02 beam is about twice as far from the centre of the pattern as the 01 (and the 03 three times as far), that is the spacing of the points of light in the diffraction pattern is roughly inversely proportional to the spacing of the lines in the lattice that give rise to them. The $h0$ row of points of light can similarly be associated with diffraction

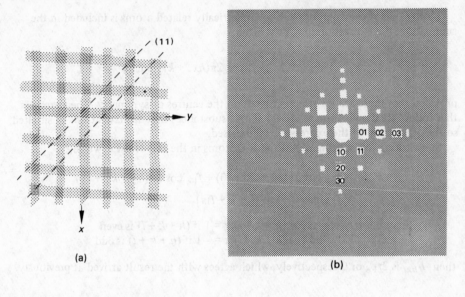

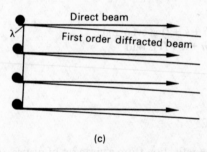

Fig. 3.11   The relation between gratings and diffraction patterns. (a) A two-dimensional grating such as a fine-woven cloth. (b) The pattern seen when a distant light is viewed through a cloth such as that in (a). (c) Demonstrates that because the wavelength of light is very short compared with the spacing of the cloth, the diffraction angles are very small. The second order, or 02, beam is thus roughly twice as far from the centre of the pattern as the first.

by the horizontal fibres, and the point labelled 11 with diffraction by the correspondingly labelled lines in the fabric; the same principle applies to other values of h and k. Note that the pattern of diffracted light itself forms a lattice.

The formation of an X-ray diffraction pattern by a crystal is an analogous process in three dimensions. Interpreting the pattern is greatly simplified if we redefine the crystal 'grating' in terms of the directions and spacings of the lattice planes; in so doing we produce a three-dimensional array of points analogous to the two-dimensional array in Fig. 3.11(b); because of the inverse relation between the spacing of the points and the planes giving rise to them, this is called the **reciprocal lattice**.

Figure 3.12(a) and (b) shows how this is constructed, and also serves to formalize the relation between Fig. 3.11(a) and (b). For simplicity we begin with an orthogonal lattice, reduce it to two dimensions by projecting it down c, and deal only with planes

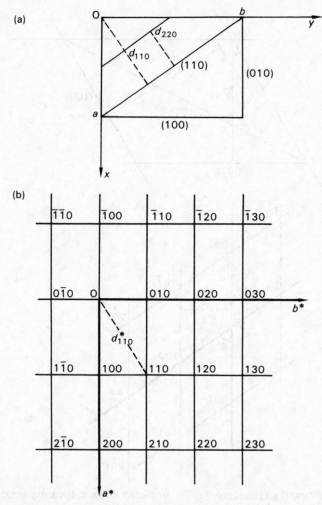

Fig. 3.12 (a) Part of an orthogonal lattice projected down c. (b) Part of the corresponding reciprocal lattice. If $a^* = 0.30$ r.u., use a ruler to find b^*. If $\lambda = 1.542$ Å, calculate a and b, and hence the scale to which (a) is drawn. Use these results to convince yourself, by direct measurement, that $d^*_{110} = \lambda/d_{110}$.

whose l index is zero. From a point O within the crystal lattice, or **real** or **direct** lattice (Fig. 3.12(a)), lines are constructed perpendicular to the lattice planes; these are then marked off at distances inversely proportional to the interplanar spacings. If the distance d^* in reciprocal space is taken as $1/d$, the dimensions of the reciprocal lattice will be Å^{-1}, or reciprocal ångstroms, but for the interpretation of diffraction patterns it is usually more convenient to take $d^* = \lambda/d$, where λ is the wavelength of the X-rays used. In this case d^* is measured in dimensionless **reciprocal units** (r.u.).

From O in Fig. 3.12(a), therefore, a line is drawn perpendicular to (100); this is the line labelled a^* in Fig. 3.12(b), and because the real lattice is orthogonal it is parallel to a. Using a suitable scale, a distance is marked off along this line proportional to $1/d_{(100)}$, thus defining the reciprocal lattice point labelled 100. The (200) plane is of

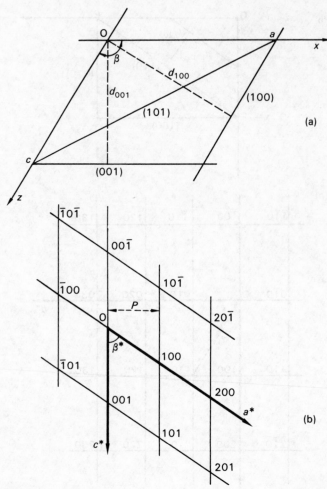

Fig. 3.13   (a) Part of a monoclinic lattice protected down b, the unique axis. (b) The corresponding reciprocal lattice.

Note that $a^* = \lambda/a \sin \beta = \lambda/d_{100}$, and conversely that $a = \lambda/a^* \sin \beta^* = \lambda/P$, where P is the perpendicular distance between rows of reciprocal lattice points. If, on this diagram, $c^* = 0.30$ r.u., use a ruler and protractor to determine a^*, β^* and P. Calculate a and convince yourself that both expressions give the same answer; calculate c (assume $\lambda = 1.542$ Å). Measure d_{101} from the diagram of the real lattice. Compare the value with that calculated from d^*_{101} measured on the reciprocal lattice.

course parallel to the (100), but with half the spacing; the 200 reciprocal lattice point thus also lies along a^*, but twice as far from the origin as 100. The positions of the other $h00$ points are similarly determined.

Similarly, the $0k0$ points lie along a line perpendicular to (010), labelled b^* in Fig. 3.12(b); again, since the lattice is orthogonal, b^* is parallel to b. The same is true of the c^* direction, which is not shown; note that a^*, etc. are commonly used to denote both the direction and length of the reciprocal axes. In the example shown, a is $2/3b$, and $d_{(100)} = 2/3\, d_{(010)}$, so that $a^* = 3/2\, b^*$ and the point marked 100 is one and a half times as far from the origin as that marked 010.

Generation of the non-axial points follows the same principles. For example, the line marked $d^*_{(110)}$ in Fig. 3.12(b) is perpendicular to the (110) plane in Fig. 3.12(a). Application of Pythagoras' theorem will show that marking off a distance along it proportional to $1/d_{(110)}$ completes the rectangle outlined with heavy lines in Fig. 3.12(b); this represents the projection of the reciprocal unit cell down c^*.

For non-orthogonal lattices, the relation between real and reciprocal lattice is less straightforward. The construction for a monoclinic lattice is shown in Fig. 3.13; β^* is

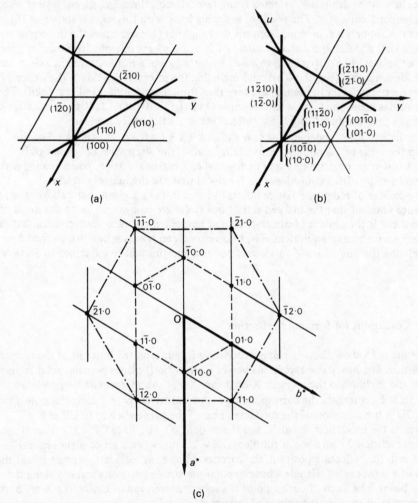

(a)

(b)

(c)

Fig. 3.14 Assigning indices to trigonal and hexagonal lattices. (a) When indices are assigned relative to two axes perpendicular to c, equivalent planes have indices that appear to be different. (b) Introducing a third axis u and an extra index i makes the equivalence more apparent; since $i = -(h + k)$ it is often omitted. (c) The corresponding reciprocal lattice, with equivalent reflections linked by dashed lines. (Note that it is not possible to define a third axis in reciprocal space that corresponds to u in real space.)

If $a^* = 0.120$ r.u., $\lambda = 1.542$ Å, calculate a; then use the value of a to calculate $d_{10.0}$. Check your working by recalculating a^*.

$180° - \beta$, and only b^* is parallel to the corresponding real axis. For triclinic crystals, none of the reciprocal axes need be parallel to the corresponding real one, and the trigonometry relating real and reciprocal cell is complicated; it is summarized in the Appendix. The important thing to remember is that for all systems, *by definition*, a^* is perpendicular to (100), and so on.

Trigonal and hexagonal crystals are a fruitful source of confusion, both in assigning indices to planes and in relating real and reciprocal lattices. The crystallographic *a* and *b* axes have to be arbitrarily selected from, respectively, three and six equivalent directions perpendicular to *c*. The result of assigning indices on this basis is shown in Fig. 3.14(a). Although it is obvious from the drawing that (for example) the three planes (110), (1$\bar{2}$0) and ($\bar{2}$10) are all equivalent, it is by no means obvious from an inspection of their indices. The difficulty is resolved by introducing a third equivalent axis in real space, designated *u* (Fig. 3.14(b)), and including the intercept on this in the indices. Planes on trigonal and hexagonal axes are thus formally given *four* indices: (*hkil*). The three planes mentioned above thus become (11$\bar{2}$0), (1$\bar{2}$10) and ($\bar{2}$110); permutation of *h, k* and *i* then produces equivalent reflections in a satisfactory manner.

The index *i* is not independent of *h* and *k*; $h + k + i = 0$, or $i = -(h + k)$. For this reason the value of *i* is not always explicitly stated; the alternative notation (*hk.l*) (Fig. 3.14(b)) automatically implies a trigonal or hexagonal lattice. When dealing with any problem involving equivalences it is helpful to write the indices out in full.

The indices of reciprocal lattice points in Fig. 3.14(c) are given in the short form; convince yourself that the marked reflections really *are* equivalent. Since the shape of the unit cell is the same for both trigonal and hexagonal crystals, the reciprocal lattices are also *geometrically* equivalent. The two systems can however be distinguished by considering the intensities of various reflections, and this will be explained in Section 3.7.

3.6   Conditions for forming a reflection

Figure 3.15 shows how the Bragg condition is reinterpreted in terms of the reciprocal lattice. The heavy line represents one of a set of (*hkl*) planes perpendicular to the paper and inclined to the incident X-ray beam XO at the appropriate Bragg angle θ. The point P represents the corresponding reciprocal lattice point, using the scale $d^* = \lambda/d$; OD is the direction of the diffracted beam. The perpendicular to OP at P intersects the incident beam at X, and the angle PXO $= \theta$. Since OP $= \lambda/d$, then if the Bragg condition $2d \sin \theta = \lambda$ is fulfilled, OX $= 2$. Thus when a set of planes in real space is in the reflecting position, the corresponding reciprocal lattice point P is at the apex of a right-angled triangle whose hypotenuse equals two units and lies along the X-ray beam. The locus of such a point is a sphere of unit radius having the X-ray beam as diameter; it is called the **sphere of reflection**.

The line CP from the centre of the sphere to P is parallel to OD, and hence to the diffracted beam. In fact, the most convenient way of interpreting diffraction effects, described in the next chapter, is to imagine the crystal to be at C, while the origin of the corresponding reciprocal lattice remains at O. This apparent 'fiddle' can be justified on the basis that the reciprocal lattice is concerned with *directions* within the crystal, and so long as the angular relationships are maintained the two lattices need not have a common origin; the fact that *it works* will probably be sufficient justification for most people.

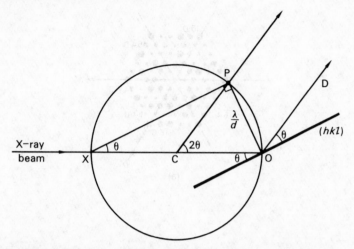

Fig. 3.15   The Bragg equation interpreted in terms of the reciprocal lattice. The heavy line through O represents one of a set of planes that is in the reflecting position; P is the corresponding reciprocal lattice point. The direction of the diffracted beam is given by OD if the crystal is considered to be at O, and by CP if, as in the usual construction, it is assumed to be at C while the origin of the reciprocal lattice remains at O.

To record a diffraction pattern, the crystal at C is usually rotated or oscillated in some way; the reciprocal lattice with its origin at O moves in parallel with it. The sphere of reflection is, of course, stationary, and each time a reciprocal lattice point passes through its surface, the Bragg condition for the corresponding set of planes is satisfied. A reflected beam is then momentarily produced and its direction is given by the line CP joining the crystal to where the reciprocal lattice point intersects the sphere of reflection. Chapter 4 will show how helpful this construction is in interpreting single crystal photographs.

3.7   The weighted reciprocal lattice

The purpose of introducing the reciprocal lattice is to provide a convenient way of visualizing and describing the diffraction pattern of the corresponding crystal. The picture that the reciprocal lattice provides is improved by assigning to each point a weight proportional to the intensity of the corresponding reflection. The resulting **weighted reciprocal lattice** (Fig. 3.16) is usually drawn by marking each point with a dot whose size is roughly proportional to the observed intensity.

Weighting the points in this way brings out the relationship between the symmetry of the crystal and the symmetry of its diffraction pattern. Assuming that Friedel's law (Section 3.3, p. 53) is obeyed, a diffraction pattern will display the point symmetry of the crystal that gives rise to it plus *a centre of symmetry*; this combination is called the **Laue symmetry** of the crystal.

This is illustrated in Fig. 3.16, which also amplifies a point made on p. 64. Figure 3.16(a) shows part of the zero layer of the weighted reciprocal lattice of a trigonal or

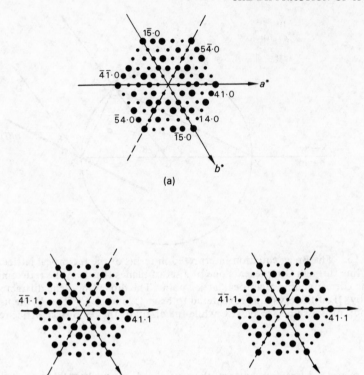

Fig. 3.16   Weighted reciprocal lattices. (a) Zero layer, trigonal or hexagonal, (b) First layer, trigonal. (c) First layer, hexagonal. If $a^* = 0.10$ Å^{-1}, what is a?

hexagonal crystal. The crystal system cannot be deduced from this layer alone; the apparent six-fold symmetry could result either from a six-fold axis in the crystal, or from a three-fold axis (which makes, for example, 41.0, $\bar{5}$4.0 and 1$\bar{5}$.0 equivalent) plus the operation of Friedel's law (which makes 41.0 $\equiv$ $\bar{4}\bar{1}$.0, etc.). However, it *is* possible to deduce that the crystal has no two-fold symmetry perpendicular to the three- or six-fold axis; if it had, pairs of reflections such as (for example) 41.0 and 14.0, or 41.0 and 5$\bar{1}$.0, should have equal intensity and they plainly do not. Upper levels of the weighted reciprocal lattice distinguish the two systems. Friedel's law does not affect the relative intensities of pairs of reflections such as 41.1 and $\bar{4}\bar{1}$.1, or in general of any hk . l and $\bar{h}\bar{k}$. l pairs; if these are all equivalent there must be a six-fold axis in the crystal.

   The geometrical arrangements of the points in the two patterns shown in Fig. 3.17 are the same, but the symmetries of the weighted patterns are quite different. In (a), a centred orthogonal cell should be chosen with its axes lying along the symmetry lines in the pattern. In (b), the presence of an orthogonal grid is not reflected in the symmetry of the pattern, and a primitive unit cell such as that indicated would normally be chosen. These patterns might represent the $h0l$ levels of a centred orthorhombic and a monoclinic crystal respectively.

   The $hk0$ and $0kl$ levels of monoclinic crystals normally show two lines of symmetry. Suppose that Fig. 3.18(a) represents the $hk0$ level of the weighted reciprocal lattice of a crystal whose point group is 2. The operation of the two-fold axis makes

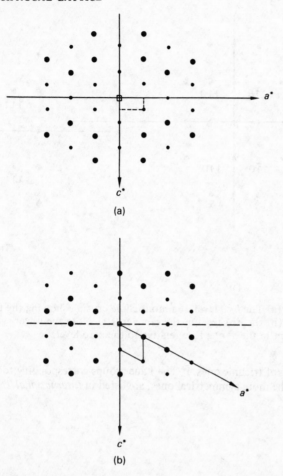

Fig. 3.17 Two arrays of points based on the same grid, but displaying different symmetries. An array like that in (a) might be observed when a centred orthorhombic crystal is being examined. Despite the orthogonal grid, the array in (b) must arise from a crystal of lower than orthorhombic symmetry.

$hk0$ and $\bar{h}k0$ equivalent in intensity; if Friedel's law is obeyed $\bar{h}\bar{k}0$ and $h\bar{k}0$ have the same intensity as well. Some sets of equivalent reflections are marked on the diagram. The $hk1$ and $\bar{h}k1$ reflections of Fig. 3.18(b) however are not related by the two-fold axis and therefore not equivalent; the two-fold axis makes $\bar{h}k\bar{1}$ (not shown) equivalent to $hk1$, and Friedel's law gives $h\bar{k}1$ the same intensity. Consequently the $hk1$ (and $hk2$, etc.) level has only one symmetry direction, although the array is still orthogonal. Unless $\beta = 90°$ it will be slightly displaced in the a^*c^* plane relative to the $hk0$ level. Similar considerations apply to the $0kl$, $1kl$, etc., levels.

As an exercise, satisfy yourself that similar relationships result if one begins with the assumption that the point group of the crystal is m. In fact the Laue group of all monoclinic crystals is the same, $2/m$; that of all orthorhombic ones is mmm (exercise: prove this by adding a centre of symmetry to 222 and finding the total symmetry that

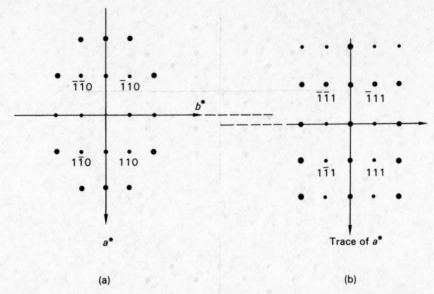

(a)   (b)

Fig. 3.18   (a) The $hk0$ level of a monoclinic crystal, showing the two directions of symmetry. (b) the $hk1$ level of the same crystal. Note the lower symmetry, and the displacement in the a^*c^* plane relative to the zero level.

results) and of triclinic ones, $\bar{1}$. The Laue groups corresponding to all point groups, including the more symmetrical ones, are listed in *International Tables*, Vol. I, pp. 351-2.

CHAPTER 4

Single crystal diffraction photographs

4.1 Selecting and mounting crystals

Before a single crystal diffraction photograph can be taken, a single crystal has to be found; both the quality of the final photographs and the ease with which they are obtained may depend on the care used in selecting and mounting this crystal. Usually it is best to start by examining a little of the sample or preparation under the polarizing microscope; this will help you to decide whether it is likely to contain suitable crystals, and may also serve to warn you if it contains more than one phase. (Bitter experience teaches that if a preparation is mainly tiny fibres, the one or two well-crystallized prisms that can be seen will usually *not* be the same phase as the bulk of the specimen.) If the material looks promising, you can then select the most suitable crystal for your purpose. A study of its shape and optics will save time in orienting it suitably.

The crystal selected should be of a suitable size. For accurate intensity work choose one whose largest dimension is about 0.1–0.5 mm (according to its composition: see p. 192); for a preliminary survey of cell dimensions and symmetry you can use a larger one to cut down film exposure times. Do not choose *too* large a crystal: it is impossible to get decent results from 'rocks' 3 mm long. If all the crystals are as large as this, they may have to be cut or cleaved with a razor blade or partially redissolved or even crushed, according to their nature, or alternatively recrystallized as described in Chapter 2. In many fields of study, the problem is more likely to be that of finding a crystal big enough to mount. If a preparation has yielded only very tiny crystals, time spent in trying to prepare larger ones will probably be time saved in the long run. Often the quality of the crystals improves with successive preparations, even though the conditions have not been changed. This may have something to do with the presence of nuclei in the environment, or if the material crystallizes from solution successive recrystallizations may remove impurities that if adsorbed onto the surface of the tiny crystals inhibit their growth. A good general rule is that slow growth favours better crystals; if the rate of crystallization can be controlled it should be adjusted with this in mind. If the crystals are being grown from the melt, then the temperature should be lowered very slowly through the freezing point; if they are being grown from solution, care should be taken to keep the degree of supersaturation low, particularly while the first crystals are forming.

The selected crystal should if possible have clean outlines, with no other crystals sticking to it. If it is birefringent it should extinguish cleanly, that is all at once. Avoid crystals that show wavy extinction, or patterns like those in Fig. 4.1. The latter are

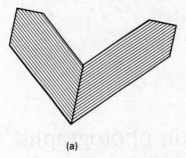
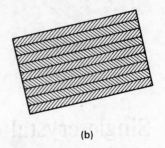

(a)   (b)

Fig. 4.1   Twinning in crystals. The extinction directions of the different individuals are indicated by the lines in the shading.

twinned; they consist of two or more individuals grown together in some definite orientation. Twins such as those shown in Fig. 4.1(a) can sometimes be separated, but some, such as the lamellar twin shown in Fig. 4.1(b), are quite intractable. Twinning can be a problem; sometimes working with twins cannot be avoided and one just has to make the best of it, but interpreting the results can be very tedious and discouraging, particularly for a beginner.

The selected crystal is normally mounted on a glass fibre (see also p. 35) and this is easier to do if the use of immersion liquid can be avoided during the microscopic examination. Where the addition of immersion liquid is unavoidable (for example if two phases can be distinguished only by their refractive indices) the crystal must be carefully dried before mounting is attempted, lest small traces of liquid cause it to stick to the slide or interfere with the action of the adhesive.

The adhesive used to mount the crystal should not give an X-ray diffraction pattern. For temporary mounting, provided the ambient temperature is not too high, there is a lot to be said for using petroleum jelly or vacuum grease: the crystal can be moved relative to the fibre, and is easily removed with a little benzene should you wish to remount it in a different orientation. For a more permanent mount, shellac (soluble in alcohol) or glue or epoxy resin (which can seldom be successfully removed) can be used, but all these have the disadvantage of setting rather quickly; unless you are handy at manipulation under the microscope, they may well have hardened by the time you actually manage to bring the fibre into contact with the crystal.

The glass fibre used should be of reasonable thickness. A suitable variety of sizes can be made by heating and pulling out soft glass rod. Avoid using fibres that dwarf the crystals mounted thereon, and *vice versa*. Glass wool fibres are suitable only for very small crystals; being so fine they are too flexible to support larger crystals, and they are also rather difficult to handle.

The fibre, with the crystal suitably attached, is mounted on a device such as that shown in Fig. 4.2, so that the crystal can be aligned precisely. This is properly called a **goniometer head**, but is often colloquially referred to as a 'set of arcs' or simply 'arcs'. The crystal is commonly adjusted to have a principal axis (say, b) parallel to the axis of the goniometer head and is then usually described as being mounted 'about the b-axis'. More rarely the description 'with the b-axis vertical' may be encountered; this is less desirable, since it is only strictly correct if the axis of the goniometer head is vertical, and in practice the head is often mounted horizontally.

Aligning the crystal is generally much easier if it can be mounted initially with a principal axis in roughly the right place, and, as implied above, the optical examination

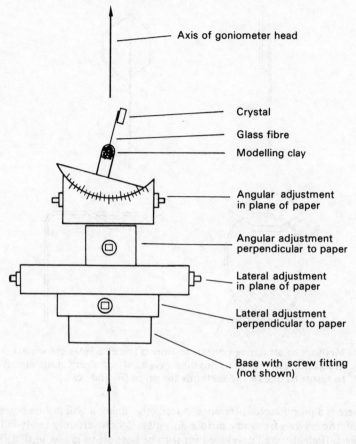

Axis of goniometer head

Crystal

Glass fibre

Modelling clay

Angular adjustment
in plane of paper

Angular adjustment
perpendicular to paper

Lateral adjustment
in plane of paper

Lateral adjustment
perpendicular to paper

Base with screw fitting
(not shown)

Fig. 4.2   The basic parts of a goniometer head or 'set of arcs'. A key is provided to fit the square pins, which operate worm gears.

can be a great help in selecting an appropriate direction. The ease, or otherwise, with which the crystal can be picked up in the required orientation varies with the shape of the crystal. Prisms, needles or lath-like crystals are easily mounted about the direction parallel to their length (Fig. 4.3(a)). Plates or flakes are also easy to mount about axes in the plane of the plate (Fig. 4.3(a)), but less easy about the perpendicular direction: a plate *can* be attached to a fibre at right angles by using a very thick fibre or a very large blob of glue, but such crudities are to be deplored. A neater method is to bend the fibre; two ways are shown in Fig. 4.3. In Fig. 4.3(b), a very fine glass fibre (from glass wool) has been bent into a loop by sticking both ends into modelling clay. In Fig. 4.3(c), a somewhat thicker fibre has been bent into an 'L' shape; this can be done by touching it with a white-hot rod or with a very small flame, and allowing it to bend under its own weight.

Cubic crystals may be very difficult to align. Those that have crystallized as recognizable cubes or octahedra do not present great problems, but cubic crystals can grow in much more complicated shapes than these, and finding an axis is then very tricky. Even worse is the problem of selecting and mounting cubic crystals grown from a melt;

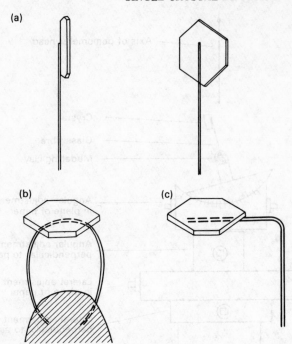

Fig. 4.3 Methods of attaching crystals to fibres. The examples shown in (a) are of relatively straightforward cases; to mount a crystal about a very short dimension, one may need to resort to one of the methods shown in (b) and (c).

unless there is a pronounced difference in refractive index it will not be possible to distinguish the crystals from any surrounding glass. Moreover, only rarely will the crystals be sufficiently well developed for it to be possible to know, until diffraction patterns are obtained, whether the piece picked up consists of one crystal or many. It is sometimes possible to separate the crystals from any remaining glass and from each other by treating the crushed mass with a suitable reagent, but all too frequently the crystals dissolve at least as rapidly as the glass. In the last resort, the process becomes one of trial and error, and can be very tedious.

Precise alignment of a crystal can seldom be achieved from optics and shape alone; one must usually make final adjustments from diffraction photographs, and some ways of doing this will be described in the relevant sections. If necessary, a crystal can be aligned *entirely* from diffraction photographs; cubic crystals without well-developed faces, for example, must be tackled in this way. This procedure is very slow, and even if study of shape or optics permits only rough alignment, much time will be saved thereby. Hence the emphasis on learning to use the polarizing microscope.

4.2   Single crystal cameras in general

The design of X-ray diffraction apparatus varies somewhat from make to make and it is unfortunately impossible within the scope of this book to describe all possible variations in detail. Therefore the precedent established for optical microscopes in

Chapter 2 will be followed: the basic principles will be described but for practical operational details you should consult an experienced colleague or a manufacturer's handbook. The rest of this chapter will be devoted to the most commonly encountered types of single crystal camera; powder cameras will be discussed in Chapter 6. Do not attempt to adjust a camera yourself: because X-rays are dangerous, this should be done only by an experienced worker.

All single crystal diffraction cameras have certain features in common. The crystal is bathed in a narrow beam of approximately parallel X-rays, produced by passing the tube output through a series of small concentric holes which collectively form the **collimator**. The film on which the pattern is recorded must be held in some form of **film-holder** or **cassette**, and kept covered with light-tight paper; Polaroid film and holders are available for some types of camera, and are useful for speeding up the setting of crystals.

If the undiffracted beam were allowed to strike the film, it would produce blackening over a wide area. To prevent this, either a small hole is punched in the film to allow the direct beam to pass through to a lead-lined **beam stop** (or **backstop**), or else the latter is suspended between the crystal and the film. In the latter method, a small part of the pattern is lost because of the shadow of the beam-stop support. Unless Polaroid film is being used, the cassette must be loaded and unloaded in a dark room, and the film is developed and fixed by normal photographic processes. Films may be labelled in pencil before or immediately after unloading: the labelling will remain throughout the subsequent processing. It should not only identify the exposure, but also indicate unambiguously how the film lay in the cassette.

It is also usual for some sort of optical system to be provided to assist in aligning and centreing the crystal. At its crudest this may consist merely of a lamp and telescope; at its most sophisticated it may approximate to an optical goniometer.

4.3 Undistorted records of the reciprocal lattice

The easiest types of X-ray diffraction patterns to interpret are those that give an undistorted picture of the reciprocal lattice; two examples are shown in Fig. 4.4. These were produced by moving the crystal and the film simultaneously, keeping the film parallel to a selected layer of the reciprocal lattice throughout. The basic geometry of the arrangement is shown in Fig. 4.5. A principal axis of the crystal is set perpendicular to the film; the film is thus parallel to a set of reciprocal lattice layers, as shown. Provided that the crystal axis is not parallel to the X-ray beam, the zero layer of the reciprocal lattice intersects the sphere of reflection in a circle, whose diameter OP is shown in Fig. 4.5. Any reciprocal lattice point that lies on this circle gives rise to a reflection; for example, a point at P would produce a reflection at P′ on the film, and the distance O′P′ is proportional to OP. If the zero layer is to be photographed, unwanted reflections from other layers of the reciprocal lattice are excluded by suitable positioning of a **layer screen** having an annular slit, such that only reflections from the cone subtended at the crystal by the zero-layer circle are permitted to reach the film.

Crystal and film are now moved together, so as to bring other reciprocal lattice points into the surface of the sphere of reflection, and the corresponding planes into the reflecting position. Providing only that the film remains perpendicular to the crystal axis, with O′ remaining in the same straight line with O and the crystal, the reflected beams strike the film to give an undistorted record of the reciprocal lattice; the scale depends on the crystal-to-film distance F (Fig. 4.5(a), similar triangles: $O'P'/OP = O'C/OC = F/1$).

Since the scale chosen when drawing the reciprocal lattice is quite arbitrary, it is permissible to use the alternative construction in Fig. 4.5(b). In this the reciprocal lattice is drawn so that 1 reciprocal unit (1 r.u.) = F, making the zero layer coincident with the film. It is a matter of individual preference as to which construction is used. Subsequent diagrams use the first, with the expanded sphere of reflection corresponding to the second faintly indicated; they may thus be visualized in terms of whichever construction is found easier to understand.

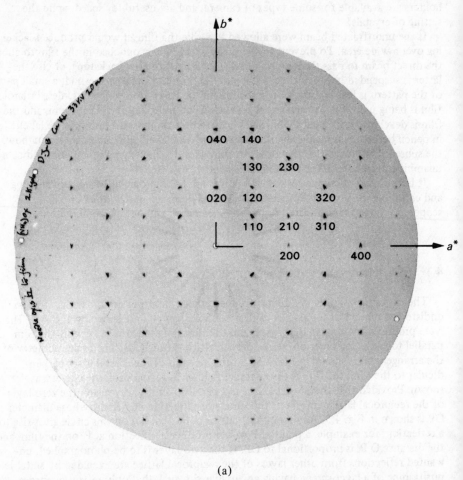

(a)

Fig. 4.4   Undistorted photographs of the reciprocal lattice of ammonium oxalate monohydrate (orthorhombic, $P2_12_12$; $a = 8.04$, $b = 10.27$, $c = 3.82$ Å). Cu radiation, Ni filter, $\lambda = 1.542$ Å. (a) de Jong–Boumann photograph of the $hk0$ layer; the a^* and b^* axes, and some key indices are labelled. Note the systematic absences caused by the screw axes (see Section 5.1). (b) A precession photograph of the $h0l$ layer of the same crystal. This layer of the reciprocal lattice is perpendicular to that in (a), an related to it by a $90°$ rotation about a^*.

Of the possible types of motion that might be imparted, two have been found useful in practice. Of these, the easier to visualize is the rotation used in the de Jong-Boumann method; the geometry for recording a zero-level photograph is shown in Fig. 4.6(a) and the photograph in Fig. 4.4(a) was recorded in this way. The geometry of recording upper layers is shown in Fig. 4.6(b); the relative positions of crystal, screen and the rotation axis of the film are unchanged, and the upper level is brought into the recording position by altering the angle of incidence of the X-ray beam. To maintain the proper relative motions of film and reciprocal lattice layer, the former must be set back along its rotation axis by a distance proportional to the height of the latter above the zero layer. The formulae relating to the recording of upper layers are given in the Appendix.

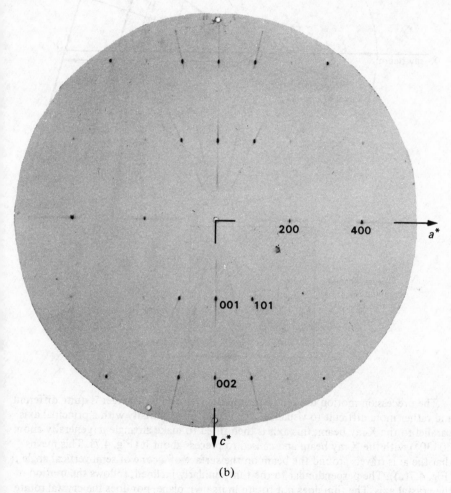

(b)

Both photographs were taken using the Stoe Reciprocal Lattice Explorer. The crystal was a needle; note the corresponding elongation of the spots along c^*, parallel to the needle axis.

Measure the photographs with a ruler; given that 52.0 mm on the film = 1 r.u., check the cell dimensions.

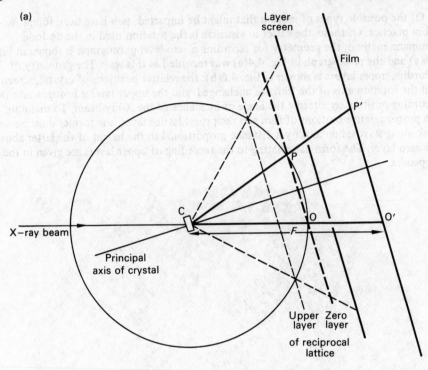

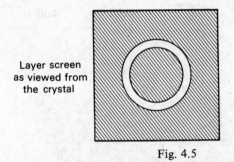

Fig. 4.5

The precession motion used in the method developed by Buerger is quite different and rather more difficult to visualize. The crystal is set initially with a principal axis parallel to the X-ray beam; this axis is then tilted to make an angle μ (generally about 20–30°) with the X-ray beam and caused to precess about it (Fig. 4.7). This means that the axis travels around the beam on the surface of a cone of semi-vertical angle μ (Fig. 4.7(a)). The perpendicular to the film, similarly inclined, follows the motion of the crystal axis. The film does not rotate in its own plane, nor does the crystal rotate about its own axis.

Figure 4.7(a) shows the arrangement for recording the zero layer, which intersects the sphere of reflection in the circle of diameter OP. As the crystal axis precesses around the X-ray beam, the tilt of the reciprocal lattice follows it. The circle OP thus rolls around O to sweep out a circular area of the zero layer. The layer screen is attached

(b)

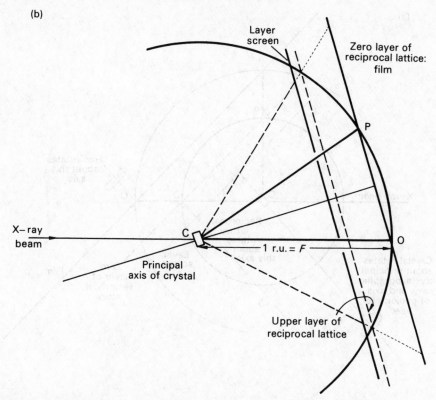

Fig. 4.5   The production of an undistorted record of the reciprocal lattice. Alternative geometrical constructions are shown in (a) and (b).

to the crystal mounting and precesses with it. A photograph recorded in this way is shown in Fig. 4.4(b). As with the de Jong–Boumann method, the geometry of recording upper levels is more complicated (Fig. 4.6(b)); in this case the required layer is selected by changing the position (and sometimes the size) of the layer screen, and here also the film position has to be changed to maintain the correct relative motions. Formulae are given in the Appendix, but usually the necessary adjustments are read off charts supplied with the instrument. A full account of the method will be found in the books by Buerger listed under suggestions for further reading.

Note that while the de Jong–Boumann method records reciprocal lattice layers *perpendicular* to the axis of the goniometer head, the precession method records layers that are *parallel* to it. Thus for an orthogonal crystal mounted about, say, c, the de Jong–Boumann method can be used to record the $hk0$, $hk1$, etc. layers and the precession method to record both the $0kl$, $1kl$, etc., and $h0l$, $h1l$, etc., layers, all without having to reset the crystal. A non-orthogonal crystal, for which c and c^* are not parallel, might need adjustment between taking the two types of photograph, but would probably not have to be remounted. To be able to obtain a complete set of undistorted reciprocal-lattice photographs without dismounting the crystal is obviously a

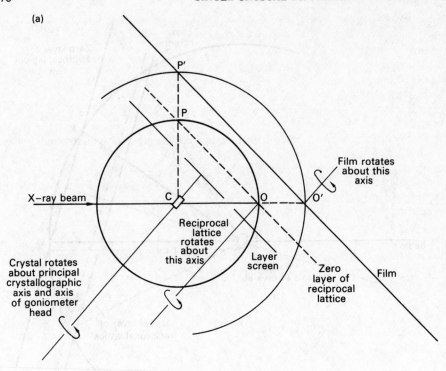

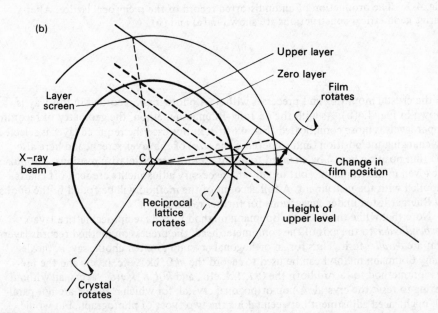

Fig. 4.6   The de Jong–Boumann method; (a) photography of the zero layer (b) photography of an upper level.

great convenience, and the commercially available 'reciprocal-lattice explorer',† carries the principle to its logical conclusion by providing for both types of recording geometry on the same instrument.

The chief drawback to both the methods so far described is that only a small part of the reciprocal lattice can be recorded. If the crystal being examined has one or more short reciprocal dimensions, this may not matter; indeed this is precisely the sort of crystal for which it is most important to have easily interpretable photographs. For crystals with larger reciprocal repeat distances, too little information may be recorded for the systematic absences to be fully investigated; the precession photograph in Fig. 4.4(b) illustrates this. The amount of information can be increased by using a radiation of shorter wavelength, thereby decreasing the scale of the reciprocal lattice, but for various reasons this may be inconvenient. One must then use other methods of recording that allow more of the reciprocal lattice to be explored at the expense of producing a distorted record (Sections 4.4 and 4.5).

There are various ways of aligning the crystal accurately or **setting** it. If the goniometer is provided with a good optical system, as a well-designed instrument should be, and the crystal has well-developed faces, light reflected from these faces can be used to set the crystal to within a few minutes of angle. Figure 4.8 shows how the system might be used to align a monoclinic crystal about b. When the reflected light

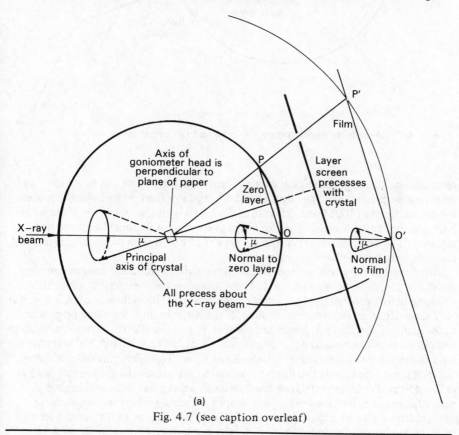

(a)

Fig. 4.7 (see caption overleaf)

† Manufactured by Stoe, Darmstadt, Germany.

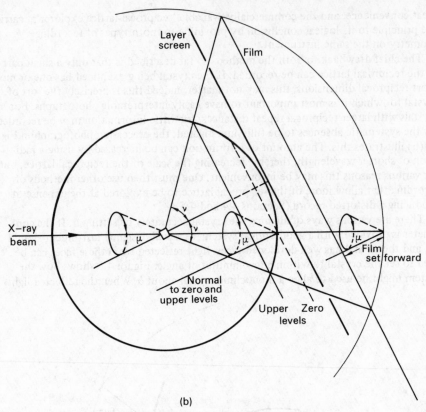

(b)

Fig. 4.7   Precession photography; (a) zero and (b) upper levels.

returns along the same path as the incident light, the (001) plane and hence the *a* and *b* axes are perpendicular to the light beam; the crystal is then rotated and the process is repeated for the (100) plane. This aligns the *b*-axis with the axis of the goniometer head and the crystal is suitably set for either precession or de Jong–Boumann photography. The same system serves for any crystal of higher than monoclinic symmetry, assuming that suitable faces are present.

   After alignment by this method, triclinic crystals, or monoclinic ones mounted about *a* or *c*, will be suitably set for de Jong–Boumann photography, but may need adjusting before precession photography is undertaken. This is illustrated in Fig. 4.9(a) for a monoclinic crystal mounted about *c*. If the X-ray beam is travelling perpendicular to the plane of the diagram, precession photographs of the *h0l*, etc. layers can be taken without further adjustment, but a simple rotation of the arcs through 90° will not serve to bring *a* into coincidence with the X-ray beam. To explore the *0kl*, etc. layers, the crystal must be adjusted to bring *c** parallel to the axis of the goniometer head as in Fig. 4.9(b). Triclinic crystals mounted about an axis in real space will in general need adjustment before precession photography no matter which section of the reciprocal lattice is to be explored (see also Fig. 4.13). For these, or for crystals whose faces are too poorly developed for optical setting, photographic methods must be used; these are usually necessary in any case for final, precise alignment.

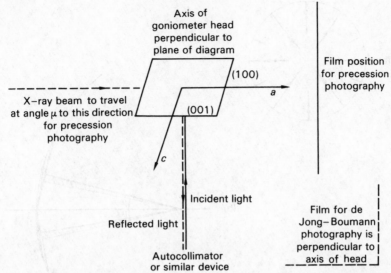

Fig. 4.8   Setting a well-formed crystal by optical means. The crystal is adjusted to bring the incident and reflected light beams into coincidence; (001) is then perpendicular to the light beam. The head is rotated and the operation repeated for (100). The b-axis is then necessarily parallel to the axis of rotation and provided that it is perpendicular to *a* and *c* (as for a monoclinic crystal) the crystal is correctly aligned for both de Jong–Boumann and precession photography; otherwise some adjustment may be needed before the latter is undertaken (see text and Fig. 4.9).

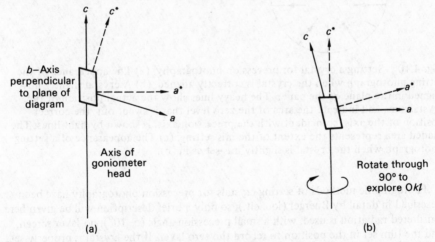

Fig. 4.9   Setting a monoclinic crystal for precession photography; the X-ray beam is assumed to be travelling perpendicular to the paper. (a) The crystal is set about *c*. The *h0l* and parallel levels can be photographed, but rotation of the head about its axis will not bring *a* parallel to the beam, or the *0kl* level into the plane of the paper. (b) The crystal is set about *c**. Both *h0l* and *0kl*, etc., levels can now be explored by rotating the head through 90°.

If the crystal were triclinic, it would in general be necessary to adjust it before *any* precession photography could be done. Once it was set about *c**, the *h0l* and *0kl* sections would be related by rotation through γ.

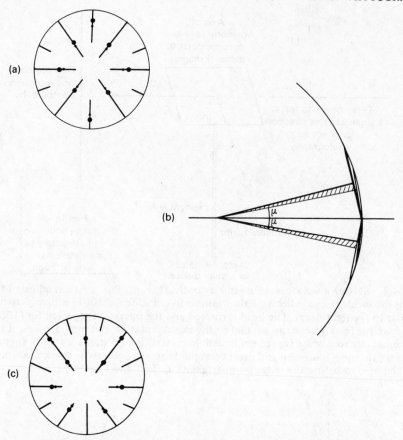

Fig. 4.10 Setting a crystal for precession photography. (a) The appearance of the setting photograph when the crystal is correctly aligned. (b) A crystal slightly mis-aligned in the plane of the paper. The heavy lines show the actual position of the crystal axis, and indicate the area of the zero level that is swept out; the correct position of the axis, coincident with the precession axis, is shown by light lines. The shaded area represents the extent of the mis-setting. (c) The appearance of a setting photograph when the crystal is slightly mis-set as in (b).

Photographic methods of setting crystals for precession photography have been described in detail by Buerger (loc. cit.), so only a brief description will be given here. Unfiltered radiation is used, with a small precession angle (5–10°), no layer screen, and the film set in the position to record the zero layer. If the crystal is properly set, the result looks something like Fig. 4.10(a). A small central portion of the zero layer of the reciprocal lattice, complete with the Kβ reflections and the streaks due to white radiation, is recorded in the centre of the film. Additional spots due to upper-layer reflections occur further out from the centre; they are easily distinguished from the zero-layer reflections because they are doubled (the film not being positioned to record upper levels) and are ignored. A crystal slightly mis-set, as in Fig. 4.10(b), sweeps out an asymmetric circular area (Fig. 4.10(c)); small adjustments must be made to the alignment of the crystal to correct the asymmetry. Formulae for calculating the

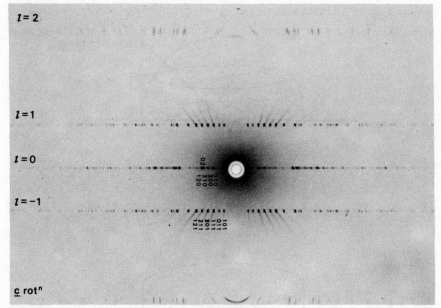

Fig. 4.11. Rotation photograph of the same crystal as in Fig. 4.4, rotating about the needle axis, c. The reflections visible in Figs. 4.4(a) and 4.21 are here compressed into the equatorial layer ($l = 0$). (Cu radiation, Ni filter).

magnitude of these corrections have been given by Buerger; charts are also available. The art lies in applying the correction in the right direction: this is relatively easy to work out with the film and instrument to hand, but not at all easy to describe on paper. Needless to say, it is essential to know how the film was placed in the holder; some instruments provide locating marks automatically. Otherwise, writing on the film in pencil before removing it from the holder will serve; should you forget to do this, it is sometimes possible to retrieve the situation by a careful study of the position of the shadow of the backstop support, but this method is not recommended for routine use. It is also a good idea to note the values of all settings of arcs and instrument before making any adjustment; if you then find that your correction has only made matters worse, you can work out where the mistake occurred and put it right.

Photographic setting for de Jong–Boumann photography, if the necessary alignment is not identical to that for precession photography, is by the oscillation techniques described in the next section.

4.4 Rotation and oscillation photographs

Figure 4.11 shows a typical **rotation photograph**, obtained using the arrangement shown in Fig. 4.12. The X-ray beam is perpendicular to a principal crystallographic axis, which in the following discussion is assumed to be c (if it were a or b the same arguments would apply, with appropriate changes of axes and indices). The crystal rotates about this axis, and the diffraction pattern is recorded on a film mounted as a cylinder concentric with the rotation axis. Although this axis is not vertical in all cameras, for simplicity we will assume that it is.

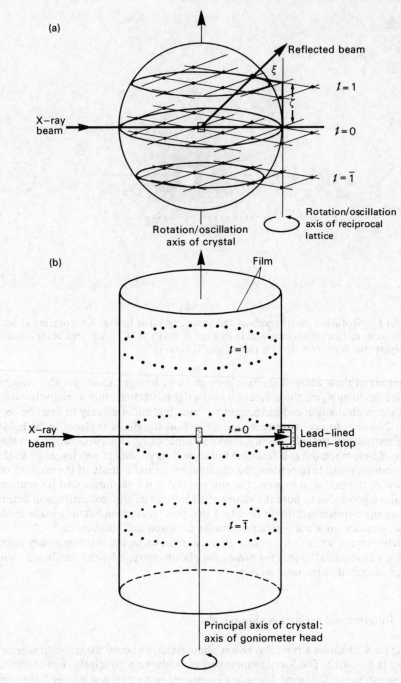

Fig. 4.12   The geometry of rotation (or oscillation) photographs. (a) The motion of the reciprocal lattice with respect to the sphere of reflection, showing the formation of a diffracted beam. The reciprocal lattice layers are perpendicular to the rotation/oscillation axis of the crystal; ζ is the vertical distance of any level above the zero layer. The

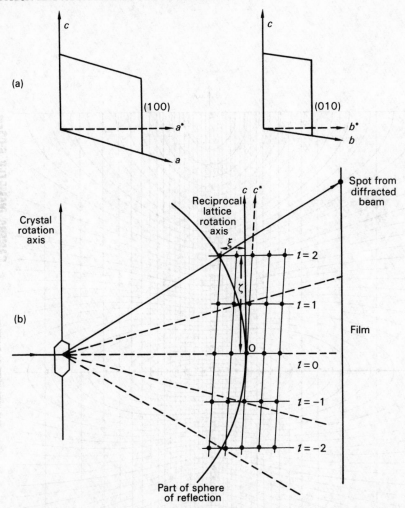

Fig. 4.13 The formation of a rotation photograph from a triclinic crystal mounted about c; (a) shows the relation of a^* and b^* to c; (b) shows that the consequence is that all reciprocal lattice layers with a given l are horizontal; hence the formation of layer lines.

The most immediately striking feature of such a photograph is the arrangement of the spots in horizontal lines, or **layer lines**. These arise because if a real axis of a crystal (of any symmetry) is vertical, two of the reciprocal axes are, by definition, horizontal. Figure 4.13(a) illustrates this for a triclinic crystal mounted about c. The reciprocal lattice points thus lie in layers perpendicular to the vertical axis; as we shall see, the

reciprocal lattice rotates about an axis through its origin and parallel to the crystal axis; ξ is the horizontal distance of any point from the rotation axis of the reciprocal lattice. (b) Recording the photograph on a cylindrical film whose axis coincides with the crystal rotation axis. The dotted lines show the position of the layers on the film corresponding to the diffracted beams produced as in (a).

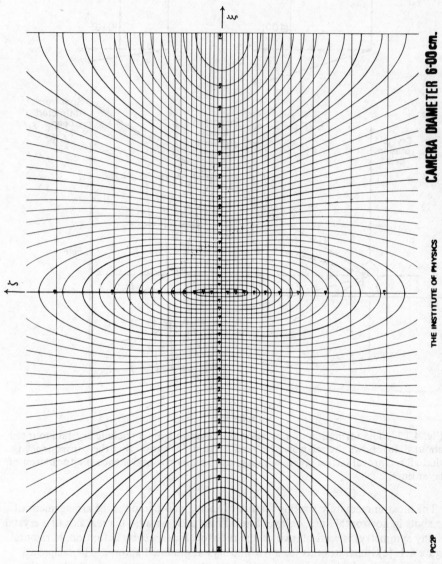

Fig. 4.14   A Bernal chart. (Reproduced by courtesy of the Institute of Physics.)

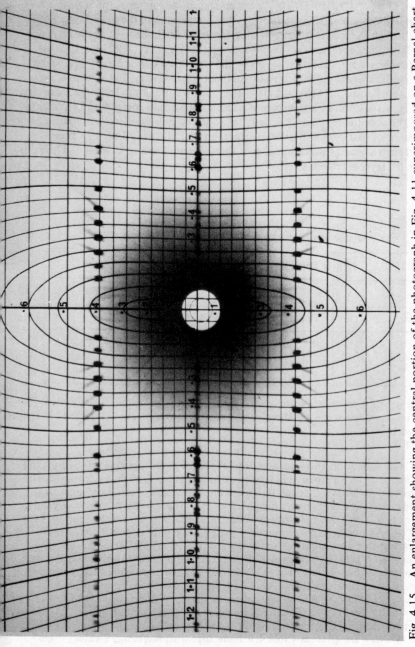

Fig. 4.15 An enlargement showing the central portion of the photograph in Fig. 4.11 superimposed on a Bernal chart. (Reproduced by courtesy of the Institute of Physics.) This shows the method of interpreting rotation (or oscillation) photographs; normally the film would be placed over the chart and both viewed together against a lighted screen. The horizontal (ξ) and vertical (ζ) coordinates determined in this way are listed in Table 4.1.

Compare the value of ζ with c^* from Fig. 4.4(b); calculate c.

position of a reflection on the film depends on the height ζ of the corresponding reciprocal lattice point above the zero layer, and its horizontal distance ξ from the rotation axis (Figs. 4.12(a), 4.13(a)). As the crystal rotates about c, the reciprocal lattice rotates about a parallel axis through O; consequently all the points on a given layer pass through the sphere of reflection at the same vertical height above O, giving rise to the layer lines observed on the photograph (cf. Figs 4.11, 4.12 and 4.13(b)).

The distance between successive layers of the reciprocal lattice can be determined by measuring the spacing on the film and applying trigonometry, but it is more convenient to use a **Bernal chart** (named after its inventor Professor J. D. Bernal) like that shown in Fig. 4.14. Copies on transparent paper or plastic are commercially available and enable the coordinates ζ and ξ for any reflection to be read directly. Figure 4.15 is an enlargement of part of the rotation photograph reproduced in Fig. 4.11 superimposed on such a chart; the coordinates of the spots are given in Table 4.1. The value of ζ for the lth layer is related to c by

$$c = l\lambda/\zeta$$

TABLE 4.1
Reciprocal coordinates from the photograph in Fig. 4.15[1]

$\xi =$	0.15	0.19	0.25	0.30	0.36	0.39	0.41	0.49	0.60	0.63	0.65	0.71	0.73	
$\zeta = 0.00$			x	x	x	x	x	x	x	x	x	x	x	$l = 0$
$\zeta = 0.40$	x	x	x	x	x		x	x	x	x	x			$l = 1$
$hk =$	10	01	11	20	21	02	12	31 22	40 32 13	41	23	42	33	

[1] For puposes of reproduction, the photograph in Fig. 4.15 is somewhat overexposed. The coordinates cannot therefore be read very accurately. (Observed reflections are indicated by x.)

Fig. 4.16 The formation and interpretation of rotation photographs. (a) The crystal is rotating about an axis perpendicular to the plane of the paper; the reciprocal lattice rotates about a parallel axis through O. The paths followed by zero-layer reciprocal lattice points at successively greater distances from O, that is with increasing ξ-values, are shown as a, b, c, etc. All the corresponding reflections appear on the same straight line on the film, at positions determined by their ξ-value only. Upper layers behave similarly, except that they intersect the sphere of reflection in a circle of reduced diameter (cf. Fig. 4.12(a)). (b) Provided that the crystal is fairly symmetrical and its cell not too large, it may be possible to work back to the reciprocal lattice, given only the ξ-values of successive row-lines. The data from Fig. 4.15 and Table 4.1 are here plotted as a series of circles. Assuming that the first two of these correspond to the paths followed by the $10l$ and $01l$ reflections respectively, an orthogonal net can be constructed which successfully accounts for the other row-lines. The hk indices assigned in this way are given in Table 4.1. Note that with increasing ξ-values it becomes progressively more difficult to assign indices unambiguously. The results may be compared with the undistorted zero-layer photograph from the same crystal reproduced in Fig. 4.4(a); compare the absences in the latter with the zero layer of Table 4.1.

(a)

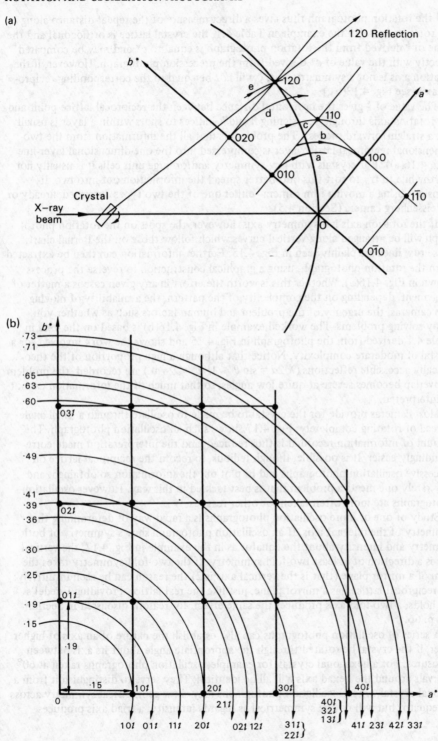

(b)

and the rotation photograph thus gives a direct measure of the repeat distance along the rotation axis. (In the example in Table 4.1, the crystal lattice is orthogonal and the value of ζ derived from the rotation photograph is equal to c^* and may be compared directly with the value of c^* derived from the precession photograph. However, if the rotation axis is not a symmetry axis, ζ will *not* be equal to the corresponding reciprocal axis; see Fig. 4.13(b).)

The value of ξ gives the horizontal distance between the reciprocal lattice point and the rotation axis through O; assigning h and k indices to spots within a layer is usually not a straightforward process. The problem is that all the information from the two-dimensional reciprocal lattice layer is compressed into the one-dimensional layer-line (Fig. 4.16(a)). For crystals with low symmetry and/or large unit cells it is usually not worthwhile to try to sort this out; better spread the information out into two dimensions using a moving film camera—either one of the two types described already or a Weissenberg camera (Section 4.5).

If the rotation axis is a symmetry axis, however, the spots on the rotation photograph will be arranged along vertical curves which follow those on the Bernal chart; these **row lines** are plainly seen in Fig. 4.15. Further information can then be extracted from the rotation photograph, using a graphical construction to reverse the process shown in Fig. 4.16(a). Whether this is worth the effort in any given case is a matter of judgement, depending on the complexity of the pattern, the availability of moving film cameras, the urgency of the problem and human factors such as whether you enjoy solving problems. The worked example in Fig. 4.16(b) is based on the data in Table 4.1 derived from the photograph in Fig. 4.15 and shows the work involved for a crystal of moderate complexity. Notice that although a high proportion of the theoretically accessible reflections ($\lambda/2d = \sin \theta \leqslant 1$; $d^* \leqslant 2$ r.u.) are recorded, the problem of overlap becomes severe at quite low angles, so that much of the information cannot be interpreted.

Most cameras provide for the crystal to be made to oscillate through a small angle instead of rotating completely; Fig. 4.17 shows such an **oscillation** photograph. The amount of information recorded is thus reduced, and the interpretation made correspondingly easier. It is possible, though tedious, to record the reciprocal lattice on successive oscillation photographs and to plot out the information so obtained, and very rarely one meets a problem that is best tackled in this way. However oscillation photographs are more often taken for other reasons.

Study of one or more oscillation photographs is a rapid way of determining the symmetry of the relevant axis. If an oscillation photograph shows symmetry of both geometry and intensity about the equator as in the example in Fig. 4.17, the vertical axis is a direction of at least two-fold symmetry. If the two-fold symmetry takes the form of a mirror plane (that is the vertical axis is $\bar{2}$) the reason can be seen intuitively; the reciprocal lattice has a mirror plane, just like the real lattice. Providing Friedel's law holds, a two-fold axis produces the same effect, for reasons discussed in Section 3.7, p. 66.

A series of oscillation photographs can also establish the nature of an axis of higher order, if the crystal be rotated through the appropriate angle about its axis between exposures. For a hexagonal crystal, for example, oscillation photographs taken at 60° intervals around the hexad axis will all be identical. They serve to distinguish it from a trigonal crystal, whose oscillation photographs may show geometrical symmetry across the equator but will not be symmetrical as regards intensity; a triad axis produces

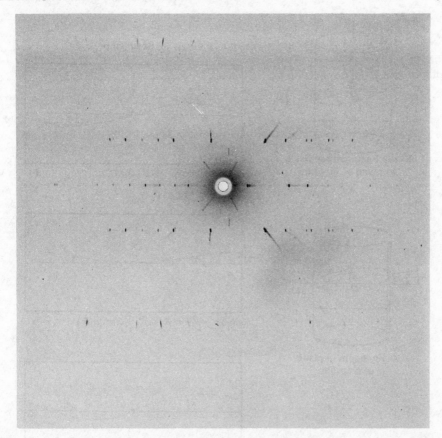

Fig. 4.17   A 15° oscillation photograph of the crystal used for Fig. 4.11 about the same axis. Note the reduction in the information density. Note also the symmetry of the reflections, as regards both position and intensity, about the equatorial layer; this shows that c must be a symmetry axis (Cu radiation, Ni filter).

identity only between photographs at intervals of 120°, the intervening ones being inverted across the equator. Although this information can be obtained equally well, and usually more conveniently, from moving film photographs, it is sometimes quicker to use the oscillation method.

The usual reason for taking an oscillation photograph is to help align the crystal, and for this purpose one may use unfiltered radiation; this reduces exposure times, and the additional spots and streaks on the photograph are frequently found to be positively helpful.

When the crystal is approximately aligned, its crystallographic axis remains slightly tilted relative to the oscillation axis and the reciprocal lattice layers tilt with it. Consequently, the layer lines on the oscillation photograph, instead of being straight, are curved, as shown in Fig. 4.18. The crystal is aligned by adjusting it to correct the tilt. One method, which works well for crystals that give sharp spots out to the edge of the

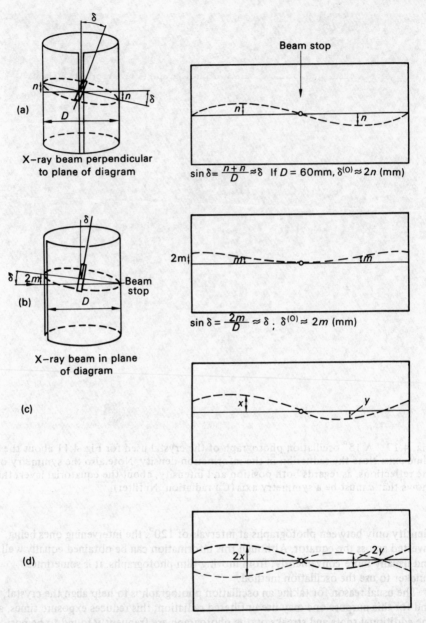

$$\sin \delta = \frac{n+n}{D} \approx \delta \quad \text{If } D = 60\text{mm}, \; \delta^{(0)} \approx 2n \text{ (mm)}$$

X-ray beam perpendicular
to plane of diagram

$$\sin \delta = \frac{2m}{D} \approx \delta \; ; \; \delta^{(0)} \approx 2m \text{ (mm)}$$

X-ray beam in plane
of diagram

Fig. 4.18 Setting a single crystal from oscillation photographs. (a) Left, the position
of the zero layer if the crystal is mis-set only in the plane perpendicular to the X-ray
beam; right, the appearance of a photograph taken with the crystal oscillating about
this position. (b) Left, the position of the zero layer when the crystal is mis-set in the
plane containing the X-ray beam; right, the corresponding oscillation photograph. (c)
The appearance of an oscillation photograph from a crystal mis-set in both planes, that
is with a combination of the above errors. For ease in calculating the necessary correction, the oscillation photograph is usually taken with one arc of the goniometer
head parallel to the X-ray beam; the other is then perpendicular to it. The necessary

film, is explained in Fig. 4.18; the deviation of the zero-layer line from the equatorial position gives the correction. When the crystal is very nearly set, the chief difficulty lies in deciding the exact position of the equator. This is resolved by making two exposures on the same film, the crystal being rotated 180° about its own axis between exposures. The resulting **double oscillation** photograph (Fig. 4.18(d)) carries two images of the zero layer, reflected in the equatorial plane, and the correction is obtained by measuring the appropriate distance between them and dividing by two. To determine the sense of the correction, it is of course necessary to be able to distinguish the two exposures. This can be done by making one exposure considerably longer than the other or by using a filter for one but not the other.

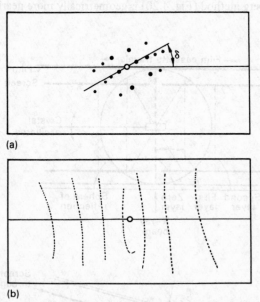

(a)

(b)

Fig. 4.19 Crystals requiring other setting techniques. (a) Oscillation photograph from a crystal whose pattern fades out below $2\theta = 90°$. The tangent to the zero-layer curve at the centre gives the approximate correction for the arc perpendicular to the X-ray beam. To determine the other correction, the arcs are rotated 90°. This method is often helpful in the preliminary stages of trial-and-error setting, when the location of a principal axis is not known even approximately. (b) Oscillation photograph from a crystal with a very long vertical axis; location of the zero layer is difficult, and it is easier to adjust the row lines.

angular correction can then be resolved between the two arcs as follows. The deviation of the zero layer is measured at $2\theta = 90°$, or $\xi = \sqrt{2}$; normally the high-θ gap in the film is negligible and one can assume that this is halfway between the middle and the edge of the film as shown. The necessary corrections in the two directions are given by $(x + y)$ and $(x - y)$, which is which being determined by inspection. In the example shown, the larger correction is clearly in the direction perpendicular to the X-ray beam, and anti-clockwise as the crystal is viewed from the direction of the approaching beam, as in (a). The smaller correction is in the direction parallel to the beam, and requires the crystal to be tilted down towards the point where the beam enters, as in (b). (d) A double oscillation photograph from a crystal mis-set as in (c). The longer exposure corresponds to the orientation of the head that produced (c).

For crystals whose patterns fade out at relatively low angles, the more rough-and-ready method shown in Fig. 4.19(a) can be used. Occasionally, if the vertical axis is extremely long and the horizontal axes relatively short (Fig. 4.19(b)), it may be easier to set the crystal by adjusting the row lines [1].

4.5 The Weissenberg camera

The two types of moving film camera already described give an undistorted picture of the reciprocal lattice, but are capable of recording only a relatively small part of it. The **Weissenberg** method (Fig. 4.20) is geometrically more nearly related to the

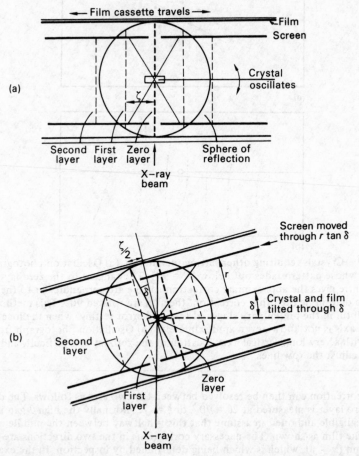

Fig. 4.20 Weissenberg photography. (a) Photography of the zero layer. (b) Photography of the first layer, using the equi-inclination setting. The crystal and film holder are tilted through δ, where $\sin \delta = \zeta/2$; the screens are moved through $r \tan \delta$. Notice that the second layer, which does not intersect the sphere of reflection in the zero-layer setting, now does so. For this reason more layers are accessible than are recorded on a rotation photograph. The practical limit is set by the limits of tilt that the instrument allows.

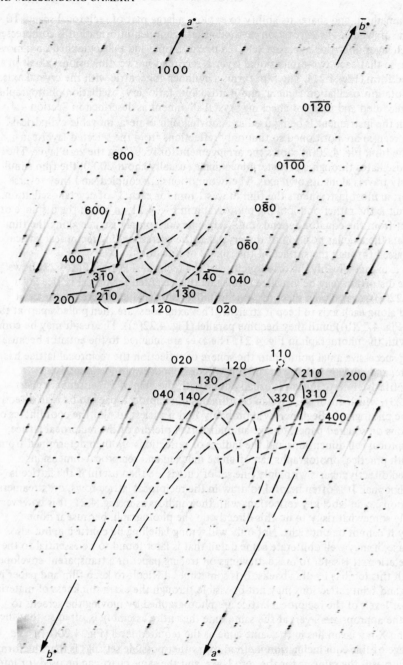

Fig. 4.21 A Weissenberg photograph of the *hk0* layer of ammonium oxalate mono-hydrate. This photograph should be compared with that in Fig. 4.4(a) and axes, 'streamers' and some indices have been marked on it for this purpose; the photographs are related in the same way as the pairs of drawings in Fig. 4.24. This photograph was taken with Cu radiation and a Ni filter; the streaking due to white radiation is rather prominent because it was over-exposed for reproduction reasons. Note that it includes many more reflections than Fig. 4.4(a), but that because it gives a distorted picture of the reciprocal lattice it is not so easy to interpret.

rotation method, and shares its ability to explore a large part of reciprocal space. To avoid the drawback of the rotation method—that too much information is compressed into each layer line—the layers are selected one at a time and photographed on a moving film, so that each two-dimensional layer is recorded in two dimensions, albeit in a distorted form (Fig. 4.21). The film forms a cylinder concentric with the crystal axis, as in a rotation/oscillation camera, and if it is kept stationary, oscillation photographs can be recorded and used for checking crystal alignment as described in Section 4.4.

When the instrument is being used as a moving film camera, movable cylindrical metal screen(s) are positioned so that only reflections from the selected layer can reach the film; Fig. 4.20(a) shows the arrangement for recording the zero layer. The crystal oscillates through a predetermined angle (usually about 200°); the film simultaneously travels along its own axis. The two motions are coupled, and they reverse together; in most instruments the film moves 1 mm for each 2° of crystal oscillation. The result is the rather odd looking photograph in Fig. 4.21, in which the distance of any spot from the equator depends on ξ, while its horizontal distance along the film represents the angular position of the crystal as the corresponding reciprocal lattice point passed through the surface of the sphere of reflection.

This is in fact a highly distorted picture of the reciprocal lattice; Fig. 4.22 shows how the distortion may be visualized. Imagine the weighted reciprocal lattice layer (Fig. 4.22(a)), drawn on a sheet of some infinitely stretchable material, with a rod inserted along each axis to keep it straight. The 'axial rods' are then pulled apart at the origin (Fig. 4.22(b)) until they become parallel (Fig. 4.22(c)). The result may be compared with the photograph in Fig. 4.21. The axes are inclined to the equator because to bring successive axial points into the sphere of reflection the reciprocal lattice has to rotate, and while it is doing so the film of course moves proportionately.

Quantitative interpretation is usually done with the help of a Weissenberg chart (Fig. 4.23), which enables Cartesian coordinates in reciprocal space to be read directly from the photograph. Beginners will probably find it easiest to plot the coordinates of reflections on squared paper, to give an undistorted picture of the reciprocal lattice; the reciprocal cell dimensions and the indices of reflections are then determined from this. With practice, photographs can often be indexed and reciprocal dimensions measured directly; charts with only one set of curves are then useful if the lattice is not orthogonal. It is often helpful to draw in the reciprocal lattice rows, or 'streamers' or 'festoons', and label key reflections with their indices as in Fig. 4.21; it is however normally somewhat risky to do this directly on the photograph, because if done wrongly it cannot be put right. Not only will wrong labelling be confusing, but also, and worse, it may well obliterate some detail that is later found to be essential to the interpretation. It is safer to make drawings on tracing paper or a transparent envelope, although this too has its drawbacks. It is sometimes difficult to keep film and paper in register and faint reflections may not be visible through the extra thickness of material.

Upper levels of the reciprocal lattice are photographed by moving the screens to isolate the appropriate layer; at the same time the entire assembly is tilted so that the incoming X-ray beam lies in the same cone as the required level (Fig. 4.20(b)). The advantage of this **equi-inclination** method over other possible settings is that the form of the curves is the same as for the zero layer, and the same chart can be used for interpreting the photographs; moreover, as Fig. 4.20 shows, it enables the maximum volume of reciprocal space to be examined. The formulae for calculating the settings are given in Fig. 4.20(b). Notice that for upper layers the circular area of reciprocal lattice explored has a radius of $\sqrt{(1 - (\zeta/2)^2)}$, and since this is spread over the same area of film as the zero layer, the scale of the upper layers is increased by

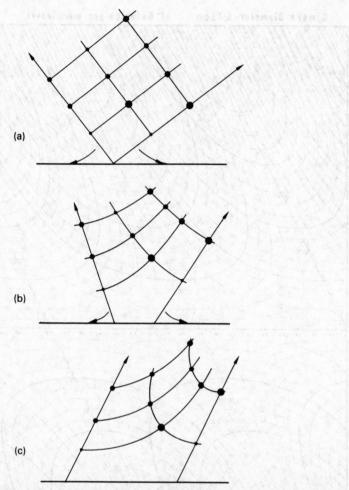

Fig. 4.22   The relationship of a Weissenberg photograph to the undistorted reciprocal lattice. (a) The weighted reciprocal lattice. (b) The axes are kept straight, but pulled apart at the origin. (c) The axes become parallel, the horizontal distance between them being proportional to the original angle.

$1/\sqrt{(1 - (\zeta/2)^2)}$. The effect is barely noticeable for small values of ζ, but increases rapidly with larger values.

If an upper-level photograph looks very similar to that of the zero level, there may be a perfectly valid structural reason, but, before seeking this, you should check that it is not simply the result of moving the layer-line screen in the wrong direction. It can readily be seen from Fig. 4.20(b) that the result of this mistake will be that the zero layer is photographed again on a slightly different scale. When the screens are in the right place, the collimator points through the gap between them.

Some typical Weissenberg patterns, together with the appropriate undistorted weighted reciprocal lattice layers, are shown in Fig. 4.24. Notice particularly how the angular separation of the axes in the undistorted lattice becomes a linear separation in the Weissenberg photographs; notice also the symmetry relations.

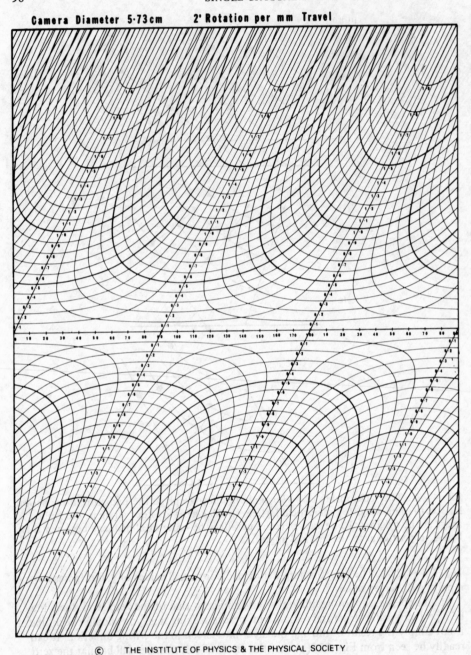

Fig. 4.23   A Weissenberg chart. (Reproduced by courtesy of the Institute of Physics.)

(a)

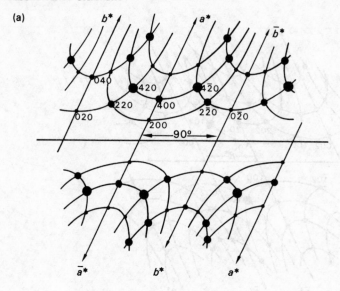

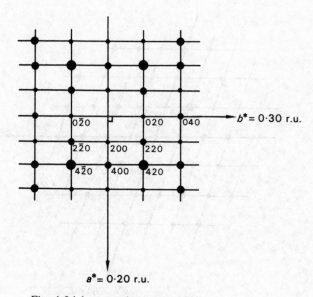

Fig. 4.24 (see caption on p. 102)

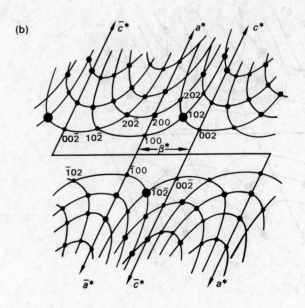

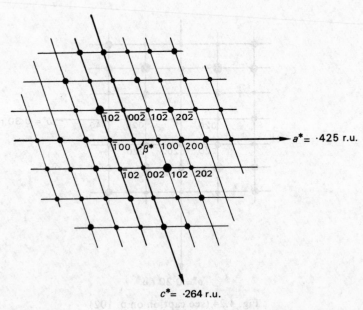

Fig. 4.24

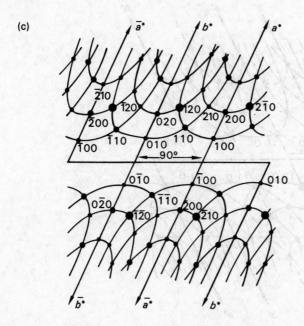

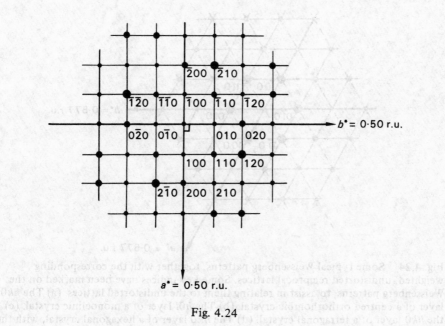

Fig. 4.24

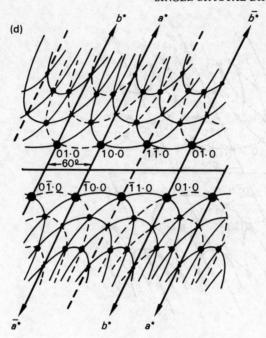

(d)

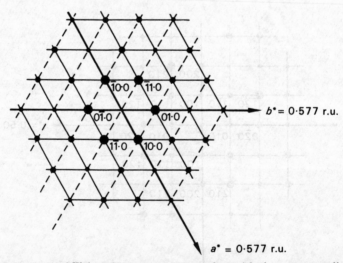

$b^* = 0.577$ r.u.

$a^* = 0.577$ r.u.

Fig. 4.24 Some typical Weissenberg patterns, together with the corresponding weighted, undistorted reciprocal lattices. Some key indices have been marked on the Weissenberg patterns, to assist in relating them to the undistorted lattices. (a) The $hk0$ layer of a centred orthorhombic crystal. (b) The $h0l$ layer of a monoclinic crystal. (c) the $hk0$ layer of a tetragonal crystal. (d) The $hk0$ layer of a hexagonal crystal, with the third set of streamers indicated by dashed lines; compare with Figs. 3.13 and 3.15.

Assuming that CuKα radiation was used for all these photographs ($\lambda = 1.542$ Å), calculate the real cell dimensions corresponding to the given reciprocal ones. In (b)

Provided that the rotation axis is a symmetry axis, a rotation or oscillation photograph plus a set of Weissenberg photographs about that axis will be sufficient to establish the unit-cell parameters. If the rotation axis is *not* a symmetry axis, the number of parameters that can be accurately determined is limited; for a triclinic crystal rotating about c, for example, the rotation photograph gives the value of c, and the zero-layer Weissenberg photograph gives a^*, b^* and γ^*. The values of α^* and β^* can be roughly estimated from the amount by which upper layers are offset, but to get accurate values $0kl$ and $h0l$ photographs are needed. If a precession camera is available, the simplest procedure is to transfer the crystal to that; adjustments will be required as described in Section 4.2 (the Weissenberg alignment bears the same relationship to the precession alignment as does the de Jong–Boumann). Otherwise it will be necessary to remount the crystal about the other two principal axes (or to mount further crystals about these axes), which is sometimes easier said than done. Thin needle-shaped or fibrous crystals, for example, may be difficult to mount except with the needle axis, and even when other orientations have been achieved, the morphology often causes the photographs to be of poor quality. For such crystals it is a great advantage to have access to a precession camera.

4.6 Laue photographs

It would be wrong to conclude this chapter without some mention of the first type of X-ray diffraction photograph ever taken [2]. This used unfiltered radiation with the crystal stationary, and it conclusively proved both the wave nature of X-rays and the periodicity of crystals. Subsequently the structures of a number of relatively simple cubic structures were successfully attacked by this method, but it was soon found that diffraction experiments that used monochromatic radiation were easier to interpret.

Stationary crystal or **Laue** photographs are more useful for determining symmetry and orientation than for determining unit cells and structure. They are used by metallurgists and materials scientists for the study of the texture of materials of known structure, but they are of little help in the identification of phases. A Laue photograph of a carefully aligned crystal exhibits its symmetry in a singularly pleasing fashion (see Fig. 4.25), although it does not give any information that could not be more easily, if less aesthetically, obtained by other means.

Very occasionally a stationary crystal photograph will help to set a crystal when other methods are getting nowhere. A true Laue photograph uses a flat-plate film and white radiation. For setting purposes it is sufficient to use an ordinary oscillation camera with unfiltered radiation, keeping the crystal stationary. The resulting film will have

---

you will need to estimate β^*; you can do this from the upper drawing if you remember that the pattern repeats every $180°$, and that horizontal distances along the film are proportional to the angular travel of the crystal. Check your result by measuring β^* directly from the lower drawing with a protractor. In (a) the reciprocal lattice shows no absences other than those due to the centreing; what is the lattice type? What sort of centreing might be present in (b)? Do you think that the crystals that gave patterns (c) and (d) have two-fold symmetry perpendicular to c?

spots arranged in curves like those in Fig. 4.25; points where large numbers of these intersect indicate the position of the zero layer, or at least of some important section through the reciprocal lattice.

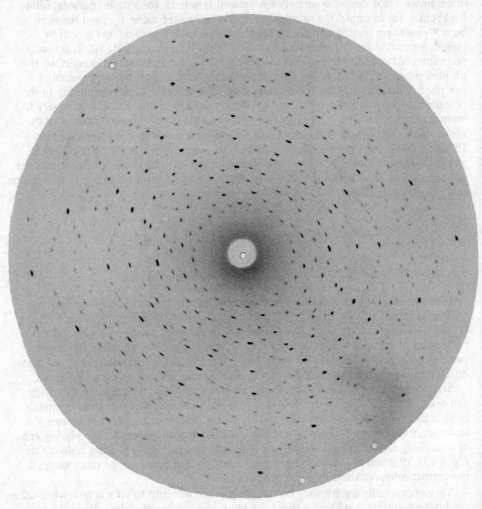

Fig. 4.25   A Laue photograph, taken using unfiltered Cu radiation and a stationary crystal. The crystal has a large tetragonal cell, and the X-ray beam is travelling along its four-fold axis.

References

[1] Mackay, A. L., *Acta Crystallogr.* **5**, 691 (1952).
[2] Friedrich, W., Knipping, P. and Laue, M., *Sitzungsberichte der (Kgl.) Bayerische Akademie der Wissenschaften,* 303–332 (1912).

CHAPTER 5

Simple single crystal studies

5.1 Unit cell and space group determination

Provided that no complications (such as twinning or disorder) arise, the use of one or more of the techniques described in the previous chapter enables a picture of the reciprocal lattice to be produced. From this it is only a short step to working out the unit cell; indeed, some of the dimensions of the real cell will probably have been determined *en route*. The necessary relationships were developed in Chapter 3; for orthogonal cells the problem of converting from reciprocal to real space and *vice versa* is almost trivial, but for non-orthogonal systems a certain amount of thought is usually needed.

The next task is to survey the reciprocal lattice to see whether there are any systematic absences. Absences due to lattice centreing (Chapter 3) occur throughout the whole of reciprocal space, and a general survey to see whether there are any rules governing the permitted values of h, k and l will enable the lattice type to be determined (cf. Table 3.1). Absences that affect only certain layers or rows of points in the reciprocal lattice may also be found; these denote the presence of glide planes and screw axes.

To see how this comes about, refer back to Fig. 1.16(a) on p. 22, which represents an a-glide plane perpendicular to c. Now imagine what happens when this pattern is projected onto the plane of the paper; that is you view it down c and ignore all z-coordinates. Under these conditions, left- and right-handed objects are indistinguishable; in the same way you cannot tell a left from a right hand if you have only its shadow on the wall to go on. The result is that in this projection the a-axis will appear to be only half as long as it really is, so when the structure is viewed down c, a is apparently halved. Transferring this into reciprocal space, for $hk0$ reflections (those from planes parallel to c) a^* is apparently doubled, which means that these reflections are missing when h is odd. The formal statement of this result is that 'in $hk0$, $h = 2n$'.

The same conclusion can be reached using the expression for the structure factor given in Chapter 3. The presence of the a-glide perpendicular to c means that for any atom at x, y, z there must be an identical atom at $x + \frac{1}{2}, y, -z$ (that is moved half a cell along a, which turns x into $x + \frac{1}{2}$, and reflected across the glide plane at $z = 0$, which turns z into $-z$). The structure factor summation must thus cover $N/2$ such pairs of atoms. The contribution from the rth pair is:

$$f_r \{\cos 2\pi [hx_r + ky_r + lz_r] + \cos 2\pi [h(x_r + \tfrac{1}{2}) + ky_r - lz_r]\}$$

For $hk0$ reflections, $l = 0$ and the expression simplifies to:

$$f_r\{\cos 2\pi[hx_r + ky_r] + \cos 2\pi[hx_r + h\tfrac{1}{2} + ky_r]\}$$

$$= f_r\{\cos 2\pi[hx_r + ky_r] + \cos [2\pi(hx_r + ky_r) + h\pi]\}$$

The two cosine terms are equal in magnitude but differ in phase by $h\pi$; they therefore cancel when h is odd, and reinforce when h is even. Consequently, the structure factor F_{hk0} is zero whenever h is odd. This is, of course, precisely the same condition that was deduced from more 'qualitative' reasoning in the previous paragraph: $hk0$ reflections occur only when h is even.

Similar arguments can be applied to other translational symmetry elements. Screw axes produce absences among reflections from the planes perpendicular to them. For example, a 4_1 axis parallel to c limits the $00l$ reflections to those with $l = 4n$, while a 2_1 axis parallel to a means that in $h00$, $h = 2n$. The effects produced by various types of symmetry elements are summarized in Table 5.1.

If, therefore, systematic absences are found that are *additional* to those due to any lattice centreing, it can be safely concluded that translational symmetry elements are present. It is, however, important to be certain that the observed conditions really are additional, and not merely a special case of the lattice absences: in a C-centred lattice, $h + k = 2n$ for *all hkl*, and the observations that $h = 2n$ in $h0l$ and $k = 2n$ in $0kl$ are consequences of the more general absence and prove nothing either way about the presence of the corresponding glide planes. Similarly, once it is established that $h = 2n$ in $h0l$, the absence of $h00$ reflections with h odd tells us nothing about whether or not there is a screw axis parallel to a.

(Refer back to Fig. 4.24(b). If you were told that the lattice was primitive, how would you then explain the systematic absence?)

The study of systematic absences should therefore begin with the most general reflections and work down to the less general. We can illustrate the process by studying Fig. 5.1, which shows part of the reciprocal lattice of an orthorhombic crystal. We first see that there are no conditions restricting the occurrence of hkl reflections overall, so the cell is primitive. The $0kl$, $h0l$ and $hk0$ layers are examined next, and we find:

in $0kl$, $k + l = 2n$

in $h0l$, $h = 2n$

in $hk0$, there are no conditions.

Satisfy yourself that you agree with these conclusions before proceeding further; you may find it helpful to make additional sketches showing the $0kl$ and $h0l$ layers. From these absences it can be deduced (if necessary with the aid of Table 5.1) that there is:

a diagonal or n-glide plane perpendicular to a,
an a-glide plane perpendicular to b,
no translational symmetry perpendicular to c.

(If you have forgotten what a diagonal glide is, refer back to Fig. 1.16.) Finally the axial reflections are examined, and although we find that in $h00$, $h = 2n$, in $0k0$, $k = 2n$ and in $00l$, $l = 2n$, these are all special cases of the glide plane absences already listed and are therefore no help in deciding whether the crystal has screw axes or not. Thus although there must be two-fold symmetry in the c-direction (because the crystal is orthorhombic) the only information we have about it is that it is not a glide plane.

TABLE 5.1

Systematic absences due to translational symmetry elements

Detection of glide planes

If absences are noted in:	the glide plane is:
$0kl$	perpendicular to a
$h0l$	perpendicular to b
$hk0$	perpendicular to c
hhl[1]	parallel to (110)

Reflections observed only if:	indicate:
$h = 2n$	a-glide plane
$k = 2n$	b-glide plane
$l = 2n$	c-glide plane
$\left. \begin{array}{c} h+k \\ \text{or} \quad k+l \\ \text{or} \quad l+h \end{array} \right\} = 2n$	n-glide plane (diagonal glide)
$\left. \begin{array}{c} h+k \\ \text{or} \quad k+l \\ \text{or} \quad l+h \\ \text{or} \quad h+k+l \end{array} \right\} = 4n$	d-glide plane[2] (diamond glide)

Detection of screw axes

If absences are noted in:	the screw axis is parallel to:
$h00$	a
$0k0$	b
$00l$	c

Reflections observed only if:	indicate:
$\left. \begin{array}{c} h \\ k \\ l \end{array} \right\} = 2n$	2_1, 4_2 or 6_3
$l = 3n$	$3_1(3_2)$ or $6_2(6_3)$ [3]
$\left. \begin{array}{c} h \\ k \\ l \end{array} \right\} = 4n$	$4_1(4_3)$
$l = 6n$	$6_1(6_5)$ [3]

[1] Not found in systems of orthorhombic or lower symmetry.

[2] Found only in centred cubic or tetragonal and in two F-centred orthorhombic space groups.

[3] Absences of this type among axial reflections occur only in trigonal and hexagonal space groups; the screw axis will then be parallel to the unique axis c, and the absences found in the $00l$ reflections only.

We can therefore write only a partial space group symbol, *Pna-*. At this point, having proceeded as far as we reasonably can from first principles, the best course is to check our observations against the absences listed in *International Tables*, Vol. I, pp. 111–119 and 133–151, or use the list on p. 350 therein, bearing in mind that if a, b, and c are interchanged an apparently different set of systematic absences will result. In fact, the absences given above are compatible with either *Pna2₁* or *Pnam*, and the standard setting for the latter is actually *Pnma* (that is with b and c exchanged relative to our original axes).

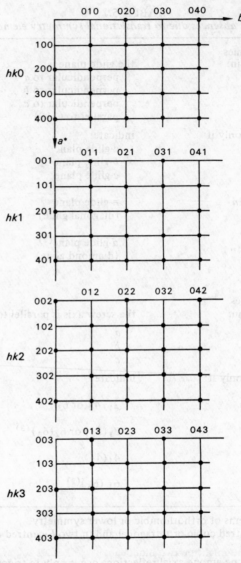

Fig. 5.1   Part of the reciprocal lattice of an orthorhombic crystal. Black dots indicate observed reflections.

It is in the orthorhombic system that the possibility of permuting axes causes most difficulty. In the monoclinic, tetragonal, trigonal and hexagonal systems, symmetry defines one axis; while at the two extremes, in both the triclinic and cubic systems the a, b and c axes can be freely permuted without changing the apparent space group (though for rather different reasons). *International Tables*, Vol. I, pp. 545–549, provides a list of equivalent space group symbols related through change of axes.

The symmetry of the diffraction pattern together with the systematic absences is thus not always sufficient to establish the space group uniquely; very often, as in the example above, there are two or more possibilities. This is in part because special sets of absences may be eclipsed by more general ones, but mainly because, as explained in the previous chapter, the symmetry of the diffraction pattern will not normally distinguish between two-fold axes and mirror planes in the crystal, or give any information with respect to the presence or otherwise of a centre of symmetry. The example above illustrates all three of these points (which are to some extent interdependent).

Sometimes other physical methods may help to distinguish between the various possibilities. If the crystals are well formed, their morphology may establish their point group; the space group can then usually be determined unequivocally. If the crystals show piezo- or pyro-electric effects (when subjected to compression, or to heating or cooling, they develop a polar separation of charge) it can be assumed that they do not have a centre of symmetry; unfortunately the reverse does not hold, since many non-centrosymmetric crystals do not show these effects to a detectable extent. Crystals that show optical activity (rotate the plane of polarized light) can belong only to certain classes. Tables summarizing these limitations will be found in the invaluable *International Tables*, Vol. I, p. 42, and information on any or all of these points should be borne in mind when space groups are being determined.

It may be possible to distinguish between the various possibilities on the basis of cell contents, calculated as described in the next section. Consider, for example, a monoclinic crystal of a molecular substance whose X-ray pattern shows no systematic absences. The three possible space groups, $P2$, Pm and $P2/m$, are illustrated in Fig. 5.2, together with the appropriate asymmetric groups. A series of imaginary examples shows the type of reasoning that might be used.

Suppose first that the cell is found to contain only one molecule. Figure 5.2 shows that the first two space groups have two asymmetric units in the cell and the last one has four. It is not therefore possible to place a single molecule in a general position—just anywhere in the cell: it must be placed in a special position, on one or more symmetry elements. That is to say, it could be placed on a two-fold axis in $P2$, or on a mirror plane in Pm, or at a centre of symmetry, where the two-fold axes and the mirror planes meet, in $P2/m$. In all these examples, the asymmetric unit is not the whole molecule, but a part of it and the molecule itself must have the symmetry of the chosen site. If it is known from other evidence (say, spectroscopic) that the molecule has, for example, a mirror plane but no two-fold axis, then the choice is limited to a mirror plane in Pm, and the space group is unequivocally fixed.

Suppose next that the cell contains two molecules. These might be placed either in the general position in $P2$ or Pm, on either the mirror plane or a two-fold axis in $P2/m$, or possibly there might be two independent molecules each lying on one of the special positions appropriate for a single molecule. Here again, a knowledge of the chemistry of the molecule may help. If, for example, individual molecules are known to be optically active but the solution from which the crystals grew was not, then the correct space group is unlikely to be $P2$ (which could accommodate two right-handed or two left-handed molecules, but not one of each) unless the crystals themselves are of two types, right- and left-handed, which might be apparent from their morphology. Conversely, if the solution of the compound *is* optically active, the space groups containing a mirror plane are excluded. (The crystals themselves may show optical activity as already mentioned, but the interpretation of this is not quite so straightforward. Its presence excludes a centre of symmetry, but not necessarily a mirror plane; see *International Tables*, Vol. I, p. 42.)

If the cell contains four molecules it becomes more difficult to draw conclusions,

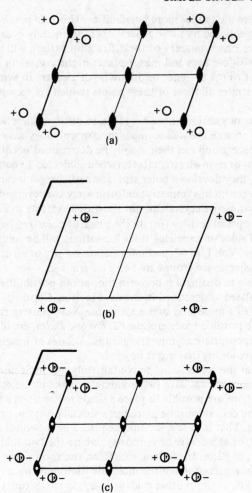

Fig. 5.2   Symmetry elements and the arrangements of asymmetric units in (a) $P2$, (b) Pm and (c) $P2/m$.

although arguments based on optical activity may still help. It may then not be possible to determine the true space group without embarking on a full structure determination; there are many examples in the literature of crystals whose space groups remained uncertain until the final stages of the structure analysis, although the true space group usually emerges earlier than this.

The above type of reasoning is not restricted to molecular substances; it is equally applicable to ionic compounds (with the proviso that these are somewhat more likely than molecular compounds to show disorder and its associated effects); many an early structure determination was based on little more than the space group determination plus a dash of informed chemical intuition. Structures that can be solved in this way are now only rarely encountered, but examples do occur from time to time.

Space group determination is occasionally complicated by a phenomenon known as **double reflection**. If the beam reflected from a set of planes $(h_1 k_1 l_1)$ strikes another set of planes $(h_2k_2l_2)$ at the appropriate angle, it may be reflected again. This doubly reflected beam will appear to arise from the $(h'k'l')$ planes of the crystal where

$$h' = h_1 + h_2$$
$$k' = k_2 + k_2$$
$$l' = l_2 + l_2$$

The doubly reflected beam will obviously be rather weak, but sometimes, if $h_1k_1l_1$ and $h_2k_2l_2$ are both strong reflections and the real $h'k'l'$ reflection is absent, a spurious reflection may result.

If, therefore, a pattern of systematic absences is violated only by one very weak reflection, the possibility of double reflection should be considered before assuming that the corresponding glide plane or screw axis is only approximate. (Lattice absences cannot be violated in this way, because the two planes giving rise to the double reflection must themselves obey the lattice conditions; adding their indices can only produce a set of indices that also obeys these conditions.) On film, double reflections may be distinguished by their appearance; because of the way they are formed, they are much sharper than the true reflections. They should disappear if the X-ray wavelength is changed. They may also vanish if the crystal is remounted in a different orientation. The final check is to search the diffraction pattern for a pair of strong reflections whose indices are appropriately related; this must of course be done in three dimensions, since a spurious 110 reflection might arise from a combination of, say, 211 and $10\bar{1}$ as easily as from 210 and $\bar{1}00$. Fortunately double reflection is not often encountered; the above is more in the nature of a caution than an account of a routine occurrence.

5.2 Density and unit cell contents

The relationship between the volume of the unit cell, V, measured in Å^3, and the density, D, measured in g cm^{-3}, is

$$D = \frac{1.66\,Z \times F}{V}$$

where F is the formula weight of the substance concerned and Z is the number of such formula units within the cell. Provided that the density can be measured, or estimated as described in Section 2.8, this relationship can be used to check analyses, to determine molecular weights and occasionally to establish compositions that are not readily determined by other means.

Densities can be determined in various ways. If ample material is available, perhaps the most satisfactory method is by means of an **air displacement pyknometer**, which compares the volume of air contained in an empty chamber with that in a chamber containing a weighed quantity of the material under test. The commercially available models give good results, but require 5–10 g of sample, and one cannot always prepare or obtain such large quantities. Where amounts in the region of 1 g are available, the classical method using a density bottle may be used, assuming that a liquid can be found that neither dissolves the test substance nor is too volatile for accurate weighing.

Very often even one gram of material represents an impossibly large amount, and suspension methods must be used. The most common one is colloquially—and descriptively—referred to as 'sink or swim'. This uses a mixture of liquids whose compo-sition can be varied until the crystals neither sink nor float; the density of the liquid mixture is then determined by conventional means. A more sophisticated version of this uses a column of liquid of continuously varying density, calibrated by floating in it standard glass beads; the density of the test material is determined from the height at which it settles. Although the actual measurements can be made very rapidly, the columns are troublesome to set up and the range of density covered by any one column is limited so the method is only really useful if large numbers of measurements have to be made on a series of materials of similar density. These suspension methods require particles of material that are large enough to be visible, and have an upper limit set by the availability of suitable high-density liquids. Bromoform-benzene mixtures are often used for materials of moderate densities (up to 2.89 g cm^{-3}). For very high density materials, concentrated solutions of thallium salts can be used; great care must be exercised with these, as they are highly poisonous.

Whatever method is used, the errors tend to make the measured density too low; all methods may be affected by crystal imperfections, and in addition those that employ liquids will be severely affected should the test sample contain small quantities of occluded air. Experience shows that the density calculated from the correct cell con-tents and the measured unit cell (the 'X-ray density') will invariably be slightly higher than the measured density. The extent of the disagreement varies with the method employed, as implied above, but the direction is constant; results that give an X-ray density that is apparently *lower* than the measured density should be regarded with extreme suspicion.

The information thus derived has various uses, depending on what is being ex-amined. For molecular substances, a check can be obtained on the molecular weight, since in general the unit cell must contain a whole number of molecules, and unless these are occupying special positions, as discussed in the previous section, the number of molecules must either equal or be a simple multiple of the number of general equivalent positions.

An example of the use of cell contents/space group considerations to establish an exact composition [1] is given in Table 5.2. The crystals were produced by devitrification of lead silicate glasses containing about 40 mole % PbO, but could never be obtained completely free either of other phases or of small amounts of uncrystal-lized glass; the composition, although known to be close to that of the original glass, could thus not be established with certainty by chemical means. The density had also to be measured on a somewhat impure sample. However, it was found possible to extract a few single crystals and determine the unit cell. The crystals were ortho-rhombic and the conditions for possible reflections were the same as those for the lattice in Fig. 5.1, discussed in the previous section: in this case physical methods proved that the crystals were non-centrosymmetric and the space group is therefore $Pna2_1$. This is shown in Fig. 5.3; it has four general equivalent positions, and since all the symmetry elements are translational ones, there are no special positions— moving an atom onto a two-fold screw axis, for example, does not reduce the number required by the symmetry operation. Therefore the number of atoms of each kind in the unit cell must be divisible by four (unless the material is disordered in some way; this is discussed in the next section). All this is summarized in Table 5.2, which also shows that for a composition corresponding to that of the original glass, 2 PbO. 3 SiO$_2$, or Pb$_2$Si$_3$O$_8$, the unit cell would contain 10 formula units or 30 Si atoms. This is unlikely, so the contents were recalculated for other ratios of PbO and SiO$_2$ close to the original one.

TABLE 5.2
Deduction of composition from crystallographic data and density

Crystal data:
 approximate composition 2 PbO . 3 SiO$_2$
 measured density 5.95 ± 0.03 g cm^{-3}
 orthorhombic with a = 9.123 Å
  b = 11.807Å
  c = 16.268 Å
 cell volume V = 1752.3 Å^3

Conditions for reflections:
 in 0kl, $k + l = 2n$ (n-glide perpendicular to a)
 in $h0l$, $h = 2n$ (a-glide perpendicular to b)
 no other conditions
 no centre of symmetry

Space group therefore $Pna2_1$ with $\begin{cases}\text{fourfold general position}\\\text{no special positions}\end{cases}$

From $D = \dfrac{1.66\,Z \times F}{V}$, $Z \times F = 6280.8$

If composition is 2 PbO . 3 SiO$_2$ (Pb$_2$Si$_3$O$_8$), F = 626.65 giving Z = 10.02.
 Cell contents would then be 20 PbO . 30 SiO$_2$ (Pb$_{20}$Si$_{30}$O$_{80}$) which is unlikely since 30 is not a multiple of 4.

Possible alternative cell contents are
 20 PbO . 28 SiO$_2$, weight 6145.3, $d_{\text{x-ray}}$ = 5.82 g cm^{-3}
 20 PbO . 32 SiO$_2$, weight 6386.7, $d_{\text{x-ray}}$ = 6.05 g cm^{-3}

The latter seems more probable, giving the composition 5 PbO . 8 SiO$_2$ and cell contents 4 (Pb$_5$Si$_8$O$_{21}$).

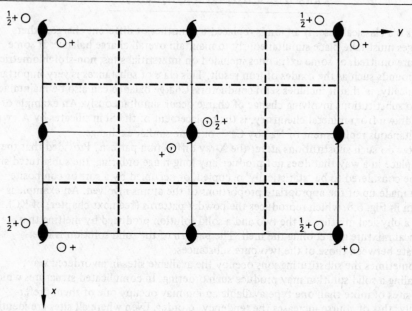

Fig. 5.3 Symmetry elements and general equivalent positions of space group $Pna2_1$.

It seems likely that the number of Pb atoms in the cell is indeed 20; the nearest alternatives, 16 or 24, both give ridiculous values for the density, Pb being by far the heaviest atom in the cell. The original value of 20 PbO is therefore retained and the assumed SiO_2 content is varied slightly. The two most probable formulae are given in the table; of these the one of higher silica content is preferred, because the X-ray density calculated from this is slightly higher than the measured density. The observation that small amounts of $PbSiO_3$ – a compound of higher PbO content – were frequently formed along with the unknown phase supports this conclusion.

5.3   Order, disorder and polytypism

Passing reference has already been made to the occurrence of imperfections and disorder in crystals, and we will now discuss briefly the effects that these may have on X-ray diffraction patterns. The subject is complicated, and if you encounter examples, you will need to seek help from more advanced works than this.

Disorder can take various forms. In inorganic chemistry (and mineralogy and metallurgy) one of the most common is **solid solution**. Typically this occurs between two substances of similar structure whose atoms or ions are of similar size and charge and can thus replace one another without undue distortion. Table 5.3 gives some examples of materials that can form solid solutions – the replacement of Al^{3+} by Cr^{3+} in the

TABLE 5.3
Materials capable of forming solid solutions

$K_2SO_4 - Cs_2SO_4$
$KCl - KBr$
$Ag_2S - PbS$
$KAl(SO_4)_2 . 12H_2O - KCr(SO_4)_2 . 12H_2O$

alums is a classical case. If an ion is replaced by another of different charge, other changes must take place simultaneously to maintain overall charge balance. If some ions are omitted, or some extra ones included on interstitial sites, **non-stoichiometric** compounds such as the oxides of iron result. This class of substances is very important technically, in that it includes semi-conductors. Charge balance can also be maintained if two substitutions involving change of charge occur simultaneously. An example of this, drawn from mineral chemistry, is the replacement of the Si in silicates by Al, with simultaneous replacement of Na^+ by Ca^{2+}, or some similar exchange.

How do such substitutions affect the X-ray diffraction pattern? Provided that they take place in a way that does not produce any long-range ordering, the substituted site can be considered to be 'statistically' occupied, or occupied by a sort of composite atom made up of the appropriate proportions of the atoms involved. An example is shown in Fig. 6.8, which reproduces the powder patterns (see next chapter) of KCl, KBr, a physical mixture of the two and a solid solution produced by melting that physical mixture and cooling the melt. The pattern of the solid solution is intermediate between those of the two pure substances.

Sometimes the substituting ions occupy the available sites in an ordered way; annealing a solid solution may produce such ordering. In complicated structures which have sites of more than one type available an ion may occupy one of them preferentially; this of course increases the tendency to order. Even where all sites are identical, occupation of one site by a larger ion may distort adjacent sites, making them more likely to be occupied by other large ions. An example of this is the replacement of the Ca in rhombohedral $CaCO_3$ (calcite) by Mg. This can take place in a completely random way, but Ca^{2+} is considerably larger than Mg^{2+} and a structure can also form in which whole layers of calcium ions parallel to the plane of the CO_3^{2-} groups are replaced by Mg^{2+}; this is the structure of the mineral dolomite.

When structures are perfectly ordered in this way, they are, strictly speaking, no longer solid solutions but compounds in their own right. They are considered here as one extreme of a continuum, at the other end of which lies complete disorder. Since many substances can exist in either an ordered or a disordered form (as in the example just given), it is not surprising that examples of partial ordering also occur. The extent to which a substance is ordered often reflects its history. For example, a substance which is ordered at low temperature may become progressively less ordered as the temperature is raised, because the increased amplitude of the atomic vibrations makes the difference between sites less critical. Sudden cooling of such materials to temperatures at which atomic migrations become sluggish may preserve indefinitely the disordering present at the higher temperature. Since many minerals behave in precisely this way, studying the degree of order preserved gives information about the thermal history of the rocks containing them, and this technique has proved invaluable to geologists.

Replacement of one sort of atom by another in an ordered way usually has a more profound effect on the diffraction pattern than the mere changes in the intensity and spacing of reflections shown by solid solutions. Ordering usually results in a decrease in symmetry, or an increase in cell size to some multiple of the original, or both, and in either case extra reflections normally appear in the diffraction pattern; when these indicate an increase in the size of the lattice repeat compared with that of the parent structure, they are often called **superlattice** reflections.

A related phenomenon found in some non-stoichiometric compounds is that of the ordering of defects or formation of **Magneli shear structures**. This is a complex subject, and for further information specialist reviews should be consulted [2]; in general the result is to superimpose an extremely large true repeat unit onto a basically simple structure. The diffraction pattern may look something like Fig. 5.4; the simple pattern

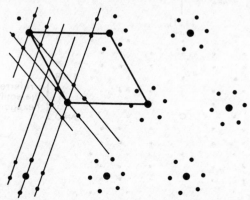

Fig. 5.4   Typical diffraction pattern from a material with a fairly simple pseudo-structure modulated over a larger distance. The reciprocal pseudo-cell is outlined by bold lines; the corresponding reciprocal lattice accounts for the strong reflections. The true reciprocal lattice, which accounts for the weak reflections as well, is shown by the fainter lines. The true reciprocal cell is much smaller, and the true real cell much bigger, than the respective pseudo-cells.

of strong reflections indicates the size and shape of the simple repeat or **pseudo-cell**, but the presence of the satellite spots shows that the true cell is very much larger. Similar patterns may be given by other structure types, and do not necessarily imply non-stoichiometry, but whenever they are encountered it is safe to assume that a simple basic pseudo-structure is being modulated in some way over a very much larger distance. A profitable way of attacking the problem is to try to solve the pseudo-structure first (often this may be obvious from analogy with a simpler, known structure) and then consider how it may be altered slightly in some ordered way to give the true structure.

Finally, we must consider the effects produced by the **stacking disorder** or **polytypism** shown by certain types of layer structure. This is best illustrated with reference to an actual example, for which we will use ZnS. This occurs in a large number of structural modifications. The two simplest are the cubic sphalerite, which can be regarded as derived from the diamond structure through replacing alternate carbon atoms by Zn and S, and the hexagonal wurtzite, which bears the same relation to sphalerite as hexagonal to cubic closest packing. In the cubic form, layers of atoms

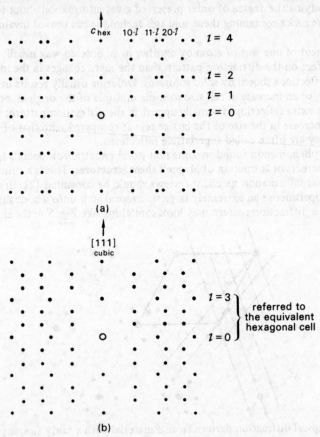

Fig. 5.5   Diagrammatic representations of the reciprocal lattices of (a) wurtzite rotated about c (2-layer stacking), (b) cubic sphalerite rotated about the equivalent [111] direction (3-layer stacking: the l indices refer to the equivalent hexagonal cell), (c) a crystal containing a mixture of 2- and 3- layer stacking, together with some

perpendicular to [111] (a body diagonal of the cube) repeat in a sequence of three (ABCABC . . .); the hexagonal form has a two-layer sequence (ABABA . . .) perpendicular to c. In ZnS, as in other compounds that can adopt these two forms, regular repeats of more complicated stacking sequences (e.g. ABABCBABABCB . . .) may occur. A crystal like this, which does not have the true structure of either simple end-member but is not sufficiently different to warrant classification as a separate structure, is called a **polytype**. It can readily be seen that an infinite variety of stacking sequences is theoretically possible, and many of these have been observed in practice. When the stacking sequence is ordered throughout the crystal, this shows in the X-ray pattern as a change in the length of the axis perpendicular to the layers. It is, however, also possible for the sequence of layers to be completely without order, and in this case the length of the c-axis becomes indeterminate; as a result, the corresponding reciprocal lattice points are extended into rods parallel to c^*. Crystals containing two or more distinct polytypes, connected by regions of disorder, give patterns of spots, corresponding to the polytypes, connected by streaks, corresponding to the disordered regions. These effects are illustrated in Fig. 5.5. Certain reflections remain unaffected by this streak-

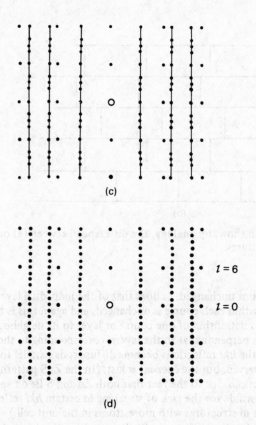

disordered regions that give rise to the streaking along the c-direction, (d) an ordered hexagonal polytype with a longer c-repeat than wurtzite (6-layer stacking).

These are rather simplified versions of the effects that can occur; in practice, crystals often exhibit more complicated patterns than these.

ing, notably the 00*l*'s; a pattern consisting of sharp 00*l* reflections accompanied by *hk*
rods is quite characteristic of layer structures showing disorder in the stacking of the
layers. A two-dimensional analogy may help to make the reason for this clearer. Figure
5.6(a) shows a brick wall with the courses properly arranged; Fig. 5.6(b) shows a wall
built with the same sort of bricks, but with the sequence of the coursing random. The

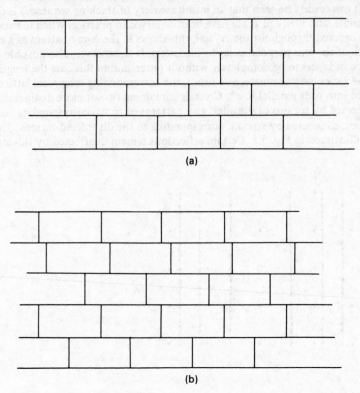

Fig. 5.6   A brick wall used to show, by analogy, the difference between (a) ordered
and (b) disordered layer structures.

thickness of the courses remains unchanged, as does that of the individual layers in a
layer structure; the pattern within each course is unchanged, and again this is true of
the layer structure. Only the relationship of one course or layer to its neighbours has
altered. Hence the reflections perpendicular to the layers, corresponding to the layer
thickness, remain sharp, but the *hkl* reflections become diffuse rods parallel to c^*, in
which the *hk* repeats are preserved, but the *l* repeat is lost. (In the ZnS pattern systematic absences in the *hkl* reflections due to the fact that both Zn and S lie on special
positions in the cell are responsible for the lack of streaking in certain *hkl* reflections;
this will not usually be found in structures with more atoms in the unit cell.)

The above very brief introduction to an exceedingly complicated subject should
enable you to recognize these effects if you encounter them; and then you must decide whether you need to go into the subject in more detail.

5.4 Topotactic studies

A single crystal can sometimes be made to undergo a 'solid state reaction' in such a way that it produces one or more single crystals of another compound. This is known as a **topotactic transformation,** and study of the relative orientation of the crystals of reactant and product materials can give interesting insights into the mechanism by which the reaction proceeded. Typical of such reactions are polymorphic transformations, decompositions (such as dehydration), and redox reactions or other changes brought about by heating the reactant crystal in a special atmosphere or by allowing it to react with a solution. Examples of reactions that have been studied extensively in this way are the transformations between the many hydroxides, oxides and oxy-hydroxides of iron and manganese and the decomposition of carbonates to the appropriate oxides.

There are several possible ways of determining the relative orientations of reactant and product. Perhaps the easiest and most satisfactory method, when it can be applied, is to arrest the reaction before it has reached completion. The specimen will then contain both reactant and product, and their relative orientations can be determined directly from their diffraction patterns. If it is not possible to stop the reaction before completion, some other way has to be devised of relating the product orientation to that of the reactant.

If the reactant crystal has a definite and easily recognizable morphology, a drawing can be made showing the positions of its crystallographic axes relative to its shape. After the reaction, the orientation of the product(s) is determined relative to the crystal outline, and hence related to that of the original crystal. If the reactant crystal has no recognizable shape, one must determine orientations relative to the instrument on which it is mounted and any adhesive used must therefore be able to withstand the conditions of the reaction. Problems of adhesion are particularly acute if the crystal is to be heated, since normal organic-based glues will carbonize at temperatures between 200 and 300°C. An inorganic cement that is quite successful for high temperature work can be made by mixing high alumina cement to a paste with a little waterglass (sodium silicate) diluted with water; the waterglass makes the mixture sufficiently tacky, and the addition of the cement causes the mixture to set and prevents the bubbling that occurs when sodium silicate is heated alone. Whatever adhesive is chosen should not, of course, react with the crystal, and due allowance should be made for any diffraction pattern arising from it. It may indeed be better to dispense with adhesive altogether and mount the crystal in a capillary or something similar.

Studies of polymorphic or other transformations that are reversible with temperature require that the photographs be taken while the crystal is being heated or cooled as appropriate. To this end various high- and low-temperature cameras have been devised; some of these are described in Section 5.6 and some in Section 6.7.

Closely related to the phenomenon of topotaxy is that of epitaxy, in which one compound grows on another in a definite orientation; indeed it is sometimes difficult to decide which phenomenon is being studied. Epitaxial growth does not necessarily imply a chemical relationship between the host and guest substances (crystals of iodoform, CHI_3, will grow epitaxially on LiF) but where it does, study of the relationships of the two materials may yield useful chemical information. An obvious example is the study of the growth of oxide films on metals.

5.5   Intensity measurements

The determination of the unit cell and space group alone may not provide as much information about your compound as you need or would like; in that case you may decide to measure the intensities of some or all of the accessible reflections, either to check deductions made from the earlier studies or as a preliminary to a full structure analysis as outlined in Chapter 7. We will assume that your crystals show no symptoms of disorder or twinning; although it is perfectly possible to tackle the structure of such crystals, it is not the sort of task with which to begin your studies.

Methods of determining intensities fall into two groups. We will consider first those that utilize the photographic techniques already described. An X-ray diffraction pattern recorded on film shows a considerable variation in the amount of blackening corresponding to different reflections; simple examination of such a film enables us to classify intensities as weak, moderate or strong, or perhaps on a scale running from very, very weak up to very, very strong, with a number of intermediate grades. This may be all that is needed to confirm a relatively simple structure; indeed many early structure determinations, even of quite complicated crystals, were based on no more than this. However, more precise numerical values for the intensities are usually needed, particularly if it is hoped to determine structural details such as bond lengths and angles with any accuracy.

To avoid problems caused by overlapping reflections, intensities are usually measured from films taken using one of the moving film cameras. The Weissenberg method is the most usual, because of the large volume of reciprocal space accessible to it; for very complicated crystals, whose patterns may well fade out at quite low angles anyway, the ease of interpretation of precession photographs may outweigh this consideration.

The blackening of film is linear with exposure only for low exposure (Fig. 5.7); the reason for this is that once a particular silver halide particle in the coating has been activated through absorbing a quantum of X-radiation, it will be reduced to silver when the film is developed, regardless of whether it receives further radiation. Consequently as the proportion of activated particles rises, the effect produced by further radiation falling on that region of the film diminishes; or, put more crudely, the film cannot be blacker than completely black. The range of intensities in most crystal patterns is so great that all cannot be measured on the same film; if the exposure is adjusted to bring the strongest reflections into the approximately linear range, the weakest ones will be too weak to observe, and conversely if the exposure be increased so that the weakest reflections are recorded, the most intense ones will be unmeasurable. Therefore each set of reflections is recorded on a series of photographs of differing exposure; the most convenient way of doing this is to use a **multiple film pack**. The camera is loaded with a pack of up to five films all stacked together;† the film nearest the crystal gives the strongest pattern because before reaching the next film the beams are attenuated by their passage through the first, and so on. If CuKα radiation is being used it is found that for many types of film the effective exposure of successive films in the pack is reduced by between 1/2 and 1/4; if the diminution is less than this, additional layers of, say, aluminium foil may be intoduced between the layers to produce the required attenuation. A factor of two between successive films represents an

---

† This technique cannot be used with precession geometry, nor with any other arrangement where the crystal-to-film distance is critical.

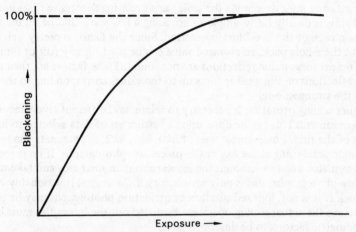

Fig. 5.7 Typical graph showing the relation between the blackening of film and exposure to X-rays; the exact shape of the curve will depend on the film and the radiation used. In all cases, estimates of exposure from the extent of blackening become less and less reliable as the exposure increases.

effective exposure ratio of 2^4 or 16 between the first and the fifth film, so that a fair range of intensities can be recorded simultaneously; a factor of four between films extends this range considerably.

The blackening of the film may be converted into relative intensities either by measurement with a **photometer (densitometer)** or by visual comparison with a prepared set of standard intensities. A photometer gives a more precise set of values, providing due allowance can be made for any irregularities in the shape of the spots; some photometers are designed to scan the spots to give an integrated value for the intensities. Sometimes this function is performed by the recording instrument, as in the 'integrating' Weissenberg or precession cameras which produce square spots by moving the film through very small distances along a grid during the exposure. In either case, for minimum effort one would like to have the photometer scan the film automatically; this is relatively easy to arrange for the undistorted arrays produced by the precession method, but much less easy for the photographs produced on a Weissenberg camera.‡

The alternative of visual matching is less precise, but a perfectly acceptable set of data can be obtained in this way. The standard intensity strip should be produced with some care. The best method is to select one of the stronger spots from the crystal being measured and record it with a series of known exposures on a strip of film, moving the film between exposures. These should be adjusted so that the weakest spot is barely visible, successive exposures increasing in intensity in known ratio to this one; a factor $\sqrt{2}$ between the intensities of successive spots is suitable. The advantage of preparing the strip in this way is that any irregularity in spot shape appears on both film and intensity strip, and this makes matching very easy and more accurate.

To get a complete set of relative intensities two different scaling operations are

---

‡ In the U.K., a microdensitometer service for scanning Weissenberg films has been established by the Science Research Council. Information may be obtained from: SRC Microdensitometer Service, Atlas Computer Laboratory, Chilton, Didcot, Oxfordshire OX11 0QY.

needed. First, one must determine the scale factor relating successive films in the multiple pack; this is usually fairly simple to do, using a few spots that lie on the measurable scale on each of the two films in question. Since the factor is pretty well constant throughout the whole pack, an averaged value can be used for any pair of films for which sufficient measurable reflections are not found. These factors are then used to scale the reflections on the weaker films up to the values corresponding to the exposure of the strongest one.

The other scaling operation is necessary to relate, say, different layers recorded on a Weissenberg camera. This can be done using a further set of data selected to intersect the layers of the first. For example, sets of $hk0, hk1, hk2, \ldots$ etc. data can be placed on a common scale using either $h0l$ or $0kl$ precession photographs. If no precession camera is available one can remount the crystal about another axis and take more Weissenberg photographs; this is only satisfactory if the crystal is reasonably equidimensional. If it is not, indexed rotation or oscillation photographs may be used for scaling. Before the actual scaling operation is carried out the intensities must be corrected for geometric factors, to be described later.

The diffracted beams need not necessarily be recorded as blackening on film; indeed, some of the earliest measurements were made using a gold-leaf electroscope as detector. The modern equivalent is to use some sort of **counter**, which converts the X-ray quanta it receives into a recordable electrical signal. An instrument that uses such a device to record a diffraction pattern is called a **diffractometer**.

For recording intensities, diffractometers are inherently somewhat more accurate than film-based methods. However, it is not so much this as the relative ease with which they can be designed to collect data automatically that makes them so attractive to crystallographers. Having set the necessary parameters, the crystallographer can go away and do something else while the data accumulate, instead of squinting at spots or manipulating a densitometer; moreover the results are produced as a punched tape or set of cards ready to be fed into a computer for further processing, which saves the labour and possible errors of transcribing the data.

There are numerous designs and a number of different modes of operation of automatic single crystal diffractometers. All that need concern us here is that they systematically explore reciprocal space; wherever a reflection is to be expected they pause and measure the diffracted intensity due to the reflection and also the adjacent background radiation. This information, together with the appropriate indices, is usually printed out so that the run can be monitored, in addition to being recorded in a form suitable for computer input. Some machines incorporate a small computer which may do some initial processing of the data in addition to controlling the movements of the crystal and counter; some are run on-line from a larger computer on a time-sharing basis and yet others need to be supplied with paper-tape instructions previously prepared on a separate computer. There is one drawback common to all: they are very expensive.

5.6   Special techniques

From time to time one may wish to maintain a crystal under special conditions while it is being studied. Perhaps it decomposes when exposed to the atmosphere, or undergoes a polymorphic transition reversible with temperature. Perhaps one wants to maintain a very low temperature in order to reduce the thermal vibrations of the atoms or to suppress the free rotations of groups of atoms (such as CO_3^{2-} or NH_4^+), or to study a substance that is a liquid or gas at room temperature.

Probably the most common requirement is to heat or cool the crystal. Provided that the required temperature is not far removed from ambient, one might enclose the whole apparatus in some sort of temperature-controlled jacket. This method is plainly unsuitable for attaining very high or very low temperatures. For studies at more extreme temperatures, one has to devise a way to heat or cool the crystal without damaging the instrument.

Much ingenuity has been expended on this problem, as a study of the bibliographies [3] will show. A number of difficulties must be overcome: the heating or cooling device must not obstruct the diffracted beams that are to be studied, the film or counter must be protected from extremes of temperature, the crystal must be mounted so that it does not move with change in temperature and, at low temperatures, ice must be prevented from forming in unsuitable places.

The problem of protecting the film or counter is generally more severe when designing high-temperature apparatus. One reason is that the minimum temperature that can be attained in a low-temperature device is still only about 300°C below ambient, whereas in a high-temperature device one may well be aiming to raise the temperature by 1000°C or more, and the larger the difference in temperature between crystal and detector, the greater the problem. Moreover, low temperatures are probably, on the whole, less damaging.

Perhaps the most successful designs have been those based on an indirect method of heating or cooling, such as blowing a jet of hot or cold air at the crystal or (less desirably) dripping liquid nitrogen onto it; induction heating, focused radiant heating, and heating or cooling by conduction through the mount have also been tried.

Many of these methods, when used in conjunction with a fairly 'open' type of instrument such as a precession camera or a diffractometer, do not produce unacceptable changes in the temperature of the film or counter. In a more enclosed system such as a Weissenberg camera, the film must be shielded and perhaps cooled if very high specimen temperatures are sought. Sometimes thermal exchange with the surroundings is minimized by provision of a vacuum and this also prevents ice forming if the crystal is being cooled.

More complicated devices such as miniature furnaces may give better temperature control and increase the potential range of temperature, but they are inherently more likely to block off part of the diffraction pattern and are therefore more suitable for powder studies (q.v.), in which only a narrow strip of diffraction pattern is needed anyway. Nevertheless, successful applications to single crystal studies have been reported; further details will be found in the Bibliography [3].

A crystal for high-temperature studies may be mounted in a capillary (usually silica) and fixed in place either with a high-temperature cement or by wedging with tiny silica fibres; or it may be fixed to a silica fibre with high-temperature cement. Although the latter method avoids loss of diffracted intensity through absorption in the walls of the capillary, it increases the likelihood of total loss of the crystal.

Crystals that are sensitive to atmosphere present another type of problem. If the difficulty is no more than a slight tendency to pick up carbon dioxide or to change hydration state, it may be sufficient to cover the surface of the crystal with a protective coating such as a thin layer of shellac, artist's lacquer or petroleum jelly. More labile materials, for example those that oxidize rapidly in air, require more positive protection. It is sometimes possible to fill the whole instrument with an inert atmosphere, but it is usually more convenient to seal the crystal itself in a capillary tube.

This latter method must be used for compounds that have to be handled by high-vacuum techniques. Sometimes these materials can be handled in a glove box, but more often the capillary must be sealed onto the high-vacuum system. If a single crystal can be grown in it from the vapour phase, the capillary is then sealed off and mounted. Otherwise the capillary is sealed onto a larger vessel and the sample is introduced into that. This vessel is then sealed off and then shaken or otherwise manipulated with the aim of getting one, and only one, crystal to enter the capillary, which is then itself sealed off. (This exercise is a bit like one of those Christmas puzzles that involves rolling ball-bearings into holes.) When one crystal has been isolated, it must be wedged securely in the capillary, so that it does not slip while its diffraction pattern is being recorded. One method is to use a slightly tapering capillary, gently tapping it so that the crystal lodges in the narrower end.

Some crystals grown from solution decompose unless kept in contact with the mother liquor or its vapour and these also must be mounted in capillary tubes; biological materials such as proteins behave in this way. These may also have to be wedged in their tubes so as to prevent movement; sometimes if only a little liquor is present they will adhere to the tube walls by capillarity [4]. When crystals have been fixed in such relatively insecure ways, radical changes in the position of the capillary are best avoided. If the bulk of the measurements are to be made with the capillary horizontal, as on a Weissenberg or precession camera, it should be kept in this position from the start; indeed even moving the crystal from one instrument to another should be avoided if possible.

Finally, one may want to study crystals under high pressure. Apparatus for producing high pressures tends to be cumbersome, which brings attendant design difficulties. One way of overcoming these is to construct the high-pressure cell of materials such as diamond or beryllium that are relatively transparent to X-rays. Single crystal attachments based on this principle are commercially available.

References

[1] Smart, R. M. and Glasser, F. P., *J. Am. Ceram. Soc.* **57**, 378–382 (1974).
[2] Wadsley, A. D., *Non-Stoichiometric Compounds* (edited by L. Mandelcorn), pp. 99–210, Academic Press, New York and London (1964); Wadsley, A. D. and Anderson, S., *Perspectives in Structural Chemistry* **3** (edited by J. D. Dunitz and J. A. Ibers), pp. 1–58, Wiley, London (1970); Bursill, L. A. and Hyde, B. G. *Progress in Solid State Chemistry* **7** (edited by H. Reiss and J. O. McCaldin), pp. 177–253, Pergamon, Oxford (1972).
[3] Goldschmidt, H., *Bibliography 1—High-Temperature X-ray Diffraction Techniques,* International Union of Crystallography (1964); Post, B., *Bibliography 2—Low-Temperature X-ray Diffraction,* International Union of Crystallography (1964).
[4] King, M. V., *Acta Crystallogr.* **7**, 601–602 (1954).

CHAPTER 6

The uses and abuses
of the powder method

6.1 What is a powder pattern?

A **powder pattern** is produced when X-rays are diffracted not by one single crystal but by a sample consisting of a very large number of randomly oriented crystalline particles, that is a powder. Figures 6.2 and 6.8 show such patterns recorded on film; they consist of a series of curved lines or rings, depending on the geometry of the camera. Powder patterns are chiefly used as a rapid means of identification, but they are sometimes used for structural studies, particularly if crystals large enough for single crystal study cannot be obtained.

The only condition governing the position of a reflected beam from a powder sample is Bragg's law; since $2d_{hkl} \sin \theta_{hkl} = \lambda$, for any given hkl all the reflections from all the tiny crystals lie on a cone of semi-vertical angle $2\theta_{hkl}$ (Fig. 6.1(a) (b)). In reciprocal lattice terms, the corresponding point may intersect the sphere of reflection anywhere on the circle PP indicated in Fig. 6.1(c). Provided that the material is sufficiently finely ground and the orientation of the particles completely random, the spots of the single crystal photograph extend into smooth lines on the powder pattern; compare Figs. 6.2, 6.3 and 4.11. Rotating the sample in the beam increases the number of planes passing through the reflecting position and helps to ensure that the lines are smooth rather than spotty.

It is sometimes difficult to ensure that the orientation of the particles *is* completely random. This is particularly true of materials that grow either as plates or needles. For obvious reasons, such crystals tend to line up during sample preparation, so that the intensity of certain types of reflection is enhanced in some regions of the diffraction cone. This is known as **preferred orientation**; methods of detecting and avoiding it will be dealt with later.

Figure 6.3 shows how the spots of the single crystal photograph become lines in the powder photograph; the powder pattern is derived from the rotation photograph by extending each spot along a line corresponding to constant d^*, where $d^* = \sqrt{(\zeta^2 + \xi^2)}$. Since only d (or d^*) can be measured from a powder pattern, all the information from the three-dimensional reciprocal lattice has thus been compressed into one dimension. In view of the complexity of most single crystal patterns, it obviously may be difficult to interpret powder patterns fully without additional information.

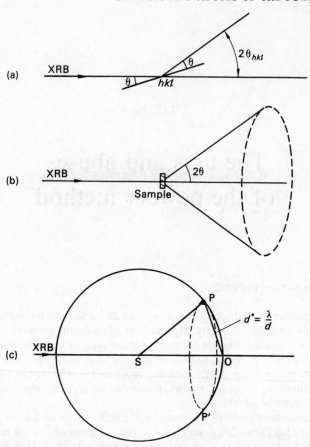

Fig. 6.1   Formation of a powder pattern. (a) The *hkl* planes of one of the tiny
crystals lie at the Bragg angle θ to the X-ray beam (XRB). (b) The *hkl* reflections from
all the randomly oriented crystals in the sample lie on a cone of semi-vertical angle 2θ.
(c) The situation in (b) redrawn in reciprocal lattice terms. The point P, representing
the reciprocal lattice point *hkl*, can intersect the sphere of reflection anywhere on the
circle PP', since there is no restriction on the direction OP.

In theory, even without additional information, it should be possible to determine
the unit cell from, and assign indices to, the lines of the powder pattern of any pure
phase; the availability of computers makes this very tempting. In practice, except for
the simplest patterns, such efforts are liable to be vitiated for several reasons. In the
first place, only the most intense reflections will be recorded in a powder pattern; most
trial-and-error methods rely on assigning tentative indices to a few of the lowest-angle
lines in the pattern, and many of these may in fact be missing. Secondly, if the unit
cell be large or complex or both, lines corresponding to different indices frequently
overlap. Finally, unless the sample is indeed a pure phase the pattern may contain ex-
traneous lines due to traces of impurity or to the presence of more than one polymorph
of the material under examination.

In short, it is always possible to determine some sort of unit cell from a powder
pattern only, but much more difficult to be certain that it is the right one. If a unit

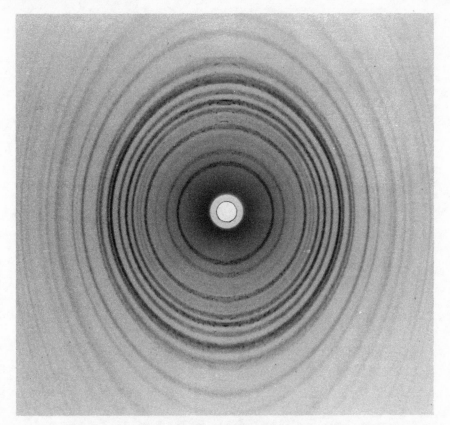

Fig. 6.2   An X-ray powder photograph of ammonium oxalate monohydrate, using the same camera as for Fig. 4.11, with which it should be compared. (Cu radiation, Ni filter). See also Fig. 6.3.

cell so determined is large and of low symmetry it should be viewed with suspicion. In practice, cubic unit cells determined from powder patterns are usually reliable even if they are quite large, particularly if the symmetry is corroborated by optical evidence. Simple patterns indexed on small hexagonal or tetragonal cells or very small ortho-rhombic ones will also often be correct. Everything else is suspect unless supported by some other evidence, such as single crystal data or analogy with related materials.

The above should not be taken to imply that the powder method is of no value; on the contrary in many fields it is invaluable. It is however largely complementary to single crystal techniques; it is not, and should not be treated as, a substitute for them.

6.2   Recording the pattern

6.2.1   Simple powder cameras

The powder pattern shown in Fig. 6.2 was recorded on the type of cylindrical camera used for rotation photographs. This method is useful if it is wished to compare single crystal and powder photographs directly (Fig. 6.3), either to see whether they

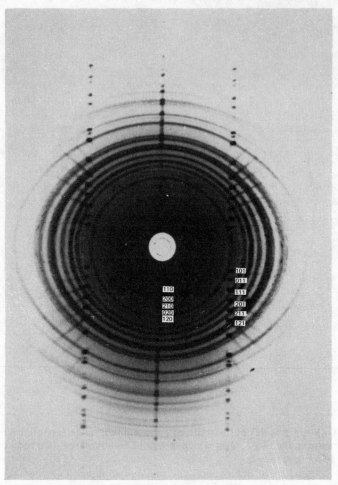

Fig. 6.3   The photographs shown in Figs. 4.11 and 6.2 have been superimposed, and
the central portion enlarged. Notice how the spots on the rotation photograph correspond to lines on the powder photograph. Some of the indices of the former, determined as described in Section 4.4, have been marked in; the corresponding powder
lines are thus indexed also.

are of identical phases or as a help in indexing the powder pattern (see below).
The diameter of the cassette is, however, rather small; although this can be an advantage when working with ill-crystallized materials, the lines of complicated patterns will
not be well resolved. Moreover, except in the special circumstances mentioned, recording powder patterns in this way wastes both film (there is no point in recording so
much pattern when only a narrow equatorial strip is needed) and equipment (a less
sophisticated camera will give the same result).

A simple Debye–Scherrer camera designed for powder work is shown in Fig. 6.4.
Basically, all that is needed is a simple light-tight cylindrical box to hold the film, a
collimator to admit a narrow beam of X-rays and a backstop to catch the direct beam,
and some means of adjusting the specimen. The latter should be roughly cylindrical; it

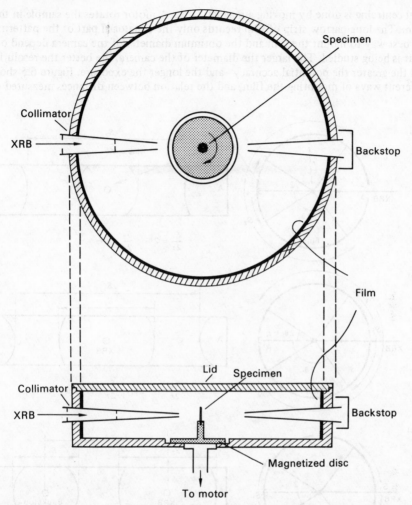

Fig. 6.4   A simple powder camera. The upper diagram shows the view from above
with the lid removed; the lower diagram is a cross-section through the collimator and
backstop with the lid in place. When the lid is in place, the camera is light-tight.

can be made by packing the powder into a thin-walled capillary tube (preferably made
from Lindemann—lithium borate—glass, which has a low absorbancy for X-rays), or by
making it into a paste with a little adhesive, such as gum arabic or tragacanth, and
rolling or extruding narrow cylinders of this. Some specimens if pressed with a spatula
form a thin flake from which a tiny rod can be cut with a razor blade; not all materials
adhere well enough for this to work, but when it does it provides a particularly simple
method of specimen preparation. The rod is then mounted on a glass fibre using the
same technique as for handling a large single crystal.

The prepared specimen is mounted in modelling clay or plasticene. Moving the
sample in the modelling clay usually gives the necessary height adjustment and allows
the sample to be roughly centred in the beam; in the camera illustrated in Fig. 6.4,

final centreing is done by moving a magnetic disc. A motor rotates the sample in the beam. The long narrow strip of film records only the equatorial part of the pattern; the best way to mount the film and the optimum diameter of the camera depend on what is being studied. The larger the diameter of the camera, the better the resolution and the greater the potential accuracy—and the longer the exposure. Figure 6.5 shows different ways of mounting the film, and the relation between distances measured on

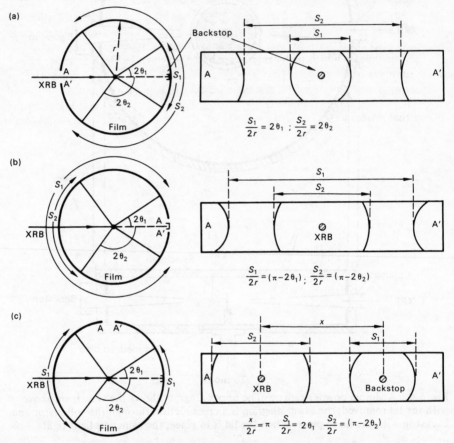

Fig. 6.5   Methods of mounting film for powder photography. (a) The simplest method if low-angle reflections are of interest. (b) The simplest method for examining high-angle reflections. (c) The Straumanis method is suitable for both high- and low-angle reflections and has a 'built-in' calibration for film shrinkage.

the resultant photograph(s) and the angle 2θ. The method shown in (a) is best if low-angle reflections are of most interest, while for studying the high-angle reflections method (b) is preferred. In either method errors arise if the film changes in size during processing; calibration can be provided by a pair of knife-edges which cast shadows at known positions on the two ends of the film. The asymmetric method of mounting shown in (c) has a built-in calibration, as indicated, and is useful for measuring both high- and low-angle reflections. For accurate work, an **internal standard** is often incorporated; that is the specimen under test is mixed with a suitable simple substance whose *d*-spacings are accurately known. This technique is applicable to any method of recording powder patterns.

6.2.2 Focusing cameras

The simple cameras described above utilize only a minute fraction of the radiation potentially available for diffraction. Focusing cameras use the available radiation more efficiently and hence greatly reduce exposure times; at the same time the resolution, or separation between lines from planes of similar spacings, is improved.

The principle on which such cameras are based is shown in Fig. 6.6: an arc of a circle subtends equal angles at all other points on the circle; thus the angles ACA', ADA', etc., are all equal, and for the same reason the angles CAD and CA'D are equal. Therefore if the sample, represented by AA', is irradiated by a beam diverging from C, planes that reflect when $2\theta = 180° - CAD$ will all give rise to diffracted beams focused

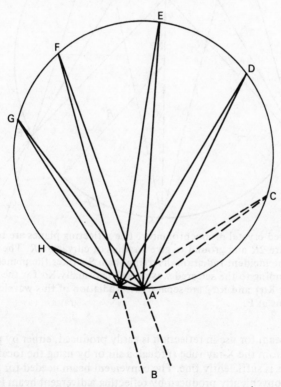

Fig. 6.6   The principle of a focusing camera. The specimen, AA', is irradiated either with divergent radiation from C or with convergent radiation B focused at F. All the angles subtended by the specimen at the circumference of the circle (ACA', ADA', etc.) are equal, and all angles subtended at the specimen by, say, the arc CD (CAD, CA'D and the angles at all points between A and A') are equal. Therefore reflections having the same 2θ value will all be brought to a focus at the same point on the circle, even though they arise from different parts of the specimen.

at D and so on. This focusing effect, therefore, is achieved simply by arranging for C, AA' and the film to lie on the same circle. This is the principle of the Seemann–Bohlin camera; an advantage of this is that it can be used to study massive polycrystalline specimens as well as powders. Alternatively, the specimen may be irradiated in transmission with a convergent beam, B, whose focus lies at F. In this case all diffracted beams for which (for example) 2θ = FAE will be brought to a focus at E; this is the principle of the Guinier camera. The specimen is commonly prepared by dusting the powder onto transparent adhesive film; care must be taken that sufficient is used to give a diffraction pattern, but not so much that the beam is totally absorbed.

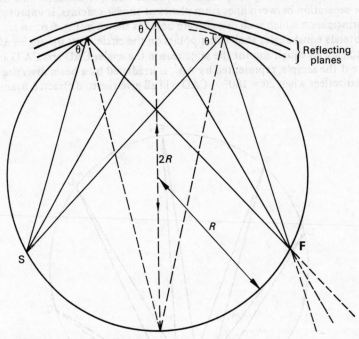

Fig. 6.7   A curved crystal monochromator. The reflecting planes are bent to have a radius of curvature $2R$ and ground to give a radius of curvature R. The value of R is chosen so that the incident radiation diverging from S strikes the planes at the Bragg angle θ corresponding to the selected wavelength (normally Kα for the incident radiation; sometimes Kα_1 and Kα_2 are separated). Radiation of this wavelength is thus brought to a focus at **F**.

A divergent beam for use in reflection is easily produced, either by passing the beam emerging from the X-ray tube through a slit or by using the focal spot of the tube itself, if this is sufficiently fine. The convergent beam needed for the transmission arrangement is conveniently produced by reflecting a divergent beam from a curved crystal monochromator, or **focusing monochromator** (Fig. 6.7). This is a single crystal cut parallel to a set of strongly reflecting planes, and then bent and ground to give the configuration shown in Fig. 6.7. The curvature is arranged so that radiation diverging from the source S always strikes the planes at the Bragg angle corresponding to its Kα component. A set of highly monochromatic beams is thus brought to a focus at **F**.

Comparison of Figs. 6.6 and 6.7 shows that to use a monochromator with the transmission type of focusing camera, the focal point **F** (Fig. 6.7) must coincide with F (Fig. 6.6), that is the monochromator is placed at the appropriate point in the path B (Fig. 6.6). Since the beam diverges again beyond **F**, a monochromator can also be used as a source of *divergent* monochromatic radiation for reflection geometry by making **F** coincide with C (Fig. 6.6).

Use of either type of focusing geometry with monochromatic radiation can give sharp, well-resolved lines on a clean background at relatively short exposures (Fig. 6.8). The optimum arrangement depends on the application: whether it is the high- or

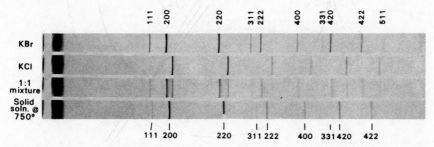

Fig. 6.8   Powder photographs taken using a Nonius focusing (Guinier) camera with monochromatized CuKα radiation. The samples are KBr, KCl, a mechanical mixture of the two (1 : 1 mole ratio), and the solid solution produced when the mixture is heated to 750°C. The indices of the lines are marked. Notice that lines with h, k and l odd are missing from the KCl pattern; this is because the scattering power of K^+ and Cl^- for X-rays is identical so that their contributions to these reflections cancel exactly (cf. Fig. 8.9).

The lines of the solid solution appear at d-spacings intermediate between those of the end-members. The slight fogging that can be observed between equivalent pairs of lines in the 1 : 1 mixture is caused by the production of small amounts of solid solution through the mechanical act of mixing the two salts.

low-angle part of the pattern that is of interest, or whether great precision of measurement is needed. The reflection arrangement shown in Fig. 6.6 with the source at C, for example, is unsuitable for studying the low-angle part of the pattern, because these reflections strike the film obliquely, as at H, making precise measurements difficult. On the other hand high-angle reflections strike the film almost normally as at E; to take maximum advantage of this the incoming beam should travel along the diameter of the camera and the reflected beams be recorded symmetrically on either side. The situation is reversed if the transmission arrangement, with the source at B, is used; the low-angle reflections then strike the film almost normally as at E, and are correspondingly sharp. Such considerations must be borne in mind when selecting (or perhaps designing) a camera; a variety of models is commercially available.

6.2.3   Powder diffractometers

The basic arrangement for a powder diffractometer is shown in Fig. 6.9(a). The specimen forms a flat plate that rotates about an axis at O, normal to the plane of the diagram, and a counter travels on a circle centred at O; the two motions are coupled so that the incoming beam and the radius to the receiving slit are both inclined to the specimen at the same angle. Since the incident beam is divergent, and each diffracted

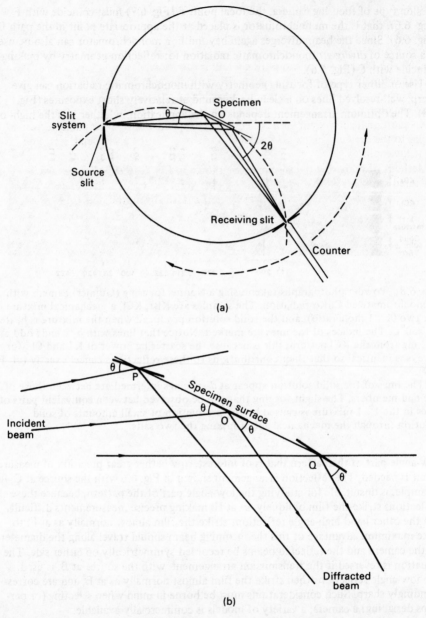

(a)

(b)

Fig. 6.9   The principle of a powder diffractometer. (The divergence and convergence of the beams are somewhat exaggerated.) (a) General arrangement. (b) Details of the formation of a diffracted beam, θ being a Bragg angle for the specimen. Rays of the incident beam make an angle θ with the surface of the specimen at the centre (O); at this point the reflecting planes (heavy lines) lie parallel to the specimen surface. Because the incident beam is diverging, rays that strike the specimen at other points, such as P and Q, are diffracted from planes (also shown as 'heavy lines') that are not quite parallel to the specimen surface. It is this that produces a covergent beam and the consequent semi-focusing effect.

ray makes an angle of 2θ with the appropriate ray of the incident beam, the diffracted beam is convergent (see detail in Fig. 6.9(b)). Consequently, the arrangement in Fig. 6.9(a), in which source slit, receiving slit and O all lie on a circle to which the specimen is tangential, has a semi-focusing effect; true focusing geometry would require that the specimen be curved, but the appropriate radius of curvature would vary with θ. Provided that the distances between source slit and sample and between receiving slit and sample are large compared with the size of the sample, the arrangement is a good approximation to focusing geometry.

An additional slit system limits the divergence of the beam in the plane perpendicular to the drawing, and a safety shield prevents radiation from being scattered about the room.

Methods of preparing the specimen are shown in Fig. 6.10. For best results, the powdered sample is packed into a window in an aluminium holder backed by a glass slide, as shown in (a). The obvious way of doing this is to fill the hole from above,

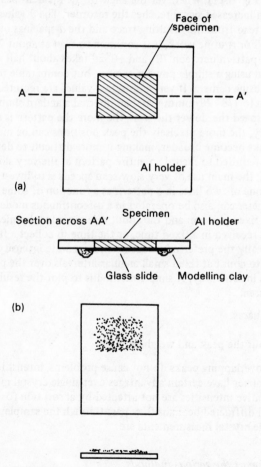

Fig. 6.10   Methods of preparing samples for powder diffractometry. (a) The pukka method. (b) the quick n' easy method. Method (a) uses more sample than (b), but it can all be easily recovered, since no adhesive is used; (a) gives accurate 2θ values; (b) is less liable to preferred orientation.

packing the sample down and smoothing the surface with another slide or with a spatula or similar implement, but this technique tends to maximize preferred orientation. It is better, if trouble from this source is expected, to lay the empty holder face down on a glass plate or other smooth surface, remove the glass slide, and pack the sample in *from the back*, finally replacing the glass slide. A more rough-and-ready method of sample preparation is shown in (b). An ordinary microscope slide is cut in half; one half of this is smeared with a thin layer of petroleum jelly and the sample sprinkled thinly onto this. This method is quick, requires very little sample, and comes as near as any method can to eliminating preferred orientation altogether; but because the specimen is not flush with the surface of the holder, it will not be correctly centred (at O, Fig. 6.9), and this introduces slight inaccuracies in the measured 2θ values.

The commonest way of operating a diffractometer is to set it to scan between the required angular limits; the signal from the counter is fed into a recorder to produce a continuous trace (Fig. 6.11). Whenever the angle of the incident beam satisfies the Bragg equation, an increased signal reaches the recorder. The θ values for the various reflections can be read from the resulting trace and the d-spacings of the reflecting planes calculated. For routine work, it is common to scan at about $2°\ 2\theta$/minute, so that to record the pattern between $70°$ and $10°\ 2\theta$ takes about half an hour; this is much quicker than using a simple powder camera, but comparable to the time for an exposure on a focusing camera. If very accurate d-values are required, a slower rate of scan is used, down to $1/8°\ 2\theta$/minute, and an internal standard should be included. For a given chart speed the slower the scan, the more the pattern is spread out on the chart and in theory, the more precisely the peak positions can be measured; at the same time the peaks become broader, making it more difficult to determine their exact centres. The time required to record an entire pattern at the very slowest speed is prohibitively long; the main use of very slow scan speeds is to investigate small shifts in the d-spacings of one or two lines in a pattern as a function of some variable.

The diffractometer can also be operated in a discontinuous mode, in which it is set to an appropriate fixed position and the count rate recorded, by measuring either the number of counts received in a fixed time, or the time to collect a fixed number of counts. This is usually the preferred method when accurate intensity data are sought, the routine being to count at fixed small angular intervals over the peak, finally integrating the results in some way. A simple method is to plot the results on graph paper and measure the area:

   by counting squares,
   by planimeter,
   or by cutting out the peak and weighing it.

Provided that overlapping peaks do not cause problems, intensities measured on a powder diffractometer have certain advantages over single crystal measurements. In particular, the relative intensities are not affected by absorption (or loss of energy from incident and diffracted beam as they pass through the sample; see Section 9.1) in the way that single crystal measurements are.

6.2.4   Comparison of the various methods

Some of the advantages and disadvantages of the various methods of recording powder patterns have already been mentioned; for convenience, these and other factors are summarized here.

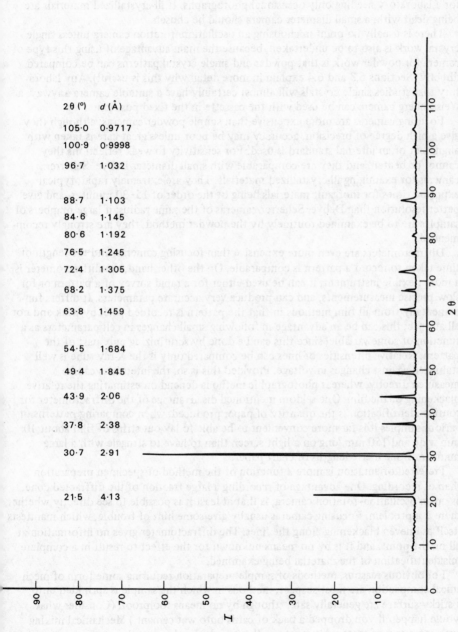

2θ (°)	d (Å)
105·0	0·9717
100·9	0·9998
96·7	1·032
88·7	1·103
84·6	1·145
80·6	1·192
76·5	1·245
72·4	1·305
68·2	1·375
63·8	1·459
54·5	1·684
49·4	1·845
43·9	2·06
37·8	2·38
30·7	2·91
21·5	4·13

Fig. 6.11 Typical diffractometer trace, recorded at 2° 2θ/min. The angle (2θ) and d-spacing corresponding to each peak are given on the left-hand side of the chart.

Debye-Scherrer cameras are relatively cheap, robust, and easy to use, and with care can give accurate d-values; on the other hand they are rather slow, up to 24 hours exposure being needed for some specimens. Such a camera would be a suitable choice for a laboratory needing only occasional photographs. If ill-crystallized materials are being dealt with, a small diameter camera should be chosen.

There is usually no point in choosing an oscillation-rotation camera unless single crystal work is also to be undertaken, because the main advantage of using this type of camera for powder work is that powder and single crystal patterns can be compared directly (Sections 6.3 and 6.4 explain in more detail why this is useful). Any laboratory that studies single crystals will almost certainly have a suitable camera anyway; a Weissenberg camera can be used with the cassette in the fixed position.

Focusing cameras are more expensive than simple powder cameras; although they give a high degree of precision, accuracy may be poor unless great care is taken with alignment or an internal standard is used. For sensitivity to weak reflections they cannot be beaten, and they are comparable with small diameter Debye-Scherrer cameras for examining ill-crystallized materials. They are extremely rapid, typical exposure times for inorganic materials being of the order of 15-30 minutes, and give better resolution than Debye-Scherrer cameras of the same radius; if large numbers of samples are to be examined routinely by the powder method, they are strongly recommended.

Diffractometers are even more expensive than focusing cameras, and the length of time taken to record a pattern is comparable. On the other hand, the diffractometer is a more flexible instrument; it can be used either for a rapid survey of a pattern or for slow precise measurements, and can produce very accurate parameters. It differs fundamentally from all film methods in that the pattern is recorded peak by peak and not all at once; this can be an advantage in following small changes in cell parameters as a function of some variable, since this can be done by scrutinizing only part of the pattern. Relative intensities of lines can be compared only if the X-ray tube is well stabilized against changes in voltage. Provided this is so, the intensities can be measured directly, whereas photographic methods depend on estimating the relative blackening of the film. One seldom mentioned disadvantage of the diffractometer for routine identification is the quantity of paper produced; when comparing patterns of various samples it is far more convenient to be able to lay out strips of film about 10 mm wide and 150 mm long on a light screen than to have to struggle with a large number of one metre lengths of chart paper.

Preferred orientation is more a function of the method of specimen preparation than of recording. One advantage of recording a large fraction of the diffracted cone, as on an oscillation-rotation camera, is that at least it is possible to see directly whether there is a problem. Focusing cameras usually give some hint of trouble, which manifests itself as uneven blackening along the lines. The diffractometer gives no information at all on the point, and it is by no means unknown for the effect to result in a complete misidentification of the material being examined.

For obvious reasons, methods of sample preparation requiring some form of mechanical compaction are most suspect; methods in which the sample is sprinkled onto a sticky surface are generally safer, though by no means foolproof. (Consider what would happen if you dropped a pack of cards onto wet cement.) Mechanical mixing with some sort of reasonably viscous adhesive which subsequently sets is perhaps safest of all. The use of common sense is always an invaluable safeguard.

6.3 'Fingerprint' methods

Perhaps the commonest single reason for recording a powder pattern is to identify the phase or phases of which the specimen consists. In general, each substance gives its own unique powder pattern which can be used to identify it—hence the term 'finger-print' methods. There is a limited number of examples of two different substances having virtually identical powder patterns, but these are sufficiently rare that they are not usually troublesome in practice.

Suppose that one is faced with the task of identifying a totally unknown substance. (It is of course rare for nothing whatever to be known about the sample, and any information about its provenance should be noted as potentially useful.) The first step should always be to examine it under the microscope to determine, if possible, whether it is a single phase or a mixture. For simplicity, we will assume that it appears to be a single phase. The pattern is then recorded by whichever of the available methods seems appropriate, and a list of d-spacings and relative intensities prepared. This will probably enable the material to be identified using the **Powder Diffraction File** [1]. The File lists, mainly on cards, the powder diffraction patterns (d-spacings and intensities) for most known crystalline phases; the unit cell, indices and optical data are, if known, also included. It is periodically brought up to date by the issue of new sets of cards, and new data published in the literature are normally included auto-matically. Various key indices are provided for rapid matching of patterns, together with full instructions for using them; space will not be used to describe these here. There are, however, a few pitfalls for the unwary that should be mentioned. Perhaps the most dangerous of these is the possibility of gross changes in relative intensity due to preferred orientation (discussed above). In extreme cases, this may make the pattern unrecognizable; less extreme ones merely complicate the identification by changing the relative intensities of the strongest lines. Another difficulty sometimes occurs with patterns recorded on a diffractometer, because the range of these instru-ments may be limited at the high-angle end of the spectrum; it is also usual to limit the low-angle end to avoid the risk of exposing the counter to the direct beam. Lines with very short or very long d-spacings may thus be missed, and occasionally they may be crucial to the identification.

Besides these technical difficulties, there may be others inherent in the nature of the substance under test. One of these has been mentioned above; two dissimilar sub-stances may have similar powder patterns. Fortunately this tends to occur mainly among fairly simple substances for which a simple chemical test is usually sufficient to complete the identification. It is not surprising that, say, materials having the sodium chloride structure should give similar patterns; if the sum of the respective ionic radii is similar, the d-spacings will follow suit, and if the relative atomic numbers are similar there will also be similarities between the relative intensities. It is less obvious that patterns from substances of quite unrelated structure may be similar, for example those from Ag_2O and CdO. Most of the diffracted radiation comes from the heavy atoms and the pattern is relatively insensitive to the arrangement of the light ones; the spatial arrangement of the heavy atoms is similar and the patterns are alike.

Materials that can form solid solutions (Section 5.3) present almost the reverse problem. In these the pattern may vary continuously from one end member to the other, and if your sample happens to be intermediate between the ones quoted in the File, its pattern will agree with neither (see Fig. 6.8). One has then to combine all known facts about the material with a dash of intuition—use intelligent guess-work. On the credit side, once you know that you are dealing with such a solid solution, careful measurements of the spacings of one or two lines from samples of known composition provide a graph of *d*-spacing *versus* composition; the composition of the unknown can then be determined.

If after making due allowance for all the above factors you cannot identify a sample, it is probably a mixture or possibly a material whose pattern is not recorded in the File. If microscopic examination also suggests a mixture, it may be possible (though tedious) to sort out the phases with a needle under the microscope, but before resorting to this, try some easier method of separation. If the phases differ enough in density and occur as separate particles, gravity separation using a liquid of intermediate density is often effective and easy. Sometimes one phase can be selectively dissolved, but you must be sure that the solvent does not also alter the remaining phase.

If separation proves impossible, you can try to guess the identity of one phase probably with help from the File; the lines due to this phase are then subtracted from the pattern and an attempt made to match the rest. This is fraught with difficulties, since there is nothing to prevent the two phases from having coincident lines, and part of the second pattern may be subtracted along with the first. This method becomes harder the more phases the mixture contains; a good practical example is the difficulty of identifying the phases present in Portland cement clinker.

There are one or two 'tricks of the trade' that can help in dealing with mixtures. One is to study the texture of the lines on a powder photograph. If one phase is considerably more coarsely crystalline than the other(s), its lines may be rather spotty; the effect is enhanced in Debye–Scherrer photographs by keeping the specimen stationary instead of rotating it. If one phase is very poorly crystallized, on the other hand, its lines will be very broad and 'fuzzy'. The presence of either effect may allow at least a partial resolution of the problem.

If the microscopic examination showed crystals large enough to give single crystal photographs, the tedious work of sorting out the phases manually can be short-circuited. A rotation photograph of one of the larger crystals, which for this purpose need not be set, can be superposed on a powder pattern taken on the same camera; lines in the powder pattern that coincide with spots on the rotation photograph belong to the same phase.

Materials whose patterns are not in the File need chemical detective work, and the method of attacking the problem depends so much upon circumstances that it is difficult to give any general guidance. One obvious line of attack is to consider where the sample came from and how it might have formed; this knowledge, combined if possible with a chemical analysis, may enable you to produce the material or suspected alternatives synthetically, and the powder patterns of these can be compared with the unknown.

An interesting example of this type of study concerns the identification of opacifying agents in ancient glasses, including the white opaque glass that decorates the Portland Vase [2]. Only a minute scrap of the latter material was available, and was much to valuable to be destroyed by subjecting it to chemical analysis. The opacifying agent, however, was crystalline, and the powder pattern from the scrap of the Portland Vase was similar to that given by another, less valuable, white glass of the same period. Chemical analysis of the latter showed that it contained a significant amount of antimony oxide, in addition to the usual constituents of a soda-lime–silica glass. A compound of CaO and Sb_2O_5 seemed probable; synthetic $Ca_2Sb_2O_7$ proved to be identical with the crystalline material in the Portland Vase opal glass. Similar studies identified other opacifying agents employed in glass-making from Egyptian times—approximately 1450 B.C.—to the present day [3].

Many problems do not require recourse to the File. If you are studying the reaction $A + B \rightarrow C$ under various conditions, and wish only to know to what extent A and B have reacted and whether C has been produced, all you need is a set of standard patterns of A, B and C, which you can easily produce yourself. A related type of study is

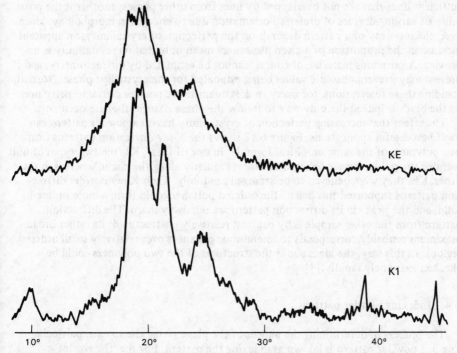

Fig. 6.12   The X-ray diffraction patterns from a disordered polymer, KE, and an ordered one, K1. Both polymers consisted of diphenylmethane and hexamethylene units joined by disulphide linkages. In K1, which melted sharply at $120°C$, these were believed to alternate regularly:

whereas in KE, which melted over the range $90-96°C$ they were believed to be arranged randomly:

where x and y vary.

   (After G. G. Cameron and S. A. Stachowiak, [4].)

of reaction kinetics, which means making an estimate of how much C forms in a given time.

This brings us to the problem of using powder patterns for quantitative estimations. In principle careful measurement of the relative intensities of the lines present in the pattern should enable the amount of the respective phases present in the mixture to be estimated. In practice even in favourable cases the accuracy is only about ±5% and it is often much poorer than this. One difficulty, in patterns of any complexity, is to find sufficient lines that are not overlapped by lines from other phases; another is the possibility of varying degrees of preferred orientation due to changes in morphology. Moreover, the intensity of a pattern depends on the perfection of crystallinity; an apparent increase in the proportion of a given phase may mean only that its crystallinity is improving. Amorphous material, of course, cannot be estimated by diffractometry, and if present may prevent absolute values being estimated for the crystalline phase. Notwithstanding these reservations, for many studies quantitative powder diffractometry may be the best, or indeed the only way to follow the phase changes that are occurring.

The effect that increasing perfection of crystallinity has on a powder pattern can itself have useful applications. Figure 6.12 shows the X-ray diffraction patterns from two polymers of the same empirical formula. In one of these, K1, the two types of unit forming the polymer were believed to repeat regularly along the chain, whereas in the other, KE, they were believed to be arranged randomly. Their X-ray powder diffraction patterns supported this belief: the ordered polymer could form a more ordered solid, and the peaks in its diffraction pattern are relatively sharp. The diffraction pattern from the other sample is by contrast relatively unstructured; its rather broad maximum probably corresponds to interatomic distances over relatively small ordered regions. In this way, the ideas about the structures of the two polymers could be checked extremely rapidly [4].

6.4   Indexing powder patterns

The process of determining the indices of the plane giving rise to each particular line in a powder pattern is known as **indexing** the pattern. For the 'fingerprint' methods just discussed, the indices of the lines are usually quite unimportant, and indexing is unnecessary. When it *is* necessary there may or may not be information from other sources about the probable shape and size of the unit cell. Some fairly trenchant remarks were made earlier (Section 6.1) regarding indiscriminate attempts to index powder patterns by trial and error. Some practical guidelines on how and when to try it now follow.

The general expression relating d-spacing to cell dimensions is most easily obtained through the reciprocal lattice. Taking $d^* = \lambda/d$, from the extension of Pythagoras' theorem:

$$d^{*2} = (ha^*)^2 + (kb^*)^2 + (lc^*)^2 + 2ha^*kb^* \cos \gamma^* + 2kb^* lc^* \cos \alpha^* + 2lc^*ha^* \cos \beta^*$$

This is simpler than the real-space equivalent. For the more symmetrical systems it simplifies further: for example, all the *cos* terms vanish if the cell is orthogonal, and for a cubic cell $a^* = b^* = c^*$ so that $d^{*2} = (h^2 + k^2 + l^2)a^{*2}$ [in real space this becomes $d = a/(h^2 + k^2 + l^2)$]. If the microscopic examination suggests that the substance is cubic, a simple slide-rule calculation will show whether the spacings are in the inverse ratios of the sums of squares (for practice, try this on the pattern in Fig. 6.11, assuming the first line to be 100: solution in Section 6.6). Even here caution is necessary.

Table 6.1 lists the first twelve lines of the powder pattern of a body-centred cubic substance with $a = 8.0$ Å, for which reflections with $(h + k + l)$ odd are missing. With one exception, the lines can be indexed equally well on a primitive cell with $a = 8/\sqrt{2}$;

TABLE 6.1

A cubic powder pattern indexed on two alternative cells. The true cell is body-centred with $a = 8.00$ Å, the false cell primitive with $a = 5.66$ Å $(= 8.00/\sqrt{2})$

Pattern d(Å)	True indices hkl	$(h^2 + k^2 + l^2)$	False indices hkl	$(h^2 + k^2 + l^2)$
5.66	110	2	100	1
4.00	200	4	110	2
3.26	211	6	111	3
2.83	220	8	200	4
2.53	310	10	210	5
2.31	222	12	211	6
2.14	321	14	?	7
2.00	400	16	220	8
1.885	330⎫ 411⎭	18	300⎫ 221⎭	9
1.788	420	20	310	10
1.704	332	22	311	11
1.630	422	24	222	12

had that one line been missed because it was weak, the resulting cell and indexing would be totally wrong. This example is fictional, but it is based on a true-life error that was not detected until single crystal photographs were available.

Given that such mistakes can occur in the cubic system, it does not require much imagination to see the possibilities for howlers presented by less symmetrical systems. *Inter alia* there have been examples of patterns from hexagonal crystals satisfactorily indexed on tetragonal cells, and on cells with hexagonal $a = (\text{true } a)/\sqrt{3}$. Hence the need for caution. It is fair enough to say of a pattern indexed in this way that 'it indexes satisfactorily on such-and-such a unit cell': it is most unwise to state dog-matically that 'the unit cell is so-and-so'.

If single crystals are available the unit cell can usually be determined unam-biguously, and it is then a simple matter to calculate the possible spacings and compare them with the pattern. For the higher symmetry systems this can be done by graphical methods, but it is usually quicker to generate the possible spacings by computer or with a desk calculator. Whichever method is used, remember that only the most intense reflections may be visible on the powder pattern; this effect is most pro-nounced with complicated patterns from crystals of low symmetry. In a pattern of any complexity there is often doubt about which of a number of possible indices to assign to a given line; the difficulty is compounded because the observed and calculated spac-ings cannot be expected to agree exactly anyway, both the measured pattern and the unit-cell parameters being subject to experimental error. It is important not to become bemused by your computer output, repeating the calculation with slight random vari-ations of the input parameters instead of getting to grips with the real problem.

The solution is to consider the relative intensities of the reflections observed on the single crystal photographs. A list of these can be prepared for the strongest reflections, and compared with the calculated indices to decide which are the most probable (you may need to allow for multiplicity: see next section). Alternatively, the single crystal photographs may be used directly, by superposing powder and rotation photographs in the manner already described; for indexing, the crystal must be set. It is usually easy to see which single crystal reflection is contributing most to a given powder line. If the rotation photograph is fully indexed, then the indices of the powder lines are also fully determined (see Fig. 6.3); if the rotation photograph is too complicated to be fully indexed, it is at least possible to determine the layer on which the reflection lies, and hence get a numerical value for the corresponding index. In the latter case, it is obviously an advantage to have rotation photographs about all three principal axes.

Many substances never yield crystals large enough to give single crystal photographs; selected area electron-diffraction patterns sometimes help in coping with these. This will be considered in Chapter 8.

Finally, it is sometimes possible to recognize in a pattern a similarity to a pattern of a substance whose unit cell is already known. This is largely a knack which comes with practice, but there are some obvious leads. If you know the chemical formula, even approximately, you can make a list of compounds that might have the same structure; this can be fairly wide ranging: Table 6.2 lists some less obvious examples of isostructural substances, drawn from simple inorganic compounds. It is even possible to perform what might be called 'structure determination by analogy' this way, if the powder pattern is shown to be similar to that of a compound of known structure.

TABLE 6.2
Some pairs of isostructural substances

Sr_3SiO_5	Cs_3CoCl_5
(Sr_3OSiO_4)	($Cs_3ClCoCl_4$)
TiO_2	MnF_2
$CaCO_3$	KNO_3
Cd_2SiO_4	Na_2SO_4
$NaAlO_2$	Na_2ZnSiO_4
($Na_2Al_2O_4$)	

Once the pattern has been indexed satisfactorily, the cell parameters can be adjusted to give the best fit between observed and calculated d-spacings, using the method of least squares; computer programs exist for this purpose. This is in fact an excellent way of determining accurate cell parameters, but it cannot be too strongly emphasized that it is a waste of time unless the pattern is correctly indexed.

6.5 The intensities of powder lines

The intensity of a diffracted beam depends on a number of factors. The amplitude and phase of the scattered wave is determined by the arrangement of the atoms of the crystal relative to the plane in question. This was discussed earlier (p. 57) and for centrosymmetric crystals was expressed mathematically by the structure factor:

$$F_{hkl} = \sum_{r=1}^{N} f_r \cos 2\pi(hx_r + ky_r + lz_r)$$

If the phase of a scattered wave is not known we can write $|F_{hkl}|$ to represent its **structure amplitude**. Since atoms have finite size, unless 2θ is zero there is a small difference in the path distance travelled by X-rays scattered by the electron cloud on opposite sides of the atom, and as Fig. 6.13(a) makes clear, this difference increases with

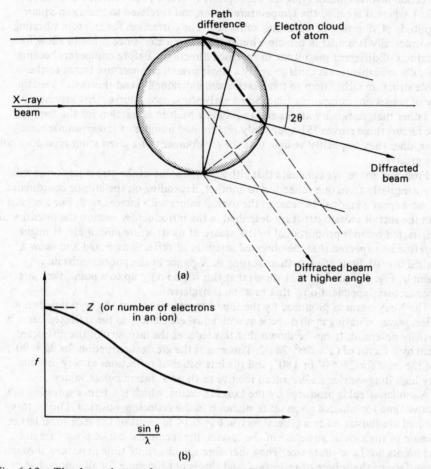

Fig. 6.13   The dependence of atomic scattering factor on the angle of the diffracted beam. (a) The path difference between waves scattered from opposite sides of the atom increases with the angle of scatter. For simplicity the electron cloud of the atom is represented crudely as a sphere. (b) The consequent decrease in atomic scattering power with scattering angle.

increasing 2θ. The consequent small phase difference between the diffracted waves from opposite sides of the atom results in a reduction of f_r, the scattering power of the atom, with increasing θ. Figure 6.13(b) shows the form of the typical curve obtained when the scattering power of an atom is plotted against $\sin\theta/\lambda$ (usually called its f-curve); the value of f is equal to Z, the number of electrons in the atoms (or ion), only when θ is zero.

Moreover, in all real crystals above absolute zero, the atoms are not stationary and fixed: their apparent coordinates represent only the mean positions about which they are vibrating. As far as the diffraction effects are concerned, this makes the atom effectively larger, producing an additional falling-off of scattering power with θ, for reasons similar to those given in the last paragraph. If the atom is vibrating isotropically, the correction involves multiplying the appropriate f value by the function $\exp(-B(\sin^2 \theta)/\lambda^2)$, where B is called the **temperature factor**, and is related to the mean-square amplitude of vibration of the atom concerned. The correction for an atom vibrating anisotropically is similar in principle but more complicated since it has to allow for vibrations of different magnitude in specified directions. Before computers became generally available it was usual to apply a single overall temperature factor to the whole structure rather than to treat each atom individually, and this is still a useful way of conserving computing time. Some early work used f-curves that assume vibrating rather than stationary atoms and thus have a built-in correction for the temperature factor; these curves [5] apply only to a limited number of rather similar structures, since they implicitly assume that the environment of a given atom type does not vary greatly.

From the above, we conclude that although the value of the structure factor will vary irregularly from one reflection to another, depending on the atomic coordinates, we can expect a gradual decrease in the overall values with increasing θ. For a crystal with the sort of mosaic structure described in the introductory section the intensity of a diffracted beam is proportional to the square of its structure amplitude. It might therefore be expected that the observed intensity of reflections would also show a gradual overall diminution with increasing θ. A glance at the photographs in, for example, Fig. 4.11 or Fig. 4.21 shows that this is true only up to a point; there are other factors dependent on θ that must be considered.

The X-ray beam as produced by the tube is unpolarized, but the crystal does not reflect waves vibrating in all directions with equal efficiency, so the reflected beam is partially polarized. It can be shown that this reduces the intensity of the diffracted beam by a factor of $(1 + \cos^2 2\theta)/2$. This causes the greatest reduction for $2\theta = 90°$, and the least for $2\theta = 0°$ or $180°$, and the intensities of reflections at very low and very high Bragg angles are enhanced relative to those at intermediate values.

A similar effect is produced by the Lorentz factor, which is a term expressing the relative time for which a given set of planes is in the reflecting position. The factors involved are illustrated in a general way in Fig. 6.14 in terms of the reciprocal lattice. Because of the mosaic structure of the crystal, the reciprocal lattice points are not true points but have finite size. They therefore spend a finite time in passing through the surface of the sphere of reflection, and this is not the same for all points. Figure 6.14 shows the path followed by some of the points as the reciprocal lattice rotates about O. Since all travel with the same angular velocity, their linear velocity increases with distance from the origin (that is with 2θ for the reflection concerned). Points near to the origin (low-angle reflections) such as A and B therefore pass through the surface more slowly than those further out (at higher angles) such as C and D, and the intensities of the corresponding reflections are enhanced. Still further from the origin, as the limit of observable reflections is approached ($2\theta \to 180°$), points such as E pass through the surface of the sphere of reflection almost tangentially, and the time spent in the reflecting position again increases, enhancing the intensity of the corresponding reflections. The exact form of correction to be used varies with the recording geometry and need not concern us here.

The increase of intensity in the high-angle region is enhanced still further in the powder method because the energy diffracted from a given set of planes is spread over

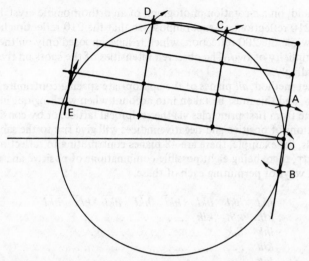

Fig. 6.14   A given set of planes is in the reflecting position for the time taken for the corresponding (finite) reciprocal lattice point to pass through the surface of the sphere of reflection. This is longer for points such as A and B than for C and D, because linear velocity increases with distance from O. For points such as E the time increases again; although their linear velocity is fairly high they are passing almost tangentially through the surface.

a cone of semi-vertical angle 2θ (Fig. 6.1). Up to $2\theta = 90°$, the surface of this cone increases with increasing values of 2θ, but beyond this point—in the back-reflection region—it decreases again.

As all the above factors are functions of θ it is convenient to correct for all of them at once. Most suites of crystallographic computer programs are designed to do this. For powder patterns other than those using focusing geometry the corrected relative intensity of the diffracted beam, I_{corr}, is related to the observed intensity, I_{obs}, by:

$$I_{obs} = \frac{1 + \cos^2 2\theta}{\sin^2 \theta \cdot \cos \theta} I_{corr}$$

This is often written as

$$\frac{4Lp}{\sin \theta} I_{corr}$$

Tables listing this function are available in, for example, *International Tables for X-ray Crystallography*, Vol. II, pp. 270–271.

It is the corrected intensity, I_{corr}, for a given set of planes that is proportional to the square of the amplitude of the scattered wave. However, in some sorts of recording geometry, waves scattered from *other* sets of planes with equivalent indices may follow the same path, thus increasing the observed intensity. The number of equivalent sets of planes capable of being so recorded is the **multiplicity** of the reflection concerned.

In moving film methods of recording, each spot on the film corresponds to one, and only one, reciprocal lattice point, and all reflections have the same multiplicity—unity.

On the other hand, on a c-rotation photograph of an orthorhombic crystal the 210, $2\bar{1}0$, $\bar{2}10$, and $\bar{2}\bar{1}0$ reflections all superimpose, so that the 210 reflection has a multiplicity of four while the 200 reflection, which is superimposed only on the $\bar{2}00$ reflection, has a multiplicity of two. The observed intensities of the spots on the film are increased accordingly.

In the powder method, *all* planes of the appropriate spacing contribute to a given diffracted beam, and this must be taken into account when working out multiplicities. This can be done from first principles via the reciprocal lattice, or by considering how many permutations of positive and negative indices will give rise to the same spacing. In cubic crystals, for example, there are 48 planes contributing to reflections of the general type hkl†, there being eight possible combinations of positive and negative indices, and six ways of permuting each of these:

$$
\begin{array}{llllllll}
hkl & \bar{h}kl & h\bar{k}l & hk\bar{l} & \bar{h}\bar{k}l & \bar{h}k\bar{l} & h\bar{k}\bar{l} & \bar{h}\bar{k}\bar{l} \\
klh & \bar{k}lh & k\bar{l}h & \ldots & \ldots & \ldots & \ldots & \ldots \\
lhk & \bar{l}hk & \ldots & \ldots & \ldots & \ldots & \ldots & \ldots \\
khl & \ldots & \ldots & \ldots & \ldots & \ldots & \ldots & \ldots \\
hlk & \ldots & \ldots & \ldots & \ldots & \ldots & \ldots & \ldots \\
lkh & \ldots & \ldots & \ldots & \ldots & \ldots & \ldots & \ldots
\end{array}
$$

For planes of less general type, that is where two or more of the indices are equal, or one or two of them are zero, there are fewer possibilities. For planes of the type hhl (112, or 225, say) hkl and khl become identical, and the multiplicity drops to 24. If an index is zero, its 'positive' and 'negative' values become identical, so there are only 24 planes of type $h0l$. The planes with the lowest multiplicities are those of the least general type: $h00$ planes have a multiplicity of six, hhh planes have a multiplicity of eight. Since in cubic crystals multiplicity increases the intensity of the most general reflections by a factor of up to eight relative to the least general, its effect is very marked.

We can now relate the observed intensities from a powder pattern to the structure of the sample; the next section gives a worked example.

6.6   A practical example

We will now use the theory so far developed to interpret the diffractometer trace shown in Fig. 6.11. This trace was taken on a standard instrument by normal techniques (without introducing any special refinements), and thus is a fair representation of the sort of results obtainable by any reasonably competent person. For the calculations, a slide rule was used, plus standard tables for converting 2θ into d; correction factors and f-curves were taken from *International Tables*.

---

† Note that in Laue group $m3$, these planes are not all equivalent. The weighted reciprocal lattice has no mirror plane through the hhl reflections, and the hkl and khl reflections have the same spacings, but not in general the same intensity. There is no simple way of disentangling the two contributions without recourse to single crystal measurements. This, together with the problem of the overlapping of reflections from unrelated planes, limits the usefulness of the powder method for determining intensities; this is a pity, because in other ways intensities measured from powder data are potentially very accurate (see Section 9.1).

The first two columns of Table 6.3 list values of 2θ and relative observed intensities (I_{rel}) taken from the trace in Fig. 6.11. The values used for I_{rel} are those of peak

TABLE 6.3
Indexing a powder pattern

1 $2\theta(°)$	2 I_{rel}	3 d_{obs} (Å)	4 $(4.13/d)^2$	5 hkl	6 a_{calc}(Å)	7 d_{calc}(Å)
21.5	39	4.13	1	100	4.13	4.126
30.7	100	2.91	2.01	110	4.12	2.918
37.8	12	2.38	3.01	111	4.12	2.382
43.9	13	2.06	4.02	200	4.12	2.063
49.4	12	1.845	5.01	210	4.125	1.845
54.5	22	1.684	6.02	211	4.125	1.684
63.8	5	1.459	8.01	220	4.127	1.459
68.2	5	1.375	9.02	{300 221}	4.125	1.375
72.4	6	1.305	10.02	310	4.127	1.305
76.5	2	1.245	11.01	311	4.129	1.244
80.6	1	1.192	12.00	222	4.129	1.191
84.6	1	1.145	13.02	320	4.128	1.144
88.7	5	1.103	14.02	321	4.127	1.103
96.7	< 1	1.032	16.01	400	4.128	1.032
100.9	1	0.998	17.07	{410 322}	4.122	1.001
105.0	2	0.9717	18.06	{330 411}	4.123	0.9725
					mean value	4.126

Columns 1 and 2 – observed data from Fig. 6.11.
Column 3 – d-spacings calculated from Column 1.
Column 4 – values of $(a/d)^2$ assuming the first line to be 100.
Column 5 – hkl indices derived from $(a/d)^2 = (h^2 + k^2 + l^2)$.
Column 6 – values of a, calculated from d_{obs} and hkl (mean value at foot of column).
Column 7 – d-spacing recalculated from the mean value of a_{calc} and hkl.

height above background (strictly speaking the area under the peak should have been used) scaled to make the maximum value one hundred. The next column (3) gives the corresponding values of d_{obs}, and from these and the intensities we identify the compound as CsCl, using the Powder Diffraction File. Most of the remaining information in the table can be obtained directly from the File, but since this is supposed to be a demonstration of how to interpret data, we will derive it from the experimental results instead.

The polarizing microscope showed that the crystals were isotropic, so we can safely assume that they are cubic. If the longest spacing is the 100 reflection, then $a \approx 4.13$ Å and calculating $(a/d)^2$ for the remaining lines should yield a series of approximately integral values representing $(h^2 + k^2 + l^2)$, as explained in Section 6.4. As column 4 in Table 6.3 shows, this is in fact so and the following column (5) gives the appropriate hkl values. All lines can be satisfactorily indexed, and all indices are present, so we conclude that the lattice is primitive. Column 6 shows values of a calculated from each d-spacing in turn, and suggests a mean value† of 4.126 Å for a compared with the value of 4.123 given with the standard pattern in the File. Finally column 7 lists a series of calculated d-spacings based on this value for a; the excellent agreement with the measured values in column 3 gives us confidence in our interpretation.

The next step is to calculate the cell contents using the relationship

$$D = \frac{1.66\, Z \times F}{V}$$

as explained in Section 5.2. The observed density is 3.97 g cm^{-3}, the formula weight 168.4 and the volume of the cell 70.2 Å^3; consequently $Z = 1$, giving an X-ray density of 3.981 g cm^{-3}.

The primitive unit cell thus contains one atom each of Cs and Cl, and a little thought shows that the only possible arrangement consistent with cubic symmetry is to place one atom (say, Cs) at the corner of the cell with coordinates 0, 0, 0, and the other (Cl) at the centre with coordinates $\frac{1}{2}, \frac{1}{2}, \frac{1}{2}$. (This is the arrangement described in Section 3.4; the derivation of the appropriate structure factor expression is, for convenience, repeated briefly at the foot of Table 6.4). Let us see if this arrangement successfully explains the observed intensities.

Table 6.4 shows the method of correcting the observed intensity data. The observed relative intensities have to be corrected for polarization and geometric factors before they can be related to the amplitudes of the scattered waves; the column headed $4Lp/\sin \theta$) gives the appropriate correction for the arrangement used in this experiment. The values were taken from *International Tables*, Vol. II, pp. 270–271, where they are tabulated against $\sin \theta$. At low angles this factor greatly enhances the intensity as measured by the counter. Beyond $\sin \theta \approx 0.5$, the effect is less dramatic; the measurements in Table 6.4 have been carried to sufficiently high angles so that, towards the bottom of the table, the factor is beginning to increase again with $\sin \theta$. The other factor that profoundly affects the intensity observed at the counter is the multiplicity of the contributing sets of planes (see p. 148), listed in the column headed m. A problem arises when two unrelated sets contribute to the same powder line, as for example (300) and (221). In this particular case it is permissible simply to add the multiplicities, because, as a glance at the final two columns or at the formula at the foot of the table shows, the value of F_c' is the same for both reflections, depending as it does solely on whether $h + k + l$ is odd or even. For more complicated structures the two reflections would be unlikely to have identical values of F_c and apportioning the observed intensity between them would then not be simple. (In cubic space groups for which $F_{hkl} \neq F_{khl}$ the problem is still more serious (cf. p. 148).) Although this severely limits the use of powder data for the solution of complicated structures, it need not trouble us in the present example.

The values of I_{rel} are corrected for the above factors: because the scale is still arbitrary, it is permissible to multiply all the results by 100 to produce a more convenient set of figures. These are listed in column 6 of Table 6.4, as I_{corr}. The final two columns, 7 and 8, give the scattering factors for Cs and Cl at the appropriate values of $\sin \theta/\lambda$, together with the appropriate signs. Already a general correspondence can be seen between the fluctuations in the value of I_{corr} and the combination of signs in the final columns; reflections with $h + k + l$ even (two positive signs) have higher values of I_{corr} than neighbouring reflections with $h + k + l$ odd.

---

† This is an unweighted average of all but the first four values.

TABLE 6.4
Reduction of intensity data

1 hkl	2 I_{rel}	3 $\sin\theta$	4 $4Lp/\sin\theta$	5 m	6 I_{corr}	7 f_{Cs}	8 f_{Cl}
100	39	0.187	54.29	6	11.97	(+) 49.6	(−) 14.7
110	100	0.265	25.68	12	32.45	(+) 46.2	(+) 13.0
111	12	0.324	16.35	8	9.18	(+) 43.8	(−) 11.6
200	13	0.375	11.63	6	18.63	(+) 41.9	(+) 10.7
210	12	0.418	8.966	24	6.97	(+) 40.2	(−) 10.1
211	22	0.458	7.170	24	12.78	(+) 38.9	(+) 9.6
220	5	0.529	5.027	12	8.29	(+) 36.4	(+) 8.8
300} 221}	5	0.561	4.365	6} 24}	3.82	(+) (+) 35.4	(−) (−) 8.6
310	6	0.591	3.872	24	6.46	(+) 34.4	(+) 8.3
311	2	0.620	3.493	24	2.38	(+) 33.6	(−) 8.1
222	1	0.647	3.216	8	3.89	(+) 32.9	(+) 8.0
320	1	0.674	3.005	24	1.39	(+) 32.1	(−) 7.8
321	5	0.700	2.859	48	3.64	(+) 31.4	(+) 7.6
400	<1	0.748	2.731	6	<6	(+) 30.1	(+) 7.4
322} 410}	1	0.772	2.737	24} 24}	0.76	(+) (+) 29.8	(−) (−) 7.3
330} 411}	2	0.794	2.787	12} 24}	1.99	(+) (+) 29.2	(+) (+) 7.2

Columns 1 and 2 – indices and observed intensities from Table 6.3.

Columns 3 and 4 – $\sin\theta$ and the corresponding correction factor.

Column 5 – the multiplicity of the plane concerned; pairs of planes such as (300) and (221), for which $h^2 + k^2 + l^2$ are identical can here be used (by dividing by the sum of the multiplicities) because the structure factors of the two planes are equal *but this will not in general be true.*

Column 6 – the corrected intensity $I_{corr} = \dfrac{I_{rel} \times 100}{m \times 4Lp/\sin\theta}$. These are still relative values.

Columns 7 and 8 – scattering factors for Cs and Cl for each plane, together with the appropriate signs.

$$
\begin{aligned}
F_c' &= f_{Cs}\cos 2\pi(h.0 + k.0 + l.0)\\
&\quad + f_{Cl}\cos 2\pi(h.\tfrac{1}{2} + k.\tfrac{1}{2} + l.\tfrac{1}{2})\\
&= f_{Cs} + f_{Cl}\cos (h + k + l)\pi\\
&= \begin{cases} f_{Cs} + f_{Cl} \text{ if } h + k + l = 2n\\ f_{Cs} - f_{Cl} \text{ if } h + k + l = 2n + 1 \end{cases}
\end{aligned}
$$

Table 6.5 makes this correspondence quantitative. The values of F_0 were derived by taking the square root of I_{corr} and scaling the results to make

$$\Sigma \sqrt{(I_{corr}/k)} \equiv \Sigma F_0 = \Sigma F_c$$

where F_c is the final calculated value. The next column, headed F_c', gives values of

TABLE 6.5
Comparison of observed and calculated F's

hkl	F_o	F_c'	F_c	$\Delta = |F_o| - |F_c|$
100	32.1	34.9	33.5	−1.4
110	52.8	59.2	52.1	0.7
111	28.1	32.2	26.7	1.4
200	40.0	52.6	41.0	−1.0
210	24.5	30.1	22.6	1.9
211	33.1	48.5	34.0	−0.9
220	26.7	45.2	28.1	−1.4
300⎫ 221⎭	18.1	26.8	16.1	2.0
310	23.6	42.7	23.5	0.1
311	14.3	25.5	13.5	0.8
222	18.3	40.9	20.4	−2.1
320	10.9	24.3	11.4	−0.5
321	17.7	39.0	17.2	0.5
400	(< 22.7)	37.5	14.6	—
322⎫ 410⎭	8.1	22.5	8.3	−0.2
330⎫ 411⎭	13.1	36.4	12.8	0.3

$$\Sigma\,|F_o| = 361.4 \qquad\qquad \Sigma\,|F_c| = 361.2 \qquad \Sigma\,|\Delta| = 15.2$$

$$R = \frac{\Sigma\,|\Delta|}{\Sigma\,|F_o|} = \frac{15.2}{361.4} = 0.042$$

$$F_c' = f_{Cs} \pm f_{Cl}$$

$$F_c = (f_{Cs} \pm f_{Cl}) \exp\,(-B\,\sin^2\theta/\lambda^2)$$

$$\text{with } B = 4.0\ \text{Å}^2$$

$$F_o = k\sqrt{I_{corr}}\ \text{where } k \text{ is chosen to give } \Sigma\,|F_o| = \Sigma\,|F_c|$$

$f_{Cs} \pm f_{Cl}$, that is the structure factor calculated assuming stationary atoms. The agreement between F_o and F_c' becomes progressively poorer with increase in angle, F_c' getting relatively larger. Obviously the agreement will be improved if we make some allowance for atomic vibrations. Although strictly speaking we should use separate temperature factors for each atom, for present purposes we will assume an overall temperature factor for the structure as a whole and write:

$$F_c = (f_{Cs} \pm f_{Cl}) \exp\,(-B\,\sin^2\theta/\lambda^2) = F_c'\exp\,(-B\,\sin^2\theta/\lambda^2) \approx F_o$$

where in an ideal world, with no experimental errors, the last equality would be a true one. In any case it can be used to estimate B, because

$$F_o/F_c' \approx \exp\,(-B\,\sin^2\theta/\lambda^2)$$

and taking logs:

$$\ln F_o/F_c' = 2.303\log_{10} F_o/F_c' \approx -B\,\sin^2\theta/\lambda^2$$

Plotting $\log_{10} F_o/F_c$ against $\sin^2 \theta/\lambda^2$ gives a fairly good straight line, from which B was estimated to be about 4.0 Å^2. (This corresponds to a root mean square vibration of about 0.2 Å for the atoms.) Multiplying the F_c' values by $\exp(-4 \sin^2 \theta/\lambda^2)$ produced the column headed F_c, and now the agreement between F_o and F_c is really very good indeed; the final column gives $\Delta = |F_0| - |F_c|$ and provides a measure of the degree of misfit. This misfit is generally quantified as

$$R = \frac{\Sigma |\Delta|}{\Sigma |F_o|}$$

which is used by crystallographers to express the extent of agreement between the assumed structural parameters and the measured data; the lower the value of R, the better the fit.

The use of R as a measure of agreement can be—and frequently has been—criticized on statistical grounds, but its use is enshrined in the literature from the days of the earliest quantitative determinations. Although there is not even general agreement as to whether R stands for Residual or for Reliability Index, the R-factor will probably continue to fill its historically determined role in structure determination.

In this example, the R-factor is 0.042, and this is satisfactory agreement, particularly since the intensity measurements were made in a rather rough-and-ready fashion; on the other hand, of course, the structure is a particularly simple one, with no positional parameters to vary. As a very rough rule of thumb, a value of 0.2–0.3 suggests that a structure is roughly correct, but that the positions of at least some of the atoms need correcting; a value of less than 0.1 indicates that all the atoms are correctly placed and their parameters known with fair accuracy.

6.7   Special techniques

Techniques for studying single crystals under conditions other than ambient were described in Section 5.5, together with some reasons for wishing to do this. Similar studies may be made with powder specimens and on the whole the design difficulties are then less acute because the adjustment of the specimen is less critical, and the aperture for observation can be reduced to a narrow slit. More extreme ranges of conditions can thus be used, and a wider variety of commercial equipment is available.

6.7.1   High-temperature studies [6]

Probably the most common requirement is for high temperature, and a variety of high-temperature cameras and attachments for diffractometers is on the market. Perhaps the most elegant is the Lenné camera, a high-temperature version of the Guinier camera. The sample is supported on a Platinum grid within an approximately spherical furnace with an equatorial slit through which the diffraction pattern emerges. The film is held in a cassette which is much broader than for the standard Guinier camera and is driven slowly past the slit by an electric motor; since the temperature of the furnace can be regulated automatically, the apparatus can be used to give a continuous record of changes in the pattern with temperature. Chemical reactions and transitions (including those that are reversed on cooling) can thus be studied, and this is particularly useful when used in conjunction with other techniques, such as differential thermal analysis, which do not lie within the scope of this book.

Design problems, like those encountered in single crystal devices (Section 5), vary with the temperature required, and the accuracy to which the temperature of the sample must be known. Slightly elevated temperatures—up to about 100°C—can be achieved with very little difficulty, the intermediate range—up to about 1000°C—requires considerably more care, and temperatures above 1000°C present formidable technical problems. Film, if used, must be kept cool; this becomes more difficult as the specimen temperature is increased. The holder is sometimes water-cooled, and screening between the furnace and the film may be provided; aluminium foil makes a good screen because it is a good reflector for radiated heat but does not unduly impede the diffracted X-rays. As a last resort, the specimen-to-film distance may be increased; this is undesirable because of the increased exposure times involved, but may be worth considering for materials that give strong diffraction patterns. The problems are less acute in designing attachments for powder diffractometers, in which the distance from sample to detector is fairly large and the instrument relatively 'open', allowing more working space.

If the dimensions of the furnace are to be kept small, as they must usually be, the problem of temperature gradients within the furnace has to be considered, together with that of measuring the exact temperature of the sample. In many cases, however, this is not so important as one might think; if a transition is being studied, for example, the exact temperature may be known from other studies, and all that is required of the high-temperature camera is that a temperature be achieved *above* the transition temperature, so that the nature of the transition may be studied. Hence the advantage of having access to supplementary techniques such as differential thermal analysis or thermogravimetric analysis.

Unless the specimen being studied is massive in form, such as a wire or slab of solid material, mounting it suitably for high-temperature studies may be a major problem (just as it is for single crystals). Even if an adhesive can be found that neither decomposes nor reacts with the sample at high temperature, the problem of thermal expansion remains, and this is often the undoing (literally!) of even the most carefully prepared specimens. From this point of view, it is most satisfactory to use a compacted specimen that remains more or less horizontal during the experiment, but this is not possible for all recording techniques. For Debye–Scherrer cameras, the sample may be packed into a silica capillary or formed into a self-supporting rod; for transmission focusing cameras the specimen has normally to be supported on a wire grid.

6.7.2 Low-temperature studies [7]

Design of equipment for low-temperature studies tends to present fewer problems, for reasons already discussed under single crystal techniques. The techniques and difficulties are much the same as in any other type of low-temperature study; suitable cryostats are commercially available, or can be specially designed, and are cooled with the appropriate liquefied gas.

6.7.3 Controlled-atmosphere studies

One sometimes wants to control the atmosphere around the sample being studied, often in conjunction with controlling the temperature. For example, high-temperature studies may need the sample to be in an inert atmosphere to prevent oxidation. Many cameras and diffractometer attachments for high- and low-temperature studies provide for this, or at least can be readily adapted to do so.

Some commercially available cameras allow the body of the camera to be evacuated or filled with an appropriate gas. Quite apart from any other advantages, evacuation of a camera body reduces scatter of the X-rays from the molecules of the air and this both cuts down the exposure time and improves the quality of the film by reducing fogging of the background.

Various *ad hoc* measures can also be devised. If a rod-like sample is suitable, the simplest thing may be to collect and seal it in a suitable capillary tube. Samples for Guinier cameras, usually mounted on transparent sticky tape anyway, can be simply protected (for room-temperature studies) by enclosing them between two layers of the same tape. Holders for diffractometer samples can easily be provided with sealed or sealable covers—thin Perspex is often suitable. Aluminium foil can be used provided it is free of pinholes; it must be suitably strengthened if it is to be subjected to a pressure differential.

6.7.4   High-pressure studies

The study of materials under very high pressure yields information that is important both to the geologist and to the materials scientist. It is however a relatively specialized field and only a brief outline will be given here; a review of developments in the field up to 1969 [8] has been given, and is the source of much of the material in this section. The principal design problem of getting the incident beam in and the diffraction pattern out of the high-pressure chamber is more easily solved for the powder method than for single crystal studies and most high-pressure studies have been tackled in this way.

At first sight a simple solution might seem to be to convert the entire camera into a high-pressure vessel, but this does not work because of film failure. Successful designs have used cells wholly or partly of X-ray transparent materials capable of withstanding high pressures; in practice this means using no elements heavier than carbon. One successful design generates the pressure with two massive opposing anvils, the sample being contained within a beryllium gasket which also serves to transmit the X-rays. Other designs have employed a cell made wholly of diamond; against the obvious drawbacks of expense and difficulty in working the material may be set the greater geometrical flexibility allowed.

References

[1] *Powder Diffraction File,* Joint Committee on Powder Diffraction Standards, 1601 Park Lane, Swarthmore, Pa. 19081.
[2] Turner, W. E. S., *J. Soc. Glass Tech.* **43**, 262–284 T (1959); Rooksby, H. P., *Ibid,* 285–288 T.
[3] Turner, W. E. S. and Rooksby, H. P., *Glastechn. Ber.* **32K**, 17–28 (1959).
[4] Cameron, G. G. and Stachowiak, S. A., *Makromolek Chem.* **176**, 1523–1528 (1975).
[5] Bragg, W. L. and West, J., *Z. Kristallogr.* **69**, 118–148 (1928).
[6] *Bibliography 1*: see Chapter 5, Reference [3].
[7] *Bibliography 2*: see Chapter 5, Reference [3].
[8] Banus, M. D., *High Temp.–High Pressures* **1**, 483–515 (1969).

CHAPTER 7

Structure determination

7.1 Trial and error

The calculations given in Section 6.6 show how to verify a structure that is known or easily guessed. Determining more complicated structures presents a variety of problems, and this chapter describes some of the ways of tackling these.

Historically, the first method used, and perhaps the simplest to understand, is that of trial-and-error, so we will consider this first. Although now seldom used in its pure form, many of the concepts are still an important part of more sophisticated methods. Basically it consists of attempting to build within the framework of the known unit cell and space group a structure that satisfies the cell contents, explains the relative magnitude of a few key intensities and also makes crystal chemical sense. Trial structures deduced in this way are then checked by comparing the calculated structure factors or intensities with the observed values. (Many successful early determinations merely used intensities estimated visually on a scale ranging from very, very weak to very, very strong.) Any parameters not fixed by space-group restrictions are adjusted to give the best possible agreement.

The example in Section 6.6 was a very elementary example of this kind of reasoning; there was only one possible arrangement within the unit cell and lattice type observed. The process in more complicated cases is best understood from an actual example. The heyday of this method was from about 1925 to 1935; a particularly rich source of examples is Zeitschrift für Kristallographie, especially those volumes published in the early thirties. From among these we choose CuO (found in nature as the mineral tenorite), partly because the early structure [1] has recently been checked [2].

The unit cell, determined from rotation and Weissenberg photographs, and other pertinent data are given in Table 7.1; the more recently determined cell parameters (in brackets) are included for comparison. The systematic absences are consistent with either of the space groups $C2/c$ or Cc; the morphology of the naturally occurring crystals suggested $C2/c$, and this proved to be correct so we will not consider Cc. The symmetry elements for $C2/c$ are shown in Fig. 7.1, together with the general equivalent positions; since there are eight of the latter and the cell contains only four each of copper and of oxygen atoms, both types of atom must occupy special positions.

Only one arrangement gave a chemically plausible structure and at the same time explained the observed intensities of a limited number of low-angle reflections. This placed Cu on a centre of symmetry at 1/4, 1/4, 0, etc., and O on the two-fold axes at 0, y, 1/4. The value of y was then adjusted to give the best possible agreement between

TABLE 7.1[1]
Crystal data for CuO

Unit cell monoclinic $a = 4.653 \ (4.6837)$Å
$b = 3.410 \ (3.4226)$Å
$c = 5.108 \ (5.1228)$Å
$\beta = 99°29' \pm 20'$
$(99.54° \pm 0.01°)$

Systematic absences: in hkl, $h + k = 2n$
$h0l$, $(h = 2n)$ $l = 2n$

Crystal habit suggests point group $2/m$; probable space group therefore $C2/c$.
$D_{meas} = 6.45$, $Z = 4$, $D_{x\text{-ray}} = 6.569 \ g \ cm^{-3}$

[1] Values in brackets are taken from [2], other data from [1].

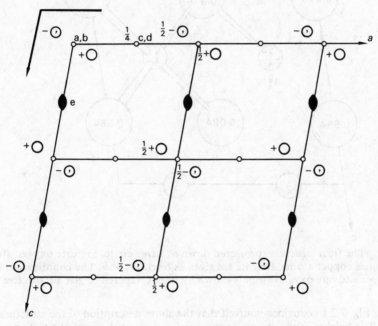

Four–fold positions:

On centres of symmetry: a $0,0,0$; $\frac{1}{2},\frac{1}{2},0$; $0,0,\frac{1}{2}$; $\frac{1}{2},\frac{1}{2},\frac{1}{2}$.

b $0,\frac{1}{2},0$; $\frac{1}{2},0,0$; $0,\frac{1}{2},\frac{1}{2}$; $\frac{1}{2},0,\frac{1}{2}$.

c $\frac{1}{4},\frac{1}{4},0$; $\frac{3}{4},\frac{3}{4},0$; $\frac{1}{4},\frac{3}{4},\frac{1}{2}$; $\frac{3}{4},\frac{1}{4},\frac{1}{2}$.

d $\frac{1}{4},\frac{3}{4},0$; $\frac{3}{4},\frac{1}{4},0$; $\frac{1}{4},\frac{1}{4},\frac{1}{2}$; $\frac{3}{4},\frac{3}{4},\frac{1}{2}$.

On two–fold axes: $0,y,\frac{1}{4}$; $\frac{1}{2},\frac{1}{2}+y,\frac{1}{4}$; $0,-y,\frac{3}{4}$; $\frac{1}{2},\frac{1}{2}-y,\frac{3}{4}$.

Fig. 7.1   Symmetry elements and general positions in space group $C2/c$. Coordinates of four-fold special positions are listed below the diagram.

The diagram has the unique (b) axis perpendicular to the plane of the paper; the directions of a and c, in the plane of the paper, are indicated.

observed and calculated intensities, the final value being 0.416. In the final arrangement, shown in Fig. 7.2, each copper atom is surrounded by four oxygen atoms,
roughly at the corners of a square, and each oxygen atom is surrounded by four
copper atoms at the corners of an irregular tetrahedron; the Cu–O distances are all
about 1.95 Å.

It is not easy to visualize a structure in three dimensions from a diagram projected
onto a printed page, and if you are not skilled at this you should spend a few minutes

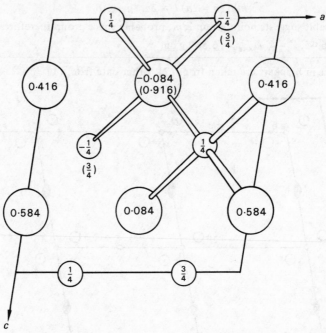

Fig. 7.2   The final structure, projected down b. Large circles indicate oxygen atoms,
smaller ones copper atoms. Heights are given as fractions of b. The coordination about
one copper and one oxygen atom is shown by bonds, tapered to give perspective.

studying Fig. 7.2 to convince yourself that the above description of the structure is
correct. The heights of the atoms are given as fractions of the vertical axis b; remember
that the structure repeats in all directions. In Fig. 7.2 some bonds have been drawn in,
tapering to indicate perspective. The oxygen atom at 0.916, for example, is bonded to
two copper atoms below it (at 3/4 in the same cell) and two more above it (at 1/4 in
the next cell up). Likewise the copper atom at 1/4 (lower centre) is connected to two
oxygen atoms above it (0.416 and 0.584 in the same cell) and two below it (0.084 in
the same cell and 0.916 in the next cell down, that is at –0.084). Now try to visualize
the bonding at some of the other atoms to make sure that you have followed this.
Finally make a mental check with the symmetry elements shown in Fig. 7.1 until you
can see clearly how the structure relates to the space group; can you trace the c-glide
plane operation?

The convention of drawing bonds as tapering rods is often used to help make the
three-dimensional arrangement clearer; in a compound containing finite molecules it is
possible to give a reasonably clear picture of the whole molecule in this way. In an

infinite three-dimensional network such as that in Fig. 7.2 only a limited amount of such bonding can be shown—trying to connect up the two atoms at the lower left-hand corner will show you what the problem is far better than any words could describe it. Another convention shown in Fig. 7.2 is that of labelling atoms whose height is fixed by symmetry with a fraction (1/4) rather than a decimal (0.250). (Heights may also be given as integral numbers representing hundredths or thousandths of the vertical repeat rather than in the decimal form used in Fig. 7.2; this would be stated in the caption.)

This structure was originally determined by manual computation using intensity data estimated visually from about forty powder lines. In a recent reinvestigation using a high-speed computer and 267 independent reflections measured on an automatic diffractometer, an R-value of $<4\%$ was obtained and the y-coordinate of the oxygen atom was found to be 0.4184 (estimated standard deviation 0.0013) instead of the original 0.416. It is only fair to add that the later investigation also included a very careful examination of the anisotropic temperature factors, which could not have been attempted with the earlier data; the accuracy of the positional parameter obtained using quite crude data is nevertheless most striking. The explanation is that if there is only one variable with which to fit forty observations, even if the observed data are not individually very accurate, the value of the variable parameter that gives the best fit can be expected to be quite reliable. It is normal in structure analysis to have a large excess of observations over unknown parameters and because of this one can work successfully with measured intensities that are accurate to perhaps only ±10%, a degree of error that would not be tolerable in most scientific work.

The crudest way of fixing a variable parameter is to vary it little by little, calculating structure factors for each value until satisfactory agreement is found. This is fairly tedious even for only one unknown, becoming more so as the number increases, so that ways of systematizing the search for a fit are desirable. An early method was to plot structure factor graphs, which show how the structure factor varies with the unknown parameter(s), for a number of key reflections. The value of the parameter that gave the best fit to the observed data was then selected. The oxygen parameter in CuO was originally determined in this way. However, this becomes impracticable as the number of variables increases and a more general method is needed. One such is described in the next section.

7.2 Fourier synthesis

The expression for calculating structure factors:

$$F_{hkl} = \sum_{r=1}^{N} f_r \exp 2\pi i (hx_r + ky_r + lz_r)$$

uses a knowledge of the arrangement of the N atoms in the cell to find the amplitude and phase of the wave scattered in a given direction. Looked at from another point of view, it expresses the distribution of scattered radiation in reciprocal space in terms of the atomic pattern, or electron density distribution, in real space. An analogous expression:

$$\rho_{XYZ} = \frac{1}{V} \sum_{h=-\infty}^{+\infty} \sum_{k=-\infty}^{+\infty} \sum_{l=-\infty}^{+\infty} F_{hkl} \exp -2\pi i (hX + kY + lZ)$$

enables us to proceed in the reverse direction, and, *given a knowledge of the ampli-tudes and phases of the scattered waves* in reciprocal space, we can calculate the electron density ρ at any point XYZ in the unit cell.

If this is done at sufficient points in the cell, an electron density map can be con-structed; by looking for the points with the highest electron density, the atoms can be located. At first sight, it seems that we need only measure as many values of F_{hkl} as possible, perform the appropriate calculation to produce an electron density map and lo! the structure is solved. It sounds too good to be true—and of course it is. The catch is in the condition 'given a knowledge of the amplitudes *and phases* of the scattered waves . . .'; the amplitudes of the waves can be measured fairly easily, but neither film nor counter tells us anything about their relative phases. This is known as the Phase Problem, and although every crystallographer engaged in structure determination spells it, at least mentally, with capital letters, if it did not exist a lot of the fun would be taken out of solving crystal structures.

Before discussing ways and means of tackling the phase problem, let us consider the relationship between the two expressions quoted above. They differ in the sign of the exponent, and this is a mathematical consequence of the fact that they are **Fourier transforms** of each other; we need not worry about just what this means, except to reiterate that they perform the complementary functions of transforming magnitudes in real space into magnitudes in reciprocal space, and *vice versa*. They also differ in that the continuous function expressing electron density can be sampled at any point XYZ of our choosing, but the Fourier transform of the unit cell contents can in practice be sampled only at specific points in reciprocal space, namely the reciprocal lattice points. In other words, the Fourier transform of the cell contents is only directly observable if Bragg's law is fulfilled.

Like the structure-factor expression, the electron-density expression for centro-symmetric structures simplifies to one with cosine terms only:

$$\rho_{XYZ} = \frac{1}{V} \sum_{h=-\infty}^{+\infty} \sum_{k=-\infty}^{+\infty} \sum_{l=-\infty}^{+\infty} F_{hkl} \cos 2\pi (hX + kY + lZ)$$

At the same time, the phase angle associated with F_{hkl}, which in the general case can have any value α, becomes either 0 or π. This means that the summation covers waves that are either exactly in phase or exactly out of phase; we have $+F_{hkl}$ for all those waves with $\alpha = 0$, and $-F_{hkl}$ for those with $\alpha = \pi$. For the centrosymmetric case therefore, the phase problem reduces to one of sign determination.

Once a trial structure has been established, either by the sort of reasoning used in the previous section or by one of the methods yet to be discussed, a Fourier synthesis using the *measured* amplitudes (F_o) with signs (or phases) taken from the *calculated* structure factors (F_c) gives an electron-density map from which improved atomic parameters may be deduced. If a partial solution has been found, missing atoms may be located by the same process. One must be intelligently selective about which terms to include in the Fourier synthesis; if the calculated term is very much smaller than the observed one, not much reliance can be placed on the phase deduced from it. A small value of F_c means that the contributions from the various atoms almost cancel and, in a centrosymmetric structure, a small shift in the atomic coordinates, or the intro-duction of one or two missing atoms, could easily change the sign of F_c; on the other hand, terms for which F_c is much bigger than F_o, although they show that all is not yet well with the trial structure, probably indicate the correct sign to attach to F_o.

Similar, but more complicated, reasoning applies to the phases to be assigned in non-centrosymmetric structures. Normally, therefore, one introduces some criterion for the inclusion of individual terms; a common one is to omit all terms for which F_o is more than three times as big as F_c.

Historically, the calculation of electron densities from the Fourier summation of observed structure amplitudes was first used as a systematic way of improving the values of those atomic coordinates not fixed by space-group considerations. Calculating a complete three-dimensional electron density map is a formidable task, and only became a routine part of crystal structure determination with the advent of high speed computers; previously it was seldom attempted. It is, however, much simpler to calculate the projection of the electron density along a line or onto a plane. For example, a summation that includes only the 00l reflections is relatively simple:

$$\rho_Z = \frac{ab}{V} \sum_{l=-\infty}^{+\infty} F_{00l} \cos 2\pi lZ = 2\frac{ab}{V} \sum_{l=0}^{+\infty} F_{00l} \cos 2\pi lZ$$

$$(\text{because } F_{00l} = F_{00\bar{l}})$$

The resulting curve represents the variation of electron density projected on the z-axis. Figure 7.3 gives an example. The structure of hexagonal ZnS, described earlier, is shown on the right of the diagram, viewed along b; the x and y coordinates of both Zn and S are fixed by symmetry, but the z coordinates are not. An 00l Fourier summation, using phases based on an approximate structure, shows peaks which indicate values for the z coordinates.

Such one-dimensional summations are not very useful; in complicated structures peaks representing different atoms overlap. Two-dimensional summations are a compromise between the amount of computation an individual can reasonably under-

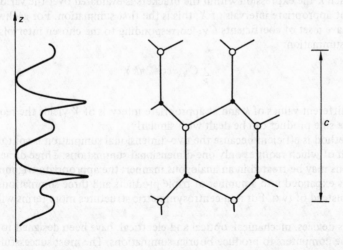

Fig. 7.3 An example of the type of problem that could be solved by a one-dimensional Fourier synthesis. The structure of hexagonal ZnS is shown on the right; small black dots represent zinc atoms, open circles sulphur atoms. Only the z co-ordinates of the atoms are not fixed by symmetry; a one-dimensional Fourier synthesis using the 00l reflections with phases from a trial structure would yield a curve similar to that shown on the left, from which more accurate values could be obtained.

take and the amount of information necessary to solve a structure; they formed the backbone of crystal structure determination for more than thirty years, from the early 1930s until comparatively recently. Various methods of easing the computational labour were devised. Perhaps the most celebrated of these were the 'Beevers–Lipson' strips [3]; the principle on which these worked is still used in present-day computer programs.

Instead of evaluating the summation point-by-point, the trigonometric expression for ρ is expanded. For example, for a centrosymmetric c-projection we have to sum $F_{hk0} \cos 2\pi(hX + kY)$ over all available h and k and at as many points X and Y as we judge necessary to get a reasonable picture of the structure. The cosine term may be expanded:

$$\cos 2\pi(hX + kY) = \cos 2\pi hX \cdot \cos 2\pi kY - \sin 2\pi hX \cdot \sin 2\pi kY$$

At first sight this appears merely to have made the expression more complicated, but in fact the computational labour is reduced, because we can deal with one index at a time. The summation of the first (cosine product) term for example:

$$\sum_h \sum_k F_{hk0} \cos 2\pi hX \cdot \cos 2\pi kY$$

may be rewritten as

$$\sum_k \left\{ \sum_h F_{hk0} \cos 2\pi hX \right\} \cos 2\pi kY$$

and evaluated in two stages. The reflections are grouped according to their k-values, and for each k the expression within the brackets is evaluated over the various values of h and at appropriate intervals of X; this is the first summation. For each value of k we now have a set of coefficients C_{Xk} corresponding to the chosen intervals of X, and a second summation:

$$\sum_k C_{Xk} \cos 2\pi kY$$

over the different values of k and at appropriate intervals of Y yields the required result. The sine product can be dealt with similarly.

The method is efficient because the two-dimensional summation is split up into two steps, each of which requires only one-dimensional summations. Three-dimensional summations may be treated in an analogous manner; the appropriate trigonometric function is expanded into a number of triple products and three summations are required instead of two. For non-centrosymmetric structures more terms will be needed.

Various devices, mechanical, optical and electrical, have been designed to function as analogue computers to produce Fourier summations. The most successful of these was probably XRAC [4]. This represented the Fourier coefficients by electrical waves; these were summed electronically and the results presented on a cathode ray oscilloscope as contours which could be photographed. XRAC was great fun to use, but having been constructed before the era of transistors and miniaturization the units that generated the necessary waves occupied a vast area of floor space. Setting up the coefficients for a synthesis was therefore by no means a sedentary occupation.

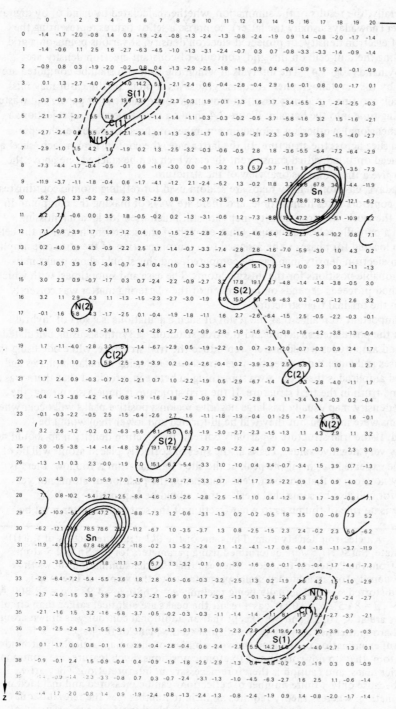

Fig. 7.4 (see caption overleaf)

Generally, the results of the summation, whether calculated by hand or by digital computer (nowadays usually the latter), comprise a set of figures representing the values of electron density, or projected electron density, at various points on a grid subdividing the unit cell; on this grid, contours of constant electron density are drawn by hand (Fig. 7.4). The intervals at which the function shall be computed are decided by the crystallographer. A coarse grid saves computing time, but may miss fine detail; too fine a grid may result in unmanageable quantities of paper, and waste computing time into the bargain. Figure 7.4 shows a two-dimensional projection; a three-dimensional synthesis is printed on a number of sheets of paper, each representing a slice across the structure. In the latter case, the contours from each 'slice' are often traced onto individual transparent sheets which can be stacked one above the other to give a three-dimensional view of the structure.

Nowadays, electron density maps are seldom used for refining atomic coordinates: drawing contours takes human time, and there are ways of making the computer do more of the work. Electron density maps are still much used for locating missing atoms in a partially solved structure. Once enough of the scattering matter in the cell has been located for phases to be assigned to a fair proportion of the structure amplitudes, an electron density map can be computed, and this should show peaks indicating probable positions for the missing atoms. The ease and smoothness with which this method proceeds depends on how much of the scattering matter was correctly placed in the original trial structure.

It is important to realize that the result of such calculations is a sort of 'hybrid' between the postulated structure and the true structure: a synthesis using calculated phases and amplitudes would merely reproduce the trial structure, while one using the true phases and amplitudes gives the true structure. One using calculated phases and measured amplitudes therefore gives something in between, provided that there was at least some truth in the trial structure. If the trial structure is hopelessly wrong, the electron density map usually has large negative regions; positive peaks will occur where trial atoms were inserted but they will be ill-formed and lower than would be expected. If the trial structure is partially correct, the electron density map should not show any very negative values. Peaks at the sites of correctly placed atoms will be of about the expected height; if the peak at the site of a trial atom is too low, there is probably no atom at that position. Peaks indicating the position of atoms not yet allowed for will also be somewhat weaker than would be expected.

There is no rule-of-thumb as to what fraction of the scattering matter must be

---

Fig. 7.4   An electron density map. The signs of the $0kl$ structure factors of tin(II) thiocyanate, $Sn(SCN)_2$, were determined using parameters for the Sn and S atoms derived from the Patterson function. The resulting Fourier summation shows the electron density (on an arbitrary scale) projected onto the yz plane. The map is slightly distorted, the cell actually being triclinic, $a = 5.680$, $b = 4.975$, $c = 10.300$ Å, $\alpha = 79.5°$, $\beta = 84.5°$, $\gamma = 100.0°$; as a result the peaks are elliptical rather than circular. Contours are at 5, 10, 20 and 30, except that an additional contour was drawn around the SCN group that lies roughly perpendicular to the plane of the paper.

Careful examination of the map shows a number of maxima, particularly around the Sn atom, that do not correspond to atomic positions. Such features are common on Fourier maps, and caution is therefore necessary in interpretation. They arise mainly because only a finite number of reflections can be measured and included in the summation, whereas theory requires an infinite number (see the relevant equations). The more limited the data used, the more liable this effect is to occur; it is known as the 'termination of series' error. (From data provided by R.A. Howie and A. Filby.)

correctly placed before this method will work. The most favourable cases are those in which one atom in the structure is considerably heavier than the rest; if this is correctly located, it may be sufficient to determine the phases, even though it constitutes only a tiny fraction of the total scattering matter in the unit cell. A classical case is that of the structure determination of vitamin B12 [5] which rested on the location of the single Co atom in a $C_{63}H_{88}O_{14}N_{14}P$ Co molecule; successive electron density maps based first on the Co alone, and then on Co and other nearby atoms, as these emerged a few at a time from the Fourier syntheses, slowly revealed more and more of the structure. In this paper, Professor Hodgkin remarks that caution in interpretation had to be used as 'it is very easy to "make" atoms and so to invent a completely unreal chemical structure'.

7.3 Getting started

7.3.1 The Patterson function

In most structures that are tackled nowadays, it is *not* possible to place atoms and derive a trial structure from space group and packing considerations alone; all the common substances that can be dealt with in this way were solved long ago.

Often, a structure determination begins by computing the **Patterson function** of the crystal. Although it is not possible to compute ρ_{XYZ} directly because of the uncertainty about the phases of the F-values, there is no such uncertainty about the $|F|^2$ values. The function

$$P_{UVW} = \frac{1}{V} \sum_{h=-\infty}^{+\infty} \sum_{k=-\infty}^{+\infty} \sum_{l=-\infty}^{+\infty} |F_{hk0}|^2 \cos 2\pi(hU + kV + lW)$$

which is always centrosymmetric, *can* be computed directly. Patterson [6] showed that the resulting function is a map, not of atomic positions, but of **interatomic vectors**. A peak in the Patterson function at UVW, in other words, implies that there are two atoms in the crystal structure at $x_1y_1z_1$ and $x_2y_2z_2$ such that $x_2 - x_1 = U$, $y_2 - y_1 = V$, and $z_2 - z_1 = W$; moreover the height of the peak in the Patterson function will be proportional to the product of the number of electrons in each of the two atoms involved. The last property is important in the interpretation of Patterson functions.

Fig. 7.5   The relationship between a structure and its vector map. (a) An imaginary structure projected down c. The 'atomic coordinates' as fractions of a (5 units) and b (8 units) are:

	x	y
A	0.100	0.125
B	0.300	0.375
C	0.500	0.750
D	0.900	0.250

(b) The corresponding vector map. The label 'AB' implies the vector from A to B, and so on. (c) The vector map decomposed into a series of images of the original structure by connecting all peaks whose first letter is A, and so on.

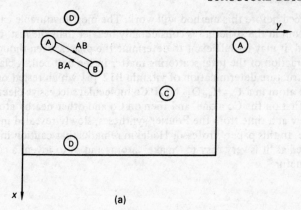

(a)

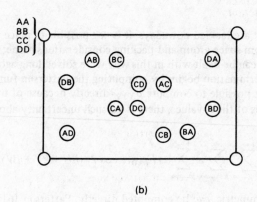

(b)

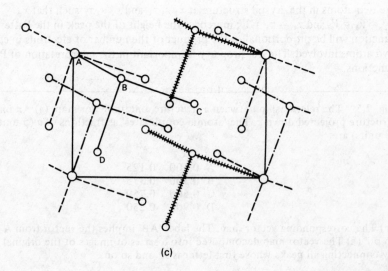

(c)

Figure 7.5(a) shows the projection of a simple four-atom structure and Fig. 7.5(b) the corresponding vector map, with the interatomic vectors labelled according to the system indicated in (a), that is to say AB is the vector from atom A to atom B, and BA the vector in the reverse direction. The connection between these two maps should be studied closely, as unless this is well understood, it will not be possible to follow the rest of the argument. It is probably worthwhile to redraw (a) on squared paper on a cell 5 x 8 units ('atomic' coordinates are given in the figure caption) and derive (b) from it before proceeding further. When doing this, remember that both the crystal structure and the corresponding vector map are periodic functions—this is emphasized in the diagram by drawing slightly more than one complete unit cell of each—otherwise it may be puzzling to see just where to plot the vectors. Note that the vector map has a large origin peak, corresponding to the vector from every atom to itself.

By now it will be obvious that for any cell containing more than two atoms, there are more vectors than atoms—generally a lot more. If there are n atoms in the cell, there are $n - 1$ vectors from each of them to the $n - 1$ other atoms, a total of $n(n - 1)$ vectors, plus the n vectors piled up at the origin; it begins to look as though it would be hopeless to try to work back from the vector map to the atomic pattern.

Figure 7.5(c) shows that the map in (b) is not quite so formless as it looks at first sight. The four peaks labelled AB, AC and AD, together with AA at the origin, reproduce the arrangement in (a), and this is also true of the set of peaks whose first letter is B, or C, or D. To try to make this clearer, these sets have been connected with distinctive lines in (c). Moreover, each of these sets is displaced from the origin of the vector map by a distance corresponding to an interatomic vector. Since the Patterson function is centrosymmetric, an arrangement that is the mirror image of the original (in (a)) is found if all peaks whose *last* letter is A, etc., are taken as a set. Plainly these observations contain the germ of an idea for sorting out the vector map; one can look for an arrangement of peaks that is repeated in other parts of the map.

In a simple structure such as that in Fig. 7.6(a) it may be possible to see the solution intuitively. In the (imaginary) triatomic molecule illustrated, one atom, represented by the black dot, is much heavier than the other two, represented by open circles. Peaks on the vector map corresponding to vectors between the two heavy atoms (black dots in Fig. 7.6(b)) are consequently very much higher than the others, and stand out prominently on the vector map; the next highest peaks can be assumed to represent heavy atom–light atom vectors, and it may be possible to pick out the shape of the molecule directly and produce a complete solution to the structure. (Note that in the example shown one would instinctively place the origin of the cell in the middle of OX, that is take the coordinates of the heavy atom as $\pm\frac{1}{2}$ OX. This shifts the origin from that shown in (a), but does not change the arrangement in any way.)

More often than not, one cannot proceed intuitively beyond the stage of locating the heavy atom. The molecule may simply be too complicated for further progress to be possible, or accidental coincidences between light atom–light atom vectors may bedevil the interpretation. When this happens, there are in general two possible ways of proceeding. The lazy way, which nevertheless usually succeeds, is to hope that the contribution of the heavy atom is sufficient to determine the phases, use its position to calculate structure factors and subsequently an electron density map and then search for the missing atoms as described in Section 7.2. Alternatively, the knowledge of the heavy atom position may be used to proceed further with deciphering the Patterson map, using a **superposition** method. The theory of these methods has been exhaustively discussed by Buerger [7] so nothing more will be said about it here. For

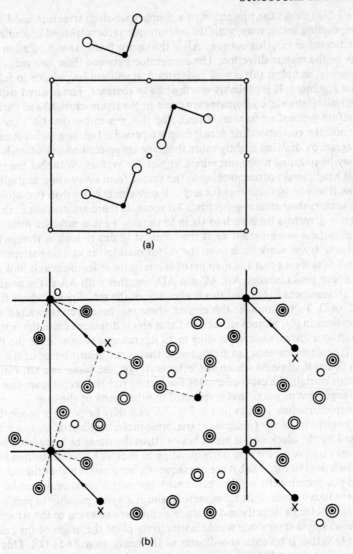

Fig. 7.6   The use of a superposition method to unravel a Patterson map. The molecule in (a) has two light atoms (open circles) attached to a heavy one (solid circles). The unit cell contains two molecules, related by a centre of symmetry. The corresponding vector map is shown in (b). The heaviest, or largest, vector peaks are represented by solid circles, the lightest by open ones, and there are two intermediate grades. The four grades represent, in order of increasing solidity,

> single weight light atom—light atom peaks
> double weight light atom—light atom peaks
> double weight heavy atom—light atom peaks
> single weight heavy atom—heavy atom peaks

The method of regenerating (a) from (b) by the use of a superposition method is explained in the text.

present purposes, it will be far more illuminating to try out a practical example for yourself, and Fig. 7.6 was designed with this in mind.

You will need two small pieces of tracing paper. On one of these, copy all the peaks from Fig. 7.6(b), including those that lie outside the cell boundaries. Now slide the tracing in the direction X-O, until the peaks X on the tracing are exactly superposed on the peaks O in the diagram in the book. At this point a couple of paper clips will come in handy to hold the diagram and tracing together in this position, while you examine the relationship between them. You will find that most of the peaks on the tracing do not coincide with those in the original drawing, but a few of them do. Mark these coincidences on the second piece of tracing paper, using a full circle for the coincidence of two heavy peaks, and an open one for that of two lighter ones. Compare the result with Fig. 7.6(a); if all has gone well the two will be identical, given the proper choice of origin.

This is not really such black magic as it may appear at first sight; it is a logical development of the concepts introduced on p. 167 in the discussion of Fig. 7.5(c). Moreover, the method is not without its pitfalls. If no suitable heavy atom–heavy atom peak is available, other peaks must be tried. A little experimentation with Fig. 7.6 and your tracing will show that a true solution is obtained only if the selected peak is **single weight**, that is the result of a single interatomic vector; multiple peaks yield multiple solutions. Moreover, if you try the same technique on the vector map in Fig. 7.5(b), derived from the non-centrosymmetric structure in Fig. 7.5(a), you will again get a multiple solution, containing the true solution and its mirror image. In theory these difficulties can be overcome by making successive superpositions, but this does not always work out in practice.

Moreover, in our examples the atoms have been nearly points, and the vector map has correspondingly sharp peaks; in practice both are continuously varying functions. More sophisticated methods are then needed to determine whether the superposed Patterson functions show a possible coincidence of vectors, and for this purpose the **minimum** function is probably the best choice. This is prepared by comparing the two (or more) maps point by point and taking the minimum value at each point. This can be done either graphically or with a computer; the former is undoubtedly more fun, but in three-dimensional work can result in unwieldy amounts of paper. Buerger [7] has given practical details for the graphical method. In either case, the result is a map whose contours show peaks only at points where peaks, or at least 'upland areas', on the contributing maps coincide; it is the equivalent of the tracing you prepared from Fig. 7.6.

7.3.2 *When the Patterson function is not enough*

There are two principal classes of problem in which the above approach fails. One comprises structures that contain, or can be induced to assimilate, a heavy atom, but which are so very complex that even though the heavy atom can be located the rest of the structure can neither be unravelled from the Patterson map nor located by Fourier synthesis, the contribution of the heavy atom to the structure factor being relatively too small to determine the phases. The other comprises structures that contain only light atoms.

The first situation is frequently encountered with biological materials such as proteins, and these are tackled by the method of **isomorphous replacement**. This works for crystals that can assimilate different heavy atoms while leaving the light atom part of the structure unchanged. Comparison of relative values of the structure amplitudes of reflections from the different crystals may then enable their phases to be determined. As a simple idealized example let us consider two centrosymmetric compounds HL and H'L, where L, the light atom part of the structure, is the same in both, and H and H' represent two different heavy atoms. Then for any given reflection:

$$|F_{HL}| = F_H + F_L \quad \text{and} \quad |F_{H'L}| = F_{H'} + F_L$$

where $|F_{HL}|$ and $|F_{H'L}|$ are the measured structure amplitudes. F_H and $F_{H'}$ are the contributions to the structure factor from the heavy atoms; these can be calculated, the heavy atoms having been located from a Patterson function in the usual way. F_L, the light atom contribution, remains the same for both compounds. Suppose, for example, that

$$\begin{aligned} |F_{HL}| &= 20 \\ |F_{H'L}| &= 25 \end{aligned} \quad \text{and} \quad \begin{aligned} F_H &= +5 \\ F_{H'} &= +10 \end{aligned} \quad \text{then } F_L = +15$$

Alternatively, if

$$\begin{aligned} |F_{HL}| &= 25 \\ |F_{H'L}| &= 20 \end{aligned} \quad \text{and} \quad \begin{aligned} F_H &= +5 \\ F_{H'} &= +10 \end{aligned} \quad \text{then } F_L = -30$$

Real examples are of course not likely to be so clear-cut as the above; difficulties in placing the measured structure amplitudes on the proper scale, and random errors of measurement are two of the most obvious snags. An additional problem has to be faced if the structure is non-centrosymmetric because then the complex nature of the structure factor means that, even in theory, application of the above reasoning is bound to lead to two possible phase angles; to distinguish between these information from a third isomorphous compound is required. The labour involved in such calculations is enormous, yet this is how the structures of proteins have been unravelled. Usually, information from the original protein and from two different heavy atom derivatives has been used. The results of these efforts represent one of the great triumphs of crystallography in recent years; accounts of some of the struggles involved will be found among the suggestions for further reading.

For the other class of structures that are unlikely to be solved through the Patterson function—those containing only light atoms—there is fortunately an alternative approach via the so-called **direct methods**. For a full account of these, the reader should consult more advanced texts, but a brief account of some of the underlying physical principles will be given.

A crystal, as we have said, can be represented by a periodic function giving the electron density at any point, and in a real crystal two conditions must be fulfilled:

(i) The electron density can never be negative.

(ii) Atoms are atom-shaped, that is the electron density about an atomic centre, or electron density maximum, is approximately spherically symmetrical. For a stationary atom, the diminution of electron density with distance from the atomic centre falls off in a manner predictable from the f-curve for that atom; in practice, atoms vibrate about their mean positions to an extent that depends on the absolute temperature and the atomic shape must be modified to take account of this.

If it can be further assumed that the distribution of scattering material about the cell is approximately random—a condition usually fulfilled reasonably well by a structure such as we are considering here, containing a large number of light atoms—various deductions can be made regarding the way in which the intensities of reflections are related.

The earliest of these [8] related the average observed intensity at a given value of $\sin \theta/\lambda$ to the value corresponding to a random assemblage of stationary atoms; from it both the temperature factor and the scaling constant necessary to convert the measured relative intensities to approximately absolute values could be deduced. It was also shown that the distribution of intensities about the average intensity could be used to test for the presence or absence of a centre of symmetry [9], which can normally not be ascertained from a simple examination of the X-ray diffraction patterns. It was next shown that for centrosymmetric structures inequality relationships can be developed that give the signs of a number of very strong reflections unambiguously [10]. To apply these relationships, the normal structure factor F_{hkl} is converted into the corresponding **unitary structure factor,** U_{hkl}:

$$U_{hkl} = F_{hkl} \bigg/ \sum_{r=1}^{N} f_r$$

where f_r is the scattering factor for the rth atom at the appropriate value of $\sin \theta/\lambda$. This expresses the value of the structure factor as a fraction of its maximum possible value ($\sum_{r=1}^{N} f_r$, for all the atoms scattering in phase). A very strong reflection is one for which this fraction, U, is large.

One of the simplest of these inequalities can be used to show that

$$U_{hkl}^2 \leqslant \tfrac{1}{2}(1 + U_{2h2k2l})$$

If the two Us are large, say 0.6, the inequality is satisfied only if the sign of U_{2h2k2l} is positive. A physical interpretation of this statement is shown in Fig. 7.7. The use of this particular inequality is limited to proving that U_{2h2k2l} is positive, but further inequalities can be developed which extend the range of determinable signs, making the method more useful than might appear at first sight. Nevertheless, it generally becomes necessary to include sign relationships that are only *probably* true (instead of *certainly* true). Largely thanks to the availability of high speed computers, these methods are now applied routinely. Comparatively recently they have been extended to non-centrosymmetric structures so that the phases can be approximately determined by analogous methods.

Once a sufficient number of phases have been determined in this way, a Fourier synthesis is computed. It should be possible to recognize most, if not all, of the structure in the resulting map, and from this point the structure determination follows the sequence outlined in Section 7.2 and/or is refined as described in the next section.

There is another method which is useful if the shape of the molecule, or of a large part of it, is known, and the problem is that of finding the orientation of the known group of atoms in the unit cell. This uses the fact noted earlier (p. 160) that the diffraction pattern of a crystal can be regarded as the Fourier transform of the cell contents observed at those points in reciprocal space where Bragg's law is satisfied, that is at the reciprocal lattice points. If the relative positions of some or all of the

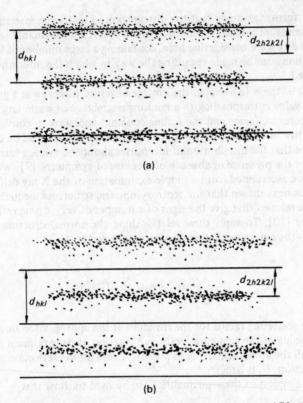

Fig. 7.7   A physical interpretation of the inequality quoted on p. 172. For waves diffracted by both hkl and $2h2k2l$ to have large amplitudes, the scattering matter must be arranged mainly in bands in one of the ways indicated by the stippling in the diagrams. The arrangment in (a) will make F_{hkl} + ve, whereas that in (b) will make F_{hkl} − ve; in either case F_{2h2k2l} will be +ve.

atoms in the cell are known, the Fourier transform of the arrangement can be calculated as a continuous function. This is then compared with the observed intensities at the reciprocal lattice points to find the orientation of the known group of atoms within the unit cell that gives the best agreement.

In practice the method has more often been applied in projection than in three dimensions. The transform can then be generated by optical diffraction methods thus saving the labour of computation. There is not space here to go into details of these methods, for which see the Bibliography. Briefly the atomic arrangement is simulated by a number of holes, one for each projected atom, punched in a mask. The optical diffraction pattern of one such group gives a representation of the Fourier transform; the pattern from a regularly repeating array of them gives a representation of the appropriate section of the reciprocal lattice.

Remembering the reciprocal nature of the operations that relate atomic arrangements and X-ray diffraction patterns, one might wonder whether the optical diffraction pattern from a mask representing the reciprocal lattice section would correspond to a projection of the structure in the appropriate direction. Unfortunately this is so only if all the diffracted X-ray beams have the same phase; for a centrosymmetric arrangement with a heavy atom on the origin (all phase angles zero) one can get quite a good picture of the projected structure in this way. Otherwise one is back with the old Phase Problem. Even if the phases are known, the utility of the method as a rapid means of Fourier synthesis is limited by the difficulty of introducing the appropriate phase changes into the optical system.

Finally, *in extremis*, one might try what have been appropriately dubbed 'Monte Carlo' methods, or trial-and-error methods without any real starting point. In these trial structures are set up more or less at random (hence the name) and tested against a limited amount of diffraction data until one that gives a reasonable degree of fit emerges. Even if the possible structures are limited by restricting them to those that make crystal chemical sense, the number of possibilities is usually so large that the method is only practicable if a very fast computer is available. Quite apart from such material considerations, the method is so totally lacking in finesse that most people would not consider it except as a last resort.

7.4   Refinement

When a solution believed to be approximately correct has been obtained, it must be **refined** to give the best possible fit between observed and calculated data. The use of the electron density map for adjusting coordinates has already been mentioned (Section 7.2), but once the coordinates are approximately correct, this is a relatively insensitive method, and progress becomes rather slow. For one thing it is usually difficult to determine the exact centre of a peak; for another, the computed electron density map is a hybrid between that of the true structure and that of the assumed one (cf. Section 7.2).

Figure 7.8(a) illustrates the latter point. P_t and P_a represent the true and assumed positions of an atom, and the dotted curves show sections across the corresponding electron densities, ρ_t and ρ_a. The solid line ρ_{map}, representing the electron density found from the Fourier synthesis, lies between the other two curves. The true position is thus *not* at the maximum of the peak on the Fourier synthesis, but on the opposite side of this from the assumed position; one way to speed up refinement is to move atoms by up to twice the distance between their assumed positions and the centre of the peak on the map. The difficulty of locating this centre with accuracy remains.

One way round this, shown in Fig. 7.8(b), is to use as Fourier coefficients not the values of F_o, but $(F_o - F_c)$. This produces a **difference** map, which consists essentially of the true electron density, with the electron density due to the assumed structure subtracted. If the assumed structure is correct, the difference map should be featureless; theoretically it should be zero everywhere, but in practice random errors in the observed data make this only approximately true even for fully refined structures. If an atom is slightly misplaced, as in Fig. 7.8(b), its assumed position will lie on a steep gradient on the difference map, not far from the zero contour, with a large negative region to one side of it, and a large positive one to the other (Fig. 7.9(a)). To correct its position, the atom should be moved *up* the steepest gradient by an amount proportional to the gradient at its centre. Exact equations relating the shift Δr to the gradient $d\rho/dr$ are to be found in more advanced works; in practice it is usually satisfactory to shift the atom by $k \cdot d\rho/dr$, where the constant k is (for three-dimensional work) of the order of 0.02–0.01 for light atoms, and less for heavy ones, and is adjusted empirically in the course of the refinement. It is usually easiest to evaluate the gradient along each of the three axial directions in turn.

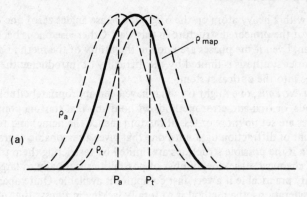

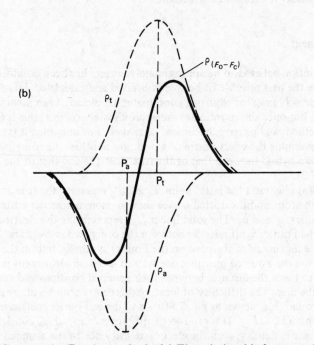

Fig. 7.8   Refinement by Fourier methods. (a) The relationship between the assumed position, P_a, the true position P_t and the electron density peak due to a slightly misplaced atom. (b) Similar relationships for a difference synthesis.

If an atom is completely misplaced, the difference map will show a large negative region at its assumed position (Fig. 7.9(b)), and one has to look for a new site; with luck the difference map will indicate this as a positive region where no atom was placed. Other features that may appear on a difference map are shown in Fig. 7.9(c) and (d). Figure 7.9(c) shows the effect of having used too small a temperature factor when calculating F_c values, thus estimating too great an electron density at the atomic centre, and too little further out; using too large a temperature factor would, of course, produce the opposite effect. Contours like those in Fig. 7.9(d) suggest that the

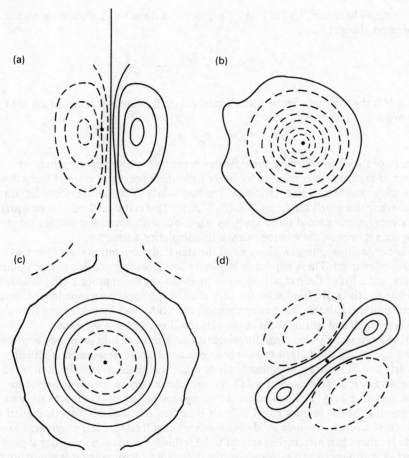

Fig. 7.9   Some typical features to be found on difference maps. The assumed atomic position is shown by a black dot; negative contours are shown as dashed lines, zero and positive ones by solid lines. (a) Atom slightly misplaced; should be moved to the right, up the gradient. (b) Atom totally misplaced. (c) Atom given too small a temperature factor; its electron density needs 'spreading out' more. (d) Atom is probably vibrating anisotropically; assigned temperature factor slightly too large.

atom is not vibrating equally in all directions, and that in calculating its contribution to the structure factors anisotropic temperature factors should be used. Most computer programs include this facility as a standard feature, but it should be used with discretion (see Chapter 9).

The other method of refinement that is commonly used in effect solves the complete set of equations

$$F_o \approx F_c = \sum_{r=1}^{N} f_r \exp\left(-B_r \frac{\sin^2 \theta}{\lambda^2}\right) \exp 2\pi i(hx_r + ky_r + lz_r).$$

This cannot be done directly, but is approached via the corresponding differential equations. If the nth parameter (B, x, y or z for the rth atom) is in error by Δn, correcting it changes F_c by $(\partial F_c/\partial n) \cdot \Delta n$, provided Δn is small. Correcting all the parameters changes F_c by

$$\Delta F_c = \sum_{n=1}^{M} \frac{\partial F_c}{\partial n} \cdot \Delta n$$

where M is the total number of variable parameters. The correct values of Δn are those that make

$$\Delta F_c = F_o - F_c$$

for each of the observed reflections. However, the values of F_o are known to be subject to experimental error; on the other hand there are many more of them than there are parameters to be determined. The best values of Δn are therefore determined by choosing those that minimize $\Sigma_{hkl}(F_o - F_c)^2$. This is the method of **least squares**. It is a very tedious procedure to apply by hand, but with the advent of high speed computers it became the routine method of completing a structure.

Most crystallographers employ one of the standard programs available for least-squares refinement. These require to be given a set of parameters that is approximately correct, and a list of the *hkl* reflections to be used with the appropriate F_o-values. To calculate F_c, the scattering factor for each atom at the angle corresponding to each reflection is needed; this requirement is most efficiently met by calculating the values once and for all and storing them in the data list along with the F_o values.

Provision is usually also made for **weighting** each reflection in some way according to how accurately it is judged to have been measured: in other words it is actually $\Sigma_{hkl} w(F_o - F_c)^2$ that is minimized, where w is the allotted weight. In addition to the parameters x, y, z and B mentioned above, one can usually refine the temperature factor anisotropically, and also refine the **occupancy factor**, or fraction of an atom that is occupying the site in question. The latter is particularly useful if statistical distribution is suspected, or where solid solutions are being treated. Most programs allow one to fix those parameters that are not to be refined: for example, positional parameters of atoms on special positions, or the occupancy factor when it is not in doubt. The program then calculates F_c and $F_o - F_c$ (or some related quantity) for each reflection, determines the required parameter shifts and the estimated standard deviations of the new parameters, and prints all this information along with the R-factor and the new parameters. The crystallographer can then examine the figures and decide whether the structure is completely refined, or whether the calculation should be repeated starting with the new parameters. Each such complete set of calculations is known as a **cycle**.

The very ease with which the calculation can be performed, the almost routine nature of the operation, can produce a false sense of security; it is all too easy to forget the limitations imposed by the (admittedly complicated) underlying mathematics. The most serious of these concerns totally or partially misplaced atoms; the least-squares routine is normally capable of making only quite small corrections to atomic positions; it will find the best position for an atom *near to where you have put it*. If you have put it in the wrong place, some warning may be given by the least-squares program through the emergence of an abnormally high-temperature factor for the atom concerned, but it is also possible for a perfectly sensible set of figures to emerge, and the error may not be detected unless the result appears to be chemically unreasonable, for example, it includes an abnormal bond length. Refinement from difference syntheses is not liable to this type of error, but requires more effort on the part of the crystallographer. The temptation to rely on successive least-squares cycles is strong; beginners seem especially prone to wasting computer time in futile refinements of wrong structures. A close check should therefore be kept on the progress of the refinement; temperature factors must be closely watched and bond lengths calculated from time to time to ensure that the structure continues to make crystal-chemical sense. Even when all has gone smoothly it is still advisable to check the final results with a difference map.

The refined structure should therefore satisfy three criteria:

(a) It should be chemically sensible.

(b) It should give reasonable agreement between observed and calculated structure factors—R should be fairly low.

(c) The difference map should be essentially featureless.

Of the three, the last is probably the most significant. To illustrate this, let me tell a cautionary tale based on personal experience. A structure containing tetrahedral groups was refined by least squares to a satisfactory R-value, with no abnormal temperature factors, and the resulting structure made chemical sense. Nevertheless, two atoms in the tetrahedron were in fact wrongly placed and when their positions were corrected the tilt of the tetrahedron was reversed. Accidental coincidences between the right and wrong parameters of the two atoms concerned appeared to account for their temperature factors remaining normal and to this extent we were perhaps unlucky; but it does go to show that you cannot be too careful! Full details of this sorry affair are in the literature [11].

Finally, what is a satisfactory value for R? It is fairly well known, and widely quoted, that random models for a structure would give R-values of 0.83 for a centrosymmetric and 0.59 for a non-centrosymmetric structure, so a trial structure should give values significantly better than these before any reliance can be placed on it. Just how much better depends on circumstances; it is difficult to give a rule of thumb. Note that a poor choice of scale factor can give an illusion of better agreement than has actually been obtained; if ΣF_o is relatively rather too big, R may have a spuriously low value. Although it should be easy to spot when this has happened, it can be temporarily deceptive.

A structure that is correct will refine rapidly and smoothly to below 0.20; a model that stops refining at rather higher values is probably only partly correct. The final R-value that you can expect to reach depends on how carefully the data were collected and corrected. Even fairly rough-and-ready data usually refine to about 0.1; with good data, values in the range 0.03–0.05 can be expected.

However, beware of trying to refine a structure beyond what the data are worth. You can always improve the agreement by introducing some more variable parameters, for example by changing from isotropic to anisotropic temperature factors, by refining site occupancies or by introducing, where appropriate, hydrogen atoms that were not initially considered. It is more difficult to decide whether the improvement is significant; a useful test has been given by Hamilton [12].

Further discussion on this topic will be found in Chapter 9.

7.5 Anomalous scattering

The structure factor of a given reflection is the vector sum of the waves scattered by the various atoms; this has so far been expressed as an equation. It can also be

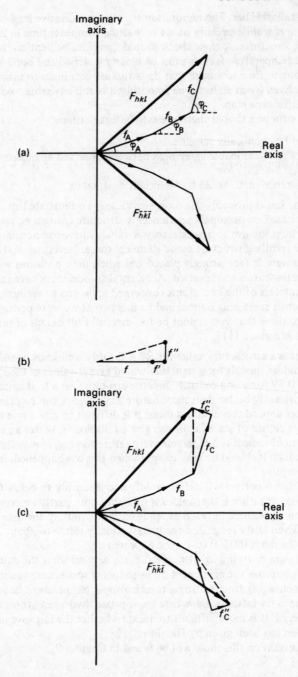

Fig. 7.10   The effect of anomalous scattering. (a) The structure factors F_{hkl} and $F_{\bar{h}\bar{k}\bar{l}}$ for a non-centrosymmetric structure shown on a vector diagram. (b) The real and imaginary parts of the scattering factor of an anomalously scattering atom, showing how a phase change is introduced. (c) The effect on F_{hkl} and $F_{\bar{h}\bar{k}\bar{l}}$ of introducing an anomalous scatterer into the structure shown in (a).

represented by a vector diagram such as Fig. 7.10(a), in which f_A, etc. are the amplitudes and ϕ_A etc. the phases of the waves scattered by the three atoms A, B and C of a non-centrosymmetric structure: although the resultants F_{hkl} and $F_{\bar{h}\bar{k}\bar{l}}$ differ in phase, they have the same magnitude, the observed intensities are equal, and Friedel's law is obeyed.

Up to this point we have assumed that the phases ϕ_A, etc., depend only on the position of the scattering atom, that is the scattering process at the atom does not introduce any additional relative phase change. It is in general true that such changes are negligible; this is why Friedel's law normally holds. There are however important exceptions: atoms that have an absorption edge (Fig. 3.2) close to the frequency of the incident radiation introduce an additional phase change, and this is known as **anomalous scattering**. For such atoms the simple scattering factor, f, which is calculated on the assumption that the electrons in the atom can be treated as free electrons, has to be modified to take account of the interaction of the incident X-rays with the bound electrons; it is of course this interaction that produces the absorption edge. The modification is shown in Fig. 7.10(b); the simple scattering factor now becomes a complex quantity $f + f' + if''$. It is the imaginary part—if''—that concerns us here as this is the component that introduces the phase difference.

The effect of the presence of an anomalous scatterer in a non-centrosymmetric structure is shown in Fig. 7.10(c). Here atom C is assumed to scatter anomalously; the real part of f_C is the same as in Fig. 7.10(a), to emphasize the effect of f_C''. The resultants F_{hkl} and $F_{\bar{h}\bar{k}\bar{l}}$ are equal neither in phase nor magnitude, and Friedel's law is not obeyed. An important consequence of the existence of this effect is that the absolute configurations of structures that have crystallized in non-centrosymmetric space groups can be determined; indeed this is how the absolute configurations of optically active compounds have been established.

References

[1]   Tunell, G., Posnjak, E. and Ksanda, C. J., *Z. Kristallogr.* **90**, 120–142 (1935).

[2]   Åsbrink, S. and Norrby, L. J., *Acta Crystallogr.* **B26**, 8–15 (1970).

[3]   Lipson, H. and Beevers, C. A., *Proc. phys. Soc.* **48**, 772–780 (1936).

[4]   Pepinsky, R., *J. appl. Phys.* **18**, 601–604 (1947).

[5]   Hodgkin, D. C., *Fortschr. Chem. org. NatStoffe* **15**, 167–220 (1958).

[6]   Patterson, A. L., *Z. Kristallogr.* **90**, 517–542 (1935).

[7]   Buerger, M. J., *Acta Crystallogr.* **4**, 531–544 (1951).

[8]   Wilson, A. J. C., *Nature, (Lond.)* **150**, 152 (1942).

[9]   Howells, E. R., Phillips, D. C. and Rogers, D., *Acta Crystallogr.* **3**, 210–214 (1950).

[10] Harker, D. and Kasper, J. S., *Acta Crystallogr.* **1**, 70–75 (1953).

[11] Jamieson, P. B. and Dent Glasser, L. S., *Acta Crystallogr.* **22**, 507–522 (1967).

[12] Hamilton, W. C., *Acta Crystallogr.* **18**, 502–510 (1965).

CHAPTER 8

Other diffraction methods

8.1 Particles and waves

Although the vast majority of crystal structure determinations are based on X-ray diffraction data, there are two other diffraction techniques of practical importance. These use beams of electrons or neutrons, and the information they provide neatly fills in some of the gaps left by X-ray diffraction.

A moving particle can also be described by a wave, whose length is given by the de Broglie equation:

$$\lambda = \frac{h}{mv}$$

where h is Planck's constant, m is the mass of the particle and v its velocity. The wavelength thus depends on the velocity of the particle, and this in turn depends on its kinetic energy, since $E = \frac{1}{2}mv^2$. Substituting

$$v = \sqrt{(2E/m)}$$

in the de Broglie equation we obtain

$$\lambda = \frac{h}{m\sqrt{(2E/m)}} = \frac{h}{\sqrt{(2mE)}}$$

The kinetic energy of neutrons depends on the temperature of the generating pile, while that of electrons depends on the accelerating voltage to which they are subject. The next two sections will consider each technique in turn.

8.2 Neutron diffraction

The neutrons emerging from a pile do not all have the same kinetic energy; rather their energies follow a Maxwell distribution, with a most probable kinetic energy kT, where k is the Boltzmann constant and T the absolute temperature. The wavelength of neutrons from a normal pile, whose temperature runs somewhere between ambient and 100°C (300–400°K), will be distributed about a most probable value of 1.0–1.5 Å; this value is eminently suitable for diffraction experiments of the usual type, but the wide range of other wavelengths present in the beam is not acceptable. A more or less monochromatic beam can be produced by reflection from a suitable set of crystal planes (cf. X-ray monochrometers, Section 6.2.2). The reflection angle θ is adjusted so that the fraction of neutrons having energies close to kT is selected (Fig. 8.1). The extent of the angular range over which the neutrons are collected is a compromise: if it is kept small, the beam will be highly monochromatic but very weak, whereas if a larger angular range is accepted the beam will be stronger but less monochromatic.

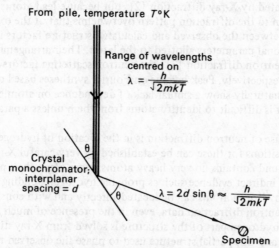

Fig. 8.1   Production of a monochromatic neutron beam; in practice neutrons diffracted over a small range of θ are collected. The larger the range of angles, the stronger the beam and the greater the range of included wavelengths. The monochromator is chosen to select neutrons with wavelengths near to the most probable value for the pile.

In any case the beam is not very strong, so for neutron diffraction single crystals must be much larger than those usually used for X-ray diffraction: at least 1 mm, and usually more, in linear dimensions. Single crystal investigations by neutron diffraction are thus limited to those materials that can be obtained as large crystals, and the intensity measurements are subject to errors due to extinction (see Section 9.1).

The diffracted beams cannot be recorded on film, but must be measured with a counter. This and the rest of the apparatus must be heavily shielded, making it very much more massive than comparable X-ray diffraction equipment. Moreover, sources of suitable neutrons are relatively rare. It is thus not surprising that neutron diffraction is much less widely used than X-ray diffraction; indeed you may well wonder why anyone should bother with it at all.

In fact the diffraction of neutrons differs fundamentally from that of X-rays, in that, with certain exceptions, neutrons are scattered by the *nuclei* of atoms and not by their electrons. The exceptions are atoms that have a magnetic moment, whose electron clouds *do* interact with neutrons. The magnetic structure of materials containing such atoms can be studied by neutron diffraction; these studies will not be discussed here but the interested reader will find the subject reviewed in [1].

Because the nucleus of an atom, unlike its electron cloud, is negligibly small in comparison with the wavelength of the scattered radiation, waves diffracted from opposite sides of the atom do not interfere destructively (cf. Fig. 6.11). Consequently neutron scattering factors are constant, instead of falling off with increasing θ like the X-ray curves. Moreover, neutron scattering factors are not proportional to atomic numbers as are X-ray values. Neutron scattering factors vary comparatively little, and quite irregularly, throughout the periodic table.

This last property means that the determination of the positions of light atoms in the presence of heavy ones, which may be difficult or impossible from X-ray data, becomes relatively easy. For example, the structure of the orthorhombic form of PbO was first investigated by X-ray diffraction [2], but because lead atoms are so heavy their contribution to the diffraction pattern overwhelms that of the oxygen atoms. The agreement between the observed and calculated structure factors is thus insensitive to the positional parameters allotted to the latter. Their arrangement had to be determined by neutron diffraction [3]: the neutron scattering factors of Pb and O are 0.96 and 0.577 respectively. Peak heights on Fourier syntheses based on neutron diffraction data naturally show a similar lack of dependence on atomic number: this may mean that it is difficult to identify atoms from them unless a parallel X-ray study has been made.

The classical use of neutron diffraction is in the location of hydrogen atoms. Approximate positions for these can be established by very careful X-ray work, provided the compound contains no very heavy atoms; more often their positions have to be inferred from indirect evidence such as probable hydrogen bonding schemes. On the other hand, the hydrogen atoms can be located directly and with considerable accuracy from neutron diffraction data, even in the presence of much heavier atoms. Usually the non-hydrogen part of the structure is solved from X-ray diffraction data in the normal way, and this partial structure used to phase the observed neutron diffraction amplitudes for a Fourier or difference synthesis.

Since neutron diffraction locates the nuclei of atoms and X-ray diffraction gives a picture of their electron clouds, a combination of the two techniques should provide information about the way electron clouds are distorted by the formation of bonds between atoms. Relatively recently, detailed pictures of electron density distributions have been obtained in this way, and the results compared with the predictions of theoretical chemistry; this is discussed in Section 9.2.

Although neutron diffraction can be used for powder investigations, this normally offers little advantage over X-ray techniques. However, the range of wavelengths in the neutron beam issuing from the pile has been put to good use in the design of high-pressure and high-temperature apparatus. If monochromatic radiation is used and diffracted intensity measured as a function of angle, a major difficulty is that a relatively large exit must be provided for the diffracted beams. If, instead, one uses 'white' radiation (containing a range of wavelengths) and measures the diffracted intensity as a function of wavelength while keeping 2θ fixed, the design problems are greatly reduced [4]. This can be done for neutrons by using the technique of time-of-flight analysis (Fig. 8.2). The monochromator used in conventional diffraction experiments is omitted, so that the incident beam is 'white'; it is pulsed by a mechanical chopper and the diffracted neutrons are collected by a fixed detector some distance away. The time taken by a neutron to travel from the chopper to the detector depends on its speed, which is inversely proportional to its wavelength. The diffracted beam is analysed in terms of the number of neutrons arriving at the detector within specified time intervals—hence the term time-of-flight analysis. Since time-of-flight is proportional to wavelength, this is equivalent to studying the diffracted intensity as a function of wavelength at fixed angle.

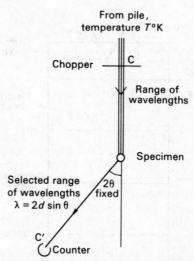

From pile,
temperature T°K

Chopper —— C

Range of
wavelengths

Specimen

Selected range   2θ
of wavelengths   fixed
$\lambda = 2d \sin \theta$

C′

Counter

Fig. 8.2   The principle of time-of-flight analysis. The beam from the pile contains a range of wavelengths, and is pulsed by the chopper at C. Neutrons whose wavelengths satisfy the Bragg equation for one of the sets of planes of the specimen, at the given 2θ value, are diffracted to the counter at C′. The time to travel the distance CC′ is measured electronically, and since $\lambda = h/mv$, it is proportional to the wavelength.

8.3   Electron diffraction,

Apparatus for electron diffraction has something in common with an X-ray tube: electrons are emitted from a hot wire and accelerated through a vacuum by applying a high voltage. The electrons, however, are not used to produce secondary radiation but are themselves diffracted.

The energy E acquired by these electrons depends on the accelerating voltage V, approximately according to

$$E = eV$$

where e is the charge on the electron. The expression is only approximate because at the high voltages usual in electron diffraction the velocity of the electrons begins to approach that of light, so that they gain mass due to the effect of relativity. However, if we ignore the relativity correction, and substitute E in the expression for λ derived in Section 8.1, we find:

$$\lambda = \frac{h}{\sqrt{(2mE)}} = \frac{h}{\sqrt{(2meV)}}$$

The wavelength is thus roughly inversely proportional to the square root of the accelerating voltage; if the latter is of the order of 10^5 volts, the wavelength of the electron beam will be roughly 0.04 Å, which is very much shorter than that of even the shortest X-rays used in diffraction work. For various reasons, including the relativity correction that is necessary at high voltages, the effective wavelength is in practice established by calibration with a standard sample rather than calculated.

A very simple electron diffraction camera is shown diagrammatically in Fig. 8.3. The essentials are the electron gun, a collimating aperture, a photographic plate to

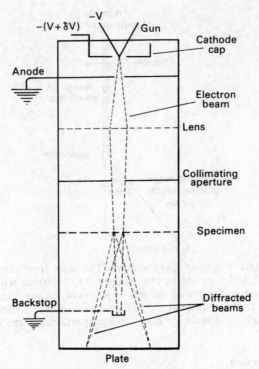

Fig. 8.3   The fundamentals of an electron diffraction camera. The stream of electrons emitted from the gun (a hot wire) is accelerated towards the anode; the cathode cap controls and focuses it. Beyond the anode, the beam may be further focused by one or more lenses. After passing through the collimating aperture, it is diffracted by the specimen, and the pattern recorded on a plate. The direct beam may be caught in a backstop, which must be earthed to prevent it from charging-up and consequently deflecting the beam.

record the pattern and of course the specimen. Because the penetrating power of electrons is not great, the specimen must be quite thin, of the order of 10^{-7} m or 1000 Å, and for the same reason the use of a backstop is optional. One or more lenses may be added between the gun and the specimen to improve the resolution of the pattern. A simple camera of this type can be adapted so that the specimen can be heated or cooled, but (unlike the electron microscope, see below) there is no provision for obtaining an electron image of the specimen. Consequently, portions of the material can be selected for study only by trial and error, and for this reason the instrument is mainly used for studying polycrystalline materials.

Electron diffraction patterns can also be obtained using an electron microscope, and this has a number of advantages. The most important is that the normal arrangement for electron microscopy gives a highly magnified image of the material on a fluorescent screen, so that one can select the portion that is to be studied before switching to electron diffraction; this technique is called **selected area electron diffraction**, and it enables diffraction patterns to be obtained from crystals that are far too small to be examined by X-rays.

An electron microscope works in roughly the same way as an optical microscope, the lenses being electromagnetic; because of the very short wavelength of the electrons the resolution, and hence the magnification, that can be achieved is very much greater than for a light microscope. Figure 8.4 shows one stage of magnification, from which it can be seen that the lens that is forming an image of the specimen is at the same time producing an image of the diffraction pattern; since the diffracted beams are parallel, the latter is to be found in the focal plane of the lens. In practice, the instrument usually has three lenses, and after a suitable portion of the specimen has been

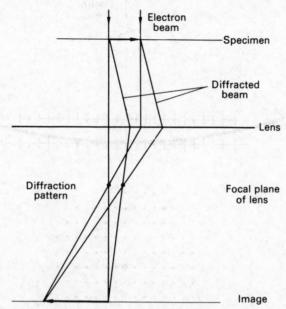

Fig. 8.4   One stage of magnification in an electron microscope. Note the formation of a diffraction pattern in the focal plane of the electromagnetic lens.

selected, the focal length of one of them is adjusted so that the image of the specimen on the fluorescent screen is replaced by that of its diffraction pattern. The screen can subsequently be removed and the pattern photographed.

The formation of an electron diffraction pattern is shown in Fig. 8.5 in terms of the reciprocal lattice. Because the wavelenth of the electron beam is very short, the radius of the sphere of reflection is very large. If a crystal is lying with a principal crystallographic axis (say c) parallel to the electron beam, its $hk0$ layer is perpendicular to the diameter of the sphere of reflection, or tangential to its surface. Because the crystal is very thin the reciprocal lattice points are somewhat elongated into rods, the dimensions of reciprocal lattice points being inversely related to the size of the ordered regions in the real crystal. The extended reciprocal lattice points intercept the almost flat surface of the large sphere of reflection and a diffraction pattern is formed even though the crystal is stationary. Moreover, the resulting pattern is a virtually undistorted picture of the relevant section of the reciprocal lattice (see Fig. 8.9).

If the crystal be slightly tilted as shown in Fig. 8.6 a rather different picture results. Both the $hk0$ and $hk1$ layers now cut the sphere of reflection, but over a smaller area. The pattern is therefore broken into curved **Laue zones**, corresponding to the various layers, and a rough estimate of the value of c can be obtained from the curvature of

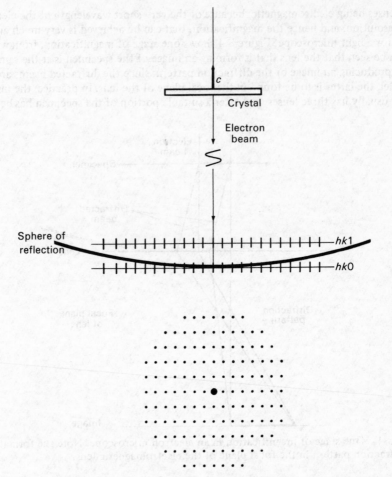

Fig. 8.5   The formation of an electron diffraction pattern. The crystal (top of diagram) is a very thin flake; its c axis is parallel to the electron beam. Part of the corresponding reciprocal lattice is shown (middle of diagram); because the crystal is so thin the 'points' are extended into rods parallel to c. The diffraction pattern is shown at the bottom of the diagram.

these zones. A picture of the reciprocal lattice can be built up by comparing the positions of reflections in successive Laue zones; the pattern in Fig. 8.6 shows the effect obtained from a primitive reciprocal lattice; Fig. 8.7, (a) and (b), shows the zero- and first-order Laue zones from an A-centred orthorhombic crystal and a C-centred monoclinic crystal respectively.

Plainly the appearance of the pattern depends on the tilt of the crystal. A specimen for electron microscopy is prepared by dispersing the fine grained material thinly on a thin film of some amorphous material supported on a grid. Early work either depended on finding crystals that were by chance suitably tilted, or used the mechanism intended for producing stereoscopic pairs of micrographs, which permitted the stage to be tilted by up to 10°. The **goniometric stage** was subsequently developed; it permits the specimen to be tilted by much larger amounts (up to 60° in some of the

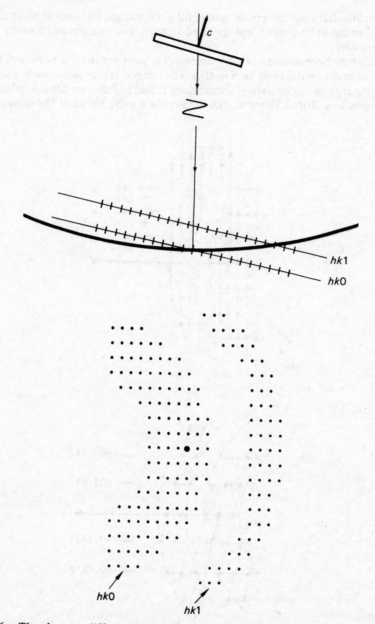

Fig. 8.6   The electron diffraction pattern from the crystal in Fig. 8.5 if its c-axis is inclined to the electron beam. The reciprocal lattice layers cut the sphere of reflection obliquely, and the diffraction pattern breaks up into Laue zones corresponding to the different layers.

latest instruments) in any desired direction giving much greater flexibility. For example, the length of an axis initially perpendicular to the stage need no longer be estimated from the curvature of the Laue zones produced when the crystal is tilted.

With a goniometric stage the crystal can be tilted far enough for other sections of the reciprocal lattice to be studied, and the third axis can then be measured directly and more accurately.

It has already been remarked that because of the poor penetrating powers of the electron beam the crystal must be very thin. The method is thus particularly suitable for studying crystals whose natural morphology is that of flakes or laths, or which cleave to give such shapes. However, the thinner the crystal, the more the elongation

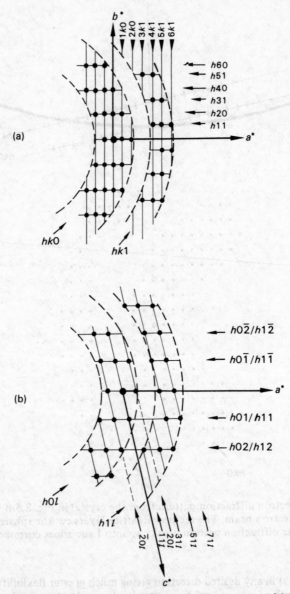

Fig. 8.7   The appearance of the zero- and first-order Laue zones of (a) an A-centred orthorhombic crystal and (b) a C-centred monoclinic crystal.

of the reciprocal lattice points; in the limit they may become virtually continuous rods, which all record at once, as shown for the 'zero' and 'first' layers in Fig. 8.8. Such a 'two-dimensional' pattern is effectively a projection of the reciprocal lattice along the direction of view. It is distinguishable from the type of pattern already discussed because it does not give Laue zones when the crystal is tilted; instead a change of spacing will be observed because the rods intercept the almost flat sphere of reflection obliquely. It is possible to obtain two unit cell dimensions from such a pattern, but not the third, nor is it in general possible to determine the lattice type: the pattern in Fig. 8.8 is consistent with either a C-centred or a body-centred reciprocal cell.

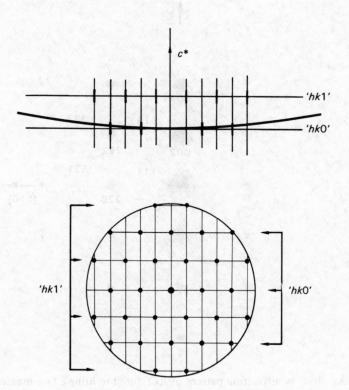

Fig. 8.8   The electron diffraction pattern from a 'two-dimensional' crystal.

The techniques used to interpret electron diffraction patterns are thus rather different from those used in X-ray and neutron diffraction. The considerations governing the observed intensities are also different. Whereas X-rays are scattered by the electron clouds of atoms, and neutrons (usually) by the nucleus, electrons are scattered to some extent by both. Although electron scattering factors are available for most elements, the use of single crystal electron diffraction intensities for structure determination has been limited because their conversion to structure factors is not straightforward. Among other things a phenomenon analogous to the 'double reflection' discussed in Section 5.1 is very important in electron diffraction. It causes 'forbidden' reflections to appear much more frequently than with X-rays, so that space group deductions must be made cautiously. The intensities of 'observed' reflections from single crystals may be altered in the same way. The problem is further complicated by the sort of multiple scattering that causes 'primary extinction' of X-rays (Section 9.1). Intensities from polycrystalline specimens are less subject to both errors and have been used successfully for structure determination.

Qualitatively, the difference between atomic scattering factors for electrons and for X-rays can be useful. KCl provides a neat example.

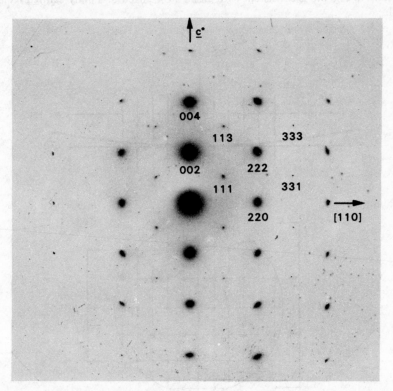

Fig. 8.9   An electron diffraction pattern of KCl, tilted to bring a face-diagonal of the unit cell parallel to the electron beam. Some of the spots are indexed; the weaker ones, with h, k and l odd, are completely absent from X-ray photographs (compare with Fig. 6.8) but appear here because the scattering powers of K^+ and Cl^- for electrons depend on the nuclear charge as well as on the electron cloud, and hence are not exactly equal. (After Gard [5].)

The electron clouds of K^+ and Cl^- are so similar that the atoms are not distinguishable to X-rays, and reflections with h, k and l all odd, although permitted by the space group, are in practice absent; the powder pattern in Fig. 6.8 shows this. Because the nuclear charges on the two atoms are different, these reflections *do* appear in the electron diffraction pattern (Fig. 8.9) [5]. These are not spurious reflections produced by double reflection, because this cannot change the lattice type—see Section 5.1.

Like neutron diffraction, electron diffraction is often most useful when it is combined with X-ray diffraction, although the combination takes a different form. By its nature, electron diffraction is eminently suited to the examination of very small crystals, and is therefore invaluable for determining some or all of the unit cell parameters of phases whose crystals are too small for single crystal X-ray diffraction studies. These data may be used to index the X-ray powder pattern, and in favourable cases the intensities from the latter can then be used for the structure analysis that is seldom possible from single crystal electron diffraction intensities alone. A slightly different combination of the two techniques is useful in studying the kinds of preparation that tend to yield a fine-grained intimate mixture of phases whose X-ray powder data alone may be very difficult to interpret. A combination of electron microscopy and electron diffraction may enable the various diffraction patterns to be correlated with the observed morphologies of the different phases, and this in turn may help to sort out the X-ray powder patterns.

One drawback of electron diffraction is that the specimen is subjected to extremely high vacuum together with bombardment by high energy electrons. Some materials may decompose or otherwise alter under these conditions, and this possibility must always be borne in mind when interpreting results.

One of the more exciting recent developments in electron microscopy/diffraction has been the use of very high resolution instruments to produce images of matter on the atomic scale. As Fig. 8.4 shows, each stage in the magnification process involves the recombination of diffracted beams to produce an image. This is the same process as that carried out mathematically when an electron density map is calculated from X-ray structure amplitudes. The successive images and diffraction patterns that form in the electron microscope are thus Fourier transforms of one another, and given sufficient magnification one might hope to see images of atoms. Although the physical limitations of the lenses prevent the image from being perfect, quite remarkable results have been achieved. Very beautiful photographs have been published showing the distribution of scattering matter in the unit cell and pinpointing defects of the type discussed in Section 5.3 [6]. The cover design of this book is based on such a photograph.

References

[1] Bacon, G. E., In *Advances in Structure Research by Diffraction Methods* 2 (edited by R. Brill and R. Mason), pp. 1–34 (1966) Interscience.

[2] Byström, A., *Arkiv Kem.* **17B**, No. 8 (1943).

[3] Kay, I., *Acta Crystallogr.* **14**, 80–81 (1961); Leciewicz, J., *Acta Crystallogr.* **14**, 66 (1961).

[4] Brugger, R. M., Bennion, R. B. and Worlton, T. G., *Physics Letters* **24A**, 714–717 (1967); Brugger, R. M., Bennion, R. B., Worlton, T. G. and Myers, W. R., *Trans. Amer. Cryst. Assoc.* **5**, 141–154 (1969).

[5] Gard, J. A. In *Proceedings of the European Regional Conference on Electron Microscopy, Delft 1960* (edited by A. L. Houvink and B. J. Spit), **1**, pp. 203–206, Nederlandse Vereniging v. Electronmicroscopie, Delft (1961).

[6] Iijima, S., *Acta Crystallogr.* **A29**, 18–24 (1973); Buseck, P. R. and Iijima, S., *Am. Mineral.* **59**, 1–21 (1974).

CHAPTER 9

Assessing crystal structure analyses

9.1 Sources of error

To be able to gauge the reliability of any given set of structural parameters, one must be aware of the likely sources of error in the measured intensities from which they were derived. The most serious are those that are inherent in the diffraction process itself and thus affect the intensity of the beams being measured. These are functions of the crystal being used and can be difficult to correct. By contrast, errors deriving from the measuring process are relatively controllable.

9.1.1   Errors inherent in the crystal

As an X-ray beam travels through matter, it is attenuated through interaction with the electron clouds of the atoms it encounters (in addition to any energy lost through diffraction); this is called **absorption**, and the reduction in intensity is given by

$$I = I_0 \exp(-\mu t)$$

where I_0 is the initial intensity of the beam, I the reduced intensity after travelling a distance t through the absorbing medium and μ the linear absorption coefficient of the medium for radiation of the appropriate wavelength. Tables of absorption coefficients are readily available; for convenience *mass* absorption coefficients are usually listed because they are independent of the state of the material. From these the linear absorption coefficient of a compound is readily calculated, provided its formula and density are known. Unfortunately, applying the correction to beams diffracted from a crystal is not at all straightforward, because it is difficult to calculate the effective value of t. The reason can be seen from Fig. 9.1(a), which shows a crystal in the reflecting position. The paths travelled by the beams reflected from the two small elements of crystal A and B are shaded; their lengths are very different. To get an estimate of the effective value of t, one has to calculate the path length for the beam reflected by each such tiny element throughout the crystal—a task of some magnitude. Worse, this has to be done for *each reflection*, since the total distance travelled plainly varies with θ (Fig. 9.1(a) and (b)) and even more plainly varies with the orientation of the crystal (Fig. 9.1(c)).

Given a high speed computer, t can be calculated provided the shape of the crystal is accurately known [1], but it is more usual to deal with the problem of absorption in a way that avoids such calculations. There are several ways of setting about this, of

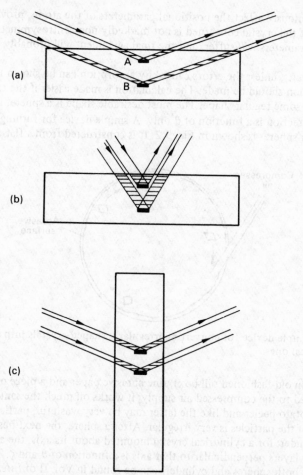

Fig. 9.1   Absorption correction for a diffracted beam. (a) The path lengths of the beams reflected from the two small elements of the crystal, A and B, are very different. To correct for absorption, the distance travelled by the beams reflected from all such elements throughout the crystal must be calculated; (b) and (c) show that the result will not be the same for other reflections.

which the most common is to ignore the problem altogether. How reasonable this is depends on circumstances; for small crystals containing only light atoms, the absorption correction is likely to be quite small for all normal wavelengths; if the crystal contains some heavy atoms absorption is minimized by restricting intensity measurements to a short wavelength radiation such as Mo Kα. Errors are also reduced by having a reasonably equant crystal; crystals shaped like the one in Fig. 9.1 obviously exacerbate the situation and should be avoided if possible. Of course, it is *not* always possible to avoid them, and in that case one ought at least to estimate the maximum and minimum path lengths through the crystal and the corresponding absorption corrections, in the hope of satisfying oneself that the error introduced by ignoring absorption will not be unacceptable. Fortunately, even in the extreme case of a platey crystal containing a high proportion of heavy atoms, ignoring the absorption correction will not seriously affect the positional parameters of the atoms, provided that the cross-section of the crystal concerned is not markedly non-centrosymmetric. However, the thermal parameters *will* suffer, and the final agreement will probably be rather poor.

For best results, unless the errors caused by absorption can be shown to be negligible, a correction should be made. The calculation is made easier if the crystal is converted into some regular shape. The most desirable shape is a sphere, for which the absorption correction is a function of θ only. A simple device for turning crystals into spheres or near-spheres is shown in Fig. 9.2. It is constructed from a flat cylindrical

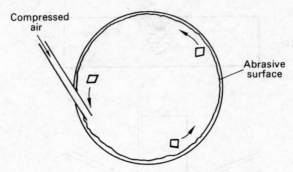

Fig. 9.2   A simple device for converting irregularly shaped crystals into approximately spherical ones.

box (such as an old-fashioned pill-box), fine abrasive paper and a piece of tubing that can be attached to the compressed air supply; it works on much the same principle as a mechanical potato-peeler and like the latter may be very wasteful, particularly if the initial shape of the particles is very irregular. After a sphere, the next best choice of shape is a cylinder; for a cylindrical crystal mounted about its axis, the absorption correction for layers perpendicular to that axis is a function of θ and ζ. Tables of the correction for both spheres and cylinders can be found in Vol. II of *International Tables*.

A needle-shaped crystal may be a sufficiently good approximation to a cylinder without further shaping. This is just as well, as shaping cylinders needs a more subtle technique than that described for shaping spheres. Soluble crystals can be shaped by mounting them securely and revolving them against a camel-hair brush moistened with solvent. If you have not a steady hand, you may need to clamp the brush. If shaping proves impracticable, calculating the absorption correction on the basis that all roughly equant crystals are approximate spheres and all needle-shaped ones are approximate cylinders is better than nothing, although plainly far from ideal.

If intensities are to be measured on a single crystal diffractometer, it is possible to measure and apply an empirical absorption correction [2] using the principle shown in Fig. 9.3. Suppose that the crystal is mounted about c; the instrument is adjusted to pick up an axial ($00l$) reflection and the crystal then rotated about its axis. The intensity recorded by the counter is noted at, say, every $15°$ as the crystal is rotated through $360°$, and the variation gives an empirical absorption correction factor that compensates for inequalities in the dimensions of the crystal perpendicular to c.

The intensity of the diffracted beams may also be reduced by **extinction**, a term that is used to cover two rather different phenomena. Figure 9.4 shows how this arises.

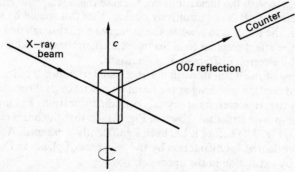

Fig. 9.3   A method of estimating an empirical absorption correction. As the crystal is rotated about *c*, the variation in the intensity of the 00*l* reflection with angle is recorded. This enables reflections in a given layer perpendicular to *c* to be corrected for the irregularity in crystal shape.

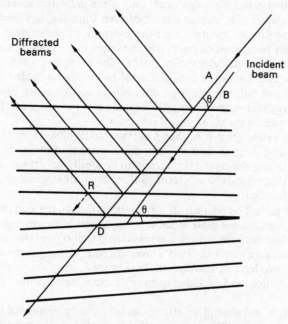

Fig. 9.4   Loss of intensity through extinction. The incident beam A is diffracted by the upper set of planes, and becomes steadily weakened until it reaches D. This is partly because energy is lost into the diffracted beams and partly because these may themselves be reflected again as at R; the doubly reflected radiation is exactly out of phase with the incident beam and destructive interference occurs. The incident beam B, suitably oriented for diffraction by the lower set of planes, has not been so weakened.

The set of planes at the top of the figure is in the reflecting position, and as the incident beam A passes through them it becomes weaker because energy is lost to the diffracted beams. The diffracted beams are themselves suitably oriented to be reflected again, as shown by the dotted line at R. After this second reflection, the radiation is exactly out of phase with the incident beam, because there is a phase change of $\pi/2$ each time it is reflected. It is not intuitively obvious that this should be so, nor is the proof simple, but the result is to weaken the primary beam through destructive interference. This is the effect referred to in Section 8.3 when the unreliability of intensities measured by electron diffraction was discussed.

This weakening of the beam through destructive interference is called **primary** extinction, and it continues so long as the beam travels through the same perfect region of the crystal. However, most crystals contain dislocations and imperfections that produce the mosaic structure shown in Fig. 1.1, so that the beam reaches a discontinuity (D, Fig. 9.4) before it has been significantly weakened. An incident beam B suitably oriented for diffraction by the lower set of planes in Fig. 9.4 has not been weakened by extinction in the upper set.

If an incident beam already weakened by extinction subsequently encounters another set of planes in the reflecting position, the weakening of the incident beam through loss of energy to the diffracted beam—or **secondary** extinction—continues, but the process of destructive interference does not carry over from the upper block. Primary extinction is therefore significant only if the individual mosaic blocks are large; secondary extinction may be important even when they are small if there are enough blocks in parallel orientation for the lower ones to be shielded from the total incident intensity because of diffraction in the upper ones. Both primary and secondary extinction weaken the radiation incident on the lower layers and consequently weaken the observed intensity of the diffracted beam relative to that for a crystal bathed in a beam of uniform intensity. Both effects become more important as the fraction of energy that passes into the diffracted beam increases, and the errors are therefore most serious for the strongest reflections.

To minimize extinction errors, therefore, the mosaic blocks should be small and sufficiently misaligned to make it unlikely that a number of them will lie in precisely the same orientation; the crystal is then said to be **ideally imperfect**. It is sometimes recommended that crystals be subjected to thermal or other shock to ensure that these conditions are fulfilled.

If extinction cannot be eliminated, it is possible, though not easy, to correct for it [3]. However, in all but the most accurate work, a satisfactory compromise is to ignore the problem until the structure is reasonably well refined; the observed and calculated F values are then examined. If reflections at low angles with large F values (intense reflections) have F_o consistently lower than F_c they are assumed to be affected by extinction, and excluded from any further least-squares cycles or given zero weights.

Both extinction and absorption effects can be virtually eliminated from intensities measured using a powder diffractometer. If the sample is finely ground and randomly oriented extinction will be negligible; provided that it is 'infinitely thick', a condition fulfilled by the standard holder, and fills the incident beam, the absorption correction is independent of angle and can be ignored unless absolute intensities are required. For compounds whose powder lines can be resolved, therefore, powder intensity data can be used to correct single crystal measurements. This is particularly helpful in dealing with extinction because low-angle reflections are the most likely to be resolvable.

9.1.2   Errors arising in the measurements

In addition to the errors inherent in the reflection process, further errors may arise in the course of measuring the intensity of the diffracted radiation that actually leaves the crystal. These are very much more controllable than the sort of error that we have just been discussing.

For intensity measurements made from photographic film, some elementary precautions have been outlined already (Section 5.5); the most important is that the spots be within the measurable range of blackening. It is advisable to have two independent workers check at least some of the measurements. It is very easy to mis-index high-angle reflections on Weissenberg photographs, and not totally unknown for more sweeping errors in indexing to occur. Allowance should be made for background scatter, as far as possible, and also for white radiation streaks. If visual matching is used, the correction necessary for reflections that lie in white radiation streaks can be made by placing the matching reflection in the same streak, as close as possible to the spot being measured. If a photometer is used, then the adjacent background must be measured for each reflection, and the intensity corrected appropriately. Normally, each reflection on a photograph will be matched by one or more equivalent ones; it is best to measure all of these and average them rather than to measure only one of each kind. The film should also be carefully inspected to see whether any low-angle reflections have been wholly or partially excluded by the shadow of the backstop.

If the intensity measurements are made with a single crystal diffractometer, rather similar considerations apply. Counters can cope with a much wider range of intensity than can be recorded satisfactorily on a single film, but they still have limitations. If two pulses arrive at the counter in close succession, the second may not be recorded because the counter is still dealing with the first. Obviously losses from this cause become more important as the counting rate increases and very strong reflections may 'swamp' the counter, resulting in serious loss in the recorded intensity.

The standard deviation of a counted intensity is $\sqrt{N}$, where N is the number of counts—on a low count, this may be an appreciable fraction of the whole. Thus the standard deviation on 100 counts is 10, or 10%, whereas on 10,000 counts it is 100, or 1%. It follows that precision will be higher for reasonably high counts than for low ones. If all reflections are counted for a fixed time, the weak ones will be only very imprecisely measured, particularly as a similar error in measuring the background has to be included. For this reason it may be better, though more time-consuming, to measure the time to accumulate a fixed number of counts.

With counters, as with film, intensity due to radiation of wavelengths other than $K\alpha$ must be eliminated. One way of doing this is to use a monochromator but this introduces other problems in single crystal X-ray work. In neutron diffraction there is no characteristic wavelength and a monochromator will be needed anyway, unless time-of-flight methods are being used.

For X-ray studies, an alternative is to use **balanced filters**, that is a pair of matched filters having the characteristics shown in Fig. 9.5. One of these is the normal β-filter for the radiation being used; the other, or α-filter, is made from the element of atomic number one or two less than the β-filter. They are ground so that their transmissions match as closely as possible in all regions except that lying between the two absorption edges. The diffracted intensity is measured with the β-filter in place ($I\beta$) and then with the α-filter ($I\alpha$); $I\beta - I\alpha$ then gives a very close approximation to the intensity due to monochromatic $K\alpha$ radiation.

Balanced filters are often backed up by including a **pulse height analyser** in the counter circuit. This discriminates between pulses of different energies, so that the counter registers only those that arrive with an energy appropriate to the characteristic radiation in use. The energy resolution of the detectors at present available is too poor for the filters to be dispensed with entirely, but the elimination of wavelengths much

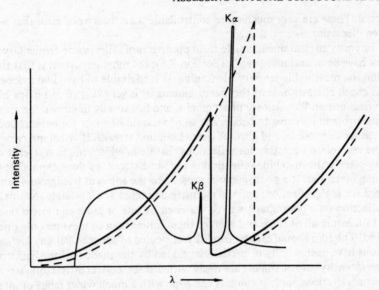

Fig. 9.5   The principle of balanced filters. The absorption curves of the β-filter (solid line) and α-filter (dotted line) are shown superimposed on the spectrum of the X-rays being used. The α- and β-filters are ground to match as closely as possible in all parts of the spectrum except the region in which the characteristic Kα band lies.

longer or shorter than that of the characteristic radiation compensates for the inevitable deficiencies in the balance of the filters.

If time permits, it is advisable to measure all the equivalent reflections, just as it is with film; this provides a built-in check against setting errors or slipping of the crystal, and may give warning of absorption effects that are too large to be ignored. If there is not time to do this, one or more 'standard' reflections should be remeasured from time to time to check the crystal orientation. If the crystal is liable to radiation damage, this should be done anyway. A useful additional precaution, if X-rays are being used, is to check the measured intensities qualitatively against any available films to ensure that no change of axes or other error has been introduced in setting the crystal up on the diffractometer.

9.2   The reliability of structural details

The earliest structure determinations gave a general picture of the arrangement of atoms in a structure; usually the coordination of each kind of atom was described and the lengths of the various bonds estimated. Tables of atomic and ionic radii were compiled in this period, and the foundations of crystal chemistry were laid. Although the intensity data used for these determinations were usually quite crude, the atomic parameters derived were, as pointed out in Chapter 7, often remarkably accurate.

As equipment and methods of refinement have become increasingly sophisticated, so have crystallographers tried to extract more and more detail from the results of their analyses. In early work thermal parameters were seldom determined individually; if used at all they took the form of a single overall temperature factor, or were built into the f-curves. The high-speed computer has changed all that, so that the norm is now the determination of individual isotropic or anisotropic temperature factors, often, in the latter case, finishing up with a computer-drawn stereographic pair showing details of the vibrational ellipsoids. The meaning to be attached to these will be discussed in the next section.

With more accurate refinements available, bond lengths and angles can be studied in increasing detail and attempts made to correlate them with chemical theory. The differences in bond length between C–C single, double and triple bonds are on a relatively gross scale and emerged long ago; distortions due to the Jahn–Teller effect are now clearly recognizable, as are the differences in bond length between X–O and X–OH bonds, and between terminal and bridging X–O bonds in condensed oxy-anions. Details such as the correlation of the X–O bridging distance with the angle X–O–X, or whether in certain situations the bonds in a benzene ring depart from equality can be studied. To assess such results usually needs a knowledge of statistics beyond the scope of this book, but a few pointers will be given.

The output from a least-squares refinement includes the estimated standard deviation (e.s.d.) for each atomic parameter; this is based on the number of parameters being refined, the quality of the fit between the observed and calculated data and the contribution made to the latter by the atom in question. The last part of that statement means that in a structure containing a mixture of light and heavy atoms, the positional parameters of the heavy atoms will be determined more accurately than those of the light ones, and moreover that light atoms will be less well determined in the presence of a heavy atom than they would be in its absence.

The first thing to note about these e.s.d.'s is that they are based only on the evidence available to the computer, and cannot therefore be expected to allow for systematic errors in the data. Consequently, they represent the *minimum* value that can reasonably be expected; if the observed data are of poor quality it is probably reasonable to multiply the e.s.d.'s by two or three when reviewing the absolute values of the bond lengths.

As a very rough rule of thumb, two bond lengths in the same structure can be taken to be significantly different if they differ by more than three times the larger of their e.s.d.'s; this is a gross over-simplification, not a proper analysis. Deciding whether the mean values of two groups of bond lengths are truly different is much more complicated; one must take into account how many measured bonds are in each of the two populations and how these are distributed about the mean, as well as the e.s.d.'s themselves. The difference between the mean values of two such groups may well be significant even if it is considerably less than three times the individual e.s.d.'s.

One of the most interesting details that could emerge from X-ray diffraction would be the distribution of electron density about the atoms, in particular any deviation from spherical symmetry caused by the formation of bonds or the presence of 'lone pairs' of electrons. It might seem that a difference map based on atomic parameters from the least squares should show any such distortions of the electron cloud. However, the least-squares refinement matches observed and calculated electron density, and if the true electron density around an atom is grossly asymmetric, the positional parameters that emerge from the least-squares routine (and the anisotropic thermal parameters, if used) will have been shifted to compensate for this. In other words, one has blotted out part of what one is trying to observe.

For very simple structures, such as sodium chloride, whose atomic coordinates are fixed by symmetry, there is no problem; provided that sufficiently accurate measurements of intensity can be made, accurate maps of electron density can be produced that show the effects of bonding and enable one to judge the state of ionization of the atoms [4]. If the atomic coordinates are not fixed by symmetry, the positions of the nuclei can be determined from neutron diffraction (see Chapter 8; neutrons are, in general, scattered by the nucleus alone), and the X-ray diffraction data then used to calculate a difference map based on these positions—often called an 'X — N' map [5]. Again assuming that the measurements are suitably accurate, the features on such a map should show the distortion produced in the electron clouds by bonding, etc. Hydrogen atoms are particularly sensitive to this effect; positions determined for these by X-ray diffraction, which, with the usual refinement techniques, locates the centre of gravity of the electron cloud, are generally displaced relative to those determined by neutron diffraction, which locates the nucleus. The displacement is towards the atom to which the hydrogen is bonded, and presumably is a result of the bonding [6].

9.3   The meaning of temperature factors

From what has already been said, it will be apparent that the temperature factors are apt to act as crystallographic scavengers, cleaning up quite a variety of errors. A wrongly placed atom may manifest itself in the least-squares refinement by an abnormally high temperature factor; the program, presented with an atom that is not really there, attempts to minimize its effect by smearing it out as much as possible. Filling a site with the wrong sort of atom also affects the temperature factor—if the atom placed there is too light, its temperature factor may be abnormally low, and *vice versa*. This effect is sometimes used deliberately by the crystallographer. In the early stages of an organic structure determination it may be difficult to distinguish nitrogen from carbon atoms. A common practice is to treat all as carbon atoms; after a few cycles of least-squares refinement the temperature factors are inspected and the atoms with the lowest temperature factors assumed to be nitrogen. A similar effect may serve to distinguish oxygen atoms from hydroxyl groups in inorganic materials.

If absorption corrections have been neglected, the overall effect is to make low-angle reflections too strong in comparison with high-angle ones, and this will be reflected in temperature factors that are too low. For small crystals containing only light atoms the effect is unlikely to be large (see Section 9.1, above) but it becomes more pronounced with heavier atoms; in extreme cases the temperature factors may be negative. If temperature factors are allowed to refine anisotropically, the values obtained will be affected by any uncorrected anisotropic absorption errors. For example, a crystal shaped like the one in Fig. 9.1 would give observed intensities that were relatively lower for reflections in which the beam passed more or less along its length. Refining temperature factors anisotropically would consequently produce values that were too large in this direction, the apparent 'smearing out' of the atoms giving a lower value of F_c for the appropriate reflections, and hence a better fit between observed and calculated data.

Before drawing conclusions from the absolute values of isotropic temperature factors or from the shape and orientation of the ellipsoids describing anisotropic ones, one should ascertain that such sources of error are absent or at least minimal: otherwise the conclusions will tell you more about deficiencies in experimental technique than about the properties of the crystal. Notwithstanding these reservations, temperature factors can and do give useful information about the behaviour of atoms in their surroundings.

Beginning with the crudest types of result, even if no correction for absorption has been made, the *relative* values of temperature factors may be informative. (Some examples have already been given in the opening paragraph of this section.) In covalently bound groupings, bridging atoms often have lower temperature factors than terminal atoms of the same kind, presumably reflecting the more restricted movement allowed to the former. The atoms in a linear molecule with a heavy atom at one end may show increased thermal vibration the further they are from the heavy atom; the latter can be regarded as relatively fixed, and the molecular tail wags more and more vigorously as it gets more distant from that fixed point. Likewise, the presence of strong hydrogen bonding or similar interactions in a structure reduces thermal motions in its vicinity.

If proper absorption corrections have been made, the absolute values of the thermal parameters reflect the rigidity of the bonding and it should be possible to make comparisons between different structures. The variation of anisotropic temperature factors within a structure can likewise be expected to reflect the atomic environment, and where accurate values are known, they confirm, in general, what common sense would suggest: the atoms in the molecular tail described above have larger amplitudes of vibration perpendicular to the chain than along it, atoms in a cyclic molecule vibrate more vigorously in the direction perpendicular to the plane of the ring than in its plane, and so on.

References

[1] Busing, W. R. and Levy, H. A., *Acta Crystallogr.* **10**, 180–182 (1957).
[2] North, A. C. T., Phillips, D. C. and Mathews, F. S., *Acta Crystallogr.* **A24**, 351–359 (1968).
[3] Zachariasen, W. H., *Acta Crystallogr.* **A24**, 421–424 (1968); Coppens, P. and Hamilton, W. C., *Acta Crystallogr.* **A26**, 71–83 (1970).
[4] Witte, H. and Wölfel, E., *Z. phys. Chem.* **3**, 296–329 (1955); Witte, H. and Wölfel, E., *Rev. mod. Phys.* **30**, 51–55 (1958).
[5] Coppens P. *Thermal Neutron Diffraction* (edited by B. T. M. Willis), pp. 82–100, Oxford University Press (1970); Coppens, P., *Science* **158**. 1577–1579 (1967); Coppens, P., Sabine, T. M., Delaplane, R. G. and Ibers, J. A., *Acta Crystallogr.* **B25**, 2451–2458 (1969); Duckworth, J. A. K., Willis, B. T. M. and Pawley, G. S., *Acta Crystallogr.* **A26**, 263–271 (1970); Taylor, J. C. and Sabine, T. M., *Acta Crystallogr.* **B28**, 3340–3351 (1972).
[6] Hamilton, W. C. and Ibers, J. A., *Hydrogen Bonding in Solids,* Wiley, New York (1968).

CHAPTER 10

A crystallographic 'cost-benefit' analysis

10.1 The information: effort ratio of various techniques

We will begin by assuming that you are working in a laboratory that is already well supplied with equipment, and consider how the information obtained by various techniques compares with the effort expended on them; in subsequent sections we will consider the questions of learning to perform these operations and of purchasing various items of equipment. We will further assume, for obvious reasons, that you are engaged in some operation that produces a reasonably crystalline solid whose properties interest you.

No matter what set of properties you are investigating, a quick check with a microscope, preferably a polarizing microscope, to see whether the material is homogeneous, is always worthwhile. It should not take more than five minutes, depending on how far you have to walk to reach the microscope, and ensures that the literature will not be further cluttered up with data relating to non-existent compounds (that were in fact mixtures, but no-one bothered to check). How much further you carry your optical examination depends on your interest in the compound. It should be possible to determine the crystal system in less than half an hour—probably very much less if the symmetry is high, indeed it may be obvious from the initial examination. If the properties that interest you are symmetry-dependent, this is obviously time well spent. Refractive index measurements take from ten minutes up to several hours, depending on the symmetry of the material and the accuracy required. They may be useful

(a) as a means of identifying an unknown,
(b) to establish that two preparations are identical,
(c) to determine the composition of a solid solution.

For all these purposes, X-ray powder diffraction studies could be used instead; the choice depends on circumstances, including the existence or otherwise of reference data. It is often a good idea to use both methods, for extra confidence in the results. If there is any chance that glass or other amorphous material is present the microscope should certainly be used because these will be missed by X-ray diffraction.

To record a powder pattern takes upwards of ten minutes, depending on the available equipment, and possibly less personal effort than a microscopic examination; it is in general the most rapid means of routine identification (but see above, on using the microscope as a check). If standard films or charts are available, the effort involved is minimal; if the measured 2θ values have to be converted into d-spacings for purposes of comparison, you will need to allow 10–30 minutes for this, depending on how complicated the pattern is and how it was recorded. Direct comparison is not only quicker but also safer.

To index a powder pattern takes from about five minutes (cubic materials with no complications) up to infinity, and the circumstances under which it may reasonably be attempted were outlined in Section 6.4. The value of the exercise is problematical; it can certainly serve to show that powder and single crystal data agree and that the powder pattern corresponds to a single phase, but both these pieces of information are obtainable in other ways. It is, however, a good way of determining accurate unit cell parameters.

Single crystal techniques encompass a wider range of time and effort. To determine a unit cell and space group may take about a week—less if you are lucky/have good crystals/find an axis quickly/really get on with it; more if you are ham-fisted/have miserable crystals with ill-defined optics/leave equipment standing idle while you go to coffee. If you are interested in fine details of structural differences that are not observable on powder photographs, you must use these techniques, and this is also true if you are studying, say, solid-state reactions in single crystals. Otherwise, in itself, the determination is unlikely to provide much new information, except that in conjunction with a density determination it may settle an otherwise uncertain composition or molecular weight; useful symmetry information may occasionally result, as discussed in Section 5.1. It is of course an essential preliminary to a complete structure determination.

To collect the data for a structure analysis using an automatic single crystal diffractometer takes from about three days to about three weeks; it may take longer if multiple film packs have to be exposed and then measured either visually or with a photometer. It is much more difficult to estimate how long it will take to solve the structure—apart from purely logistical considerations like the speed and efficiency of the computing service, so much depends on the problem itself.

If you are dealing with a reasonably sized unit cell (say around $1000 \, \text{Å}^3$) containing one or more suitable heavy atoms, and everything goes smoothly, you can expect to have the answer in under three weeks from completing the data collection. Ideally the schedule might run:

Day 1—sort and correct data; compute Patterson function overnight.

Day 2—interpret Patterson function.

Day 3—calculate structure factors based on coordinates of heavy atom; calculate Fourier synthesis overnight.

Day 4—locate rest of atoms (or most of them); calculate full trial structure.

Days 5–8—refine structure; at least one more Fourier synthesis will be needed.

Day 9—calculate bond lengths and angles and make a drawing or construct a model of the structure.

Day 10—write the paper.

But of course it seldom works out like this. Even supposing you have no other demands on your time, it is unlikely that neither you nor the computer will make mistakes; one must allow a day or two for the inevitable errors.

If complications arise, it may all take very much longer. For example, the heavy atoms may be on special positions, and hence not contribute to certain classes of reflection. It may not be possible to interpret the Patterson function unambiguously, so that several arrangements may have to be tried. There may be no heavy atom present, so that the phases must be determined by direct methods—although this often takes no longer than computing a Patterson function. Worse, there may be too many heavy atoms, so that the light ones cannot be located.

Even after the outline of the structure is well established, complications may arise. A molecule or ligand may adopt two alternative conformations at random, or an ion may occupy a site statistically; in either case site occupancies have to be refined. Unsuspected molecules of solvent may appear. A peculiar distribution of bond lengths may be found, and one then has to decide whether this is genuine and has to be explained, or whether it is the result of errors in the data and if so what errors and what are you going to do about them?

Lest the above sounds too depressing, it should be added that most structure analyses *do* in fact proceed fairly smoothly, complications being much more common among ionic materials than among coordination compounds and organic materials generally. (With the latter, if complications arise it may be easiest to abandon that particular determination and 'try another derivative', an option that is unfortunately not usually open to inorganic crystallographers.) The point is merely that it is unwise to bank on having a particular result by a week on Friday.

Whether to undertake a structure analysis is thus a question with no easy answer. Much depends on how badly you want to know the result, and whether great accuracy is needed. If all that is required is a general idea of the shape of a molecule, or the structure and arrangement of ions in a salt, it is not necessary to go to great lengths to correct the data for possible errors. If more detailed information is sought, such as the effect of different substituents on the length of an adjacent covalent bond, then data collection becomes a much more painstaking affair, to which more time and effort must be devoted.

10.2 Learning crystallography

The previous section estimated how long various operations take once you are reasonably skilled; the next question you may need to consider is how long it will take to acquire that skill, and how to set about it. You must realize that you will not learn to become a crystallographer by reading this, or any other, book or by attending a course of lectures, any more than you could learn to drive a car that way. You have to learn it 'by doing'. It helps a lot if you can learn the ropes from an experienced and patient crystallographer, and a certain amount of natural aptitude is also beneficial, but in the end it all boils down to the amount of effort *you* put into it.

Having said that, it is still true that some operations are very easily learnt. You could learn to record powder patterns in a very few minutes, provided that you were content to use them merely as 'fingerprints' and never seek a deeper interpretation. Many people do just that. Likewise you could learn in a few hours to use a polarizing microscope to the level of competence necessary to study materials as described in Chapter 2. Both of these skills are invaluable for identifying crystalline materials, and are plainly well worth acquiring. To an extent, one can apply these methods (particularly X-ray powder diffraction) with little knowledge of the underlying theory, but, quite apart from the fact that most people prefer to understand what they are doing, a knowledge of the theory can be a valuable safeguard. Some time should therefore be allowed for acquiring this; if you have read Chapters 2 and 6 you should have a fair idea of how long this would be likely to take you.

It does not take long to learn to use single crystal equipment, although it takes longer to acquire the knack of selecting and setting the crystals. Learning how to interpret the photographs is the real 'energy barrier', and requires a fair amount of mental effort. If your interest is in topotactic reactions, or polytypes, or solid state structures generally, there is really no choice in the matter: you will just have to get to grips with the techniques and theory. It is the person who is not primarily a crystallographer but has some nice crystals of an interesting substance who has to make a decision as to how to proceed.

If you want to do it yourself the choice is broadly between (a) pitching in yourself and battling it out, turning to a more experienced colleague for advice only when you are stuck, or (b) leaning more heavily upon said colleague for guidance and interpretation. The second method will get quicker results, but you will learn more from the first. Which you choose is partly a matter of temperament and partly a question of whether you may need to repeat the performance with other crystals later on: even the most patient of colleagues will eventually tire of being leant upon, so if you expect to have a number of crystals to examine you may as well take a professional approach from the start.

If you are content to act as a 'pair of hands' under competent guidance, the unit cell and space-group determination will probably take very little longer than the times quoted in Section 10.1. If you work through it for yourself, it will probably take very much longer, at least the first time.

Time lost by working it out for yourself may well be made up later if a full structure determination is to be attempted, because you will be more familiar with the problem and therefore less likely to make mistakes. If, for example, intensity data are to be collected from film you are less likely to make mistakes in indexing. If the data are to be collected by automatic diffractometer, you are most unlikely to be allowed to use the machine unsupervised, but familiarity with the reciprocal lattice will still be helpful when you examine the results because it will help you to spot errors, which can be either human or mechanical in origin: it is quite wrong to suppose that machines never make mistakes!

In the final or computing stage, there are two considerations. First, are you going to learn some elementary computing? It is undoubtedly a great help to have a nodding acquaintance with the language in which the programs are written; experience shows that even if quite detailed instructions are given, mistakes will otherwise be common, and it is anyway terribly frustrating to have to await further instructions before being able to progress. Second, are you going to get to grips with the theory, and yourself interpret as much of the output as you can? If you decide to do this it will undoubtedly take longer to solve your first structure, but you will learn a lot and probably feel more satisfied when it is finished.

Sometimes there is another option open. Many departments include a skilled crystallographer who can be induced to tackle the structure of any half-way decent crystal that comes along, in much the same spirit as other people solve crossword puzzles. Should you number one of these among your acquaintances, you may well be able to get your structure solved without doing any work at all—if that is what you want.

10.3 Equipment

In conclusion, we will try to draw up a similar sort of balance sheet for crystallographic apparatus. It is pointless to quote prices in detail, since these can change so rapidly, but a guide to orders of magnitude will be attempted.

Any laboratory in which crystalline solids are being studied ought to have a polarizing microscope. This need not be one of the more expensive models; a very elaborate one is wasted unless there is someone really expert to use it, and may even confuse the less experienced through having a large number of adjustments that are not really needed. One of the so-called 'student' models should be adequate for all-purpose use, and its cost will be of the order of a few hundred pounds.

If identification of samples or comparison of one product with another is frequently necessary, then powder diffraction equipment should be available as well. Section 6.2.4 discussed the considerations that govern the choice of recording equipment, and the price scale runs from about a hundred or so pounds for the simplest type of powder camera up to a matter of thousands for a diffractometer. A generator will also be needed, and the cost of this will be from about a thousand pounds upwards. Prices vary widely, depending on the degree of sophistication, and it is worth bearing in mind that photographic recording does not demand such a stable beam output as a diffractometer. It may thus be possible to economize considerably on the generator if film is used, although perhaps at the expense of increased exposure times; obviously the likely volume of work must be considered.

If single crystals are to be studied, priority should probably be given to the purchase of a Weissenberg camera. This is undoubtedly the most versatile type of camera, although for maximum flexibility it should be backed up by a precession-type camera. Prices here are in the thousand-pound range. If the crystals to be studied are expected to have very large or complicated unit cells, for example non-stoichiometric compounds or biological materials, then perhaps a precession or other camera able to give an undistorted picture of the reciprocal lattice should be the first choice. A cheaper but less versatile alternative would be a simple rotation–oscillation camera.

If structure determination is contemplated, the range of possible expenditure becomes very large indeed. At the upper limit, the price of an automatic single crystal diffractometer is measured in tens of thousands of pounds, and the purchase of one is justified only if it can be kept running virtually full time. This normally means that it will be used jointly by a number of members of the same laboratory, or perhaps co-operatively by several groups of workers. However, convenient as these instruments are, they are by no means essential to structure determination; if your institution does not possess one, and you wish to determine the occasional structure, you should not be deterred; if you have a Weissenberg camera, or indeed any other sort of single crystal camera, a set of films suitable for intensity measurement can be produced at no extra expense, except possibly that incurred in modifying the cassette to enable it to take a multiple film pack. To measure these visually yourself takes time, but otherwise costs nothing. If you have, or can get access to, a photometer the measurements will probably be more precise and may well be more quickly made; some organizations and laboratories are equipped to make such measurements automatically, and may either allow you to use their equipment or measure your films for you. (The SRC operates a service in the U.K.: see footnote, p. 121.) Finally, you might be able to rent time on an automatic diffractometer, or you might be lucky enough to be offered time free by a group with spare capacity on their instrument; the latter is more likely to happen if you have already shown that you are keen by tackling one or two structures with such apparatus as you yourself have available.

If you really want to know the answer, you will not be stopped—any more than were the pioneers of the subject—merely because you do not have the latest fully automatic equipment.

Appendix

USEFUL BUT COMPLICATED FORMULAE

1 Relation of triclinic real and reciprocal cells

$$a^* = \frac{\lambda bc \sin \alpha}{V} \; ; \quad a = \frac{\lambda b^* c^* \sin \alpha^*}{V^*} \; ; \text{etc.}$$

where

$$V = abc \; \{1 - 2 \cos \alpha \cos \beta \cos \gamma - \cos^2 \alpha - \cos^2 \beta - \cos^2 \gamma\}^{1/2}$$

and $V^* = 1/V$

$$\cos \alpha^* = \frac{\cos \beta \cos \gamma - \cos \alpha}{\sin \beta \sin \gamma} \; ; \quad \cos \alpha = \frac{\cos \beta^* \cos \gamma^* - \cos \alpha^*}{\sin \beta^* \sin \alpha^*} \; , \text{etc.}$$

The angle δ between a and a^* is given by

$$\tan \delta = \frac{\cos \alpha^* - \cos \beta^* \cos \gamma^*}{\cos \beta^* \sin \gamma^*}$$

The above formulae, with appropriate permutations, apply to other reciprocal axes and angles.

2 Undistorted photographs of the reciprocal lattice

Let the unit cell translation along the relevant principal axis of the crystal (Fig 4.5) be t. Let the angle between this axis and the X-ray beam be μ, and let the semi-angle subtended at the crystal by the cone of reflections to be photographed be ν. For zero-level photographs, $\mu = \nu$. Let the magnification factor be F, as shown in the figure.

(a) de Jong-Boumann photography

A convenient arrangement is shown in Fig. 4.6(a), in which $\mu = \nu = 45°$ for zero-layer photography. The layer screen thus subtends a $90°$ cone at the crystal, and this is kept constant; upper layers are recorded as shown in Fig. 4.6(b), by changing μ.

For the nth layer:

$$\sin \mu_n = \cos \nu - \frac{n\lambda}{t} = \frac{1}{\sqrt{2}} - \frac{n\lambda}{t}$$

since ν is fixed. The film is moved *away* from the crystal by

$$\frac{F \cdot n\lambda}{t}$$

(b) Precession photography

The position of the layer screen depends on the value chosen for the precession angle μ (Fig. 4.7); common values are $20°$, $25°$ and $30°$. The distance s between the layer screen and the crystal is given by $s = r \cot \nu$, where r is the radius of the annular slot in the screen. For zero-layer photographs $\mu = \nu$; for upper layers $\cos \nu_n = \cos \mu - (n\lambda)/t$. In practice the appropriate value of s is normally read from a set of graphs supplied with the instrument. The film is moved *towards* the crystal (Fig. 4.7(b)) through $(F \cdot n\lambda)/t$.

Answers to problems

(Those based on measuring diagrams are only approximate.)

Chapter 3

Figure 3.12 $b* = 0.20$ r.u. $a = 5.14$, $b = 7.71$ Å
Scale of diagram (a), 1 cm = 2.00 Å

$d^*_{110} = 0.36$ r.u. $d_{110} = 4.24$ Å $\dfrac{1.542}{4.24} = 0.36$ r.u.

Fig. 3.13 $a* = 0.25$ r.u. $\beta* = 57°$ P = 0.21 r.u.
$a* \sin \beta = 0.21$ r.u. $a = 1.542/0.21 = 7.34$ Å

$c = \dfrac{1.542}{c* \sin \beta*} = \dfrac{1.542}{0.2516} = 6.13$ Å

Scale of real lattice: 1 cm = 1.59 Å
d_{101} (measured) = 3.15 Å
$d^*_{101} = 0.49$ r.u. $d = \lambda/d* = 3.15$ Å

Fig. 3.14 $a = \lambda/a* \sin 60° = 1.542/(0.120 \times 0.866) = 14.84$ Å
Note that conversely $a* = \lambda/d_{10.0}$
$d_{10.0} = a \sin 60° = 12.85$ Å; $a* = 1.542/12.85 = 0.12$ r.u.

Fig. 3.16 $a = \lambda/a* \sin 60° = 1.542/(0.10 \times 0.866) = 17.81$ Å.

Chapter 4

Figure 4.4(a)   Mean distance between spots along
$a*$: 11.45 mm = 0.1908 r.u.:
∴ $a = 1.542/0.190 = 8.08$ Å.
Along $b* = 8.91$ mm = 0.1485 r.u. $b = 10.38$ Å
(b) Along $a*$, mean distance between spots: 11.44 mm = 0.1906 r.u.
along $c*$: 24.55 mm = 0.404 r.u.; $c = 3.82$ Å

Fig. 4.15 $\zeta = 0.405$; $c = 1.542/0.405 = 3.81$ Å

Fig. 4.24 (a) $a = 7.71$ $b = 5.14$ Å
The reciprocal lattice has h, k, l all even or all odd (body centred): the real lattice therefore is F.

(b) $\beta^* = \dfrac{14.4}{37.0} \times 180 = 70.0°$; measured value = 70°

$a = \lambda/a^* \sin \beta^* = 1.542/0.399 = 3.86$ Å
$c = \lambda/c^* \sin \beta^* = 1.542/0.248 = 6.22$ Å

The cell might be A-centred ($k + l$ even throughout hkl)
    (c) $a = b = 1.542/0.50 = 3.08$ Å
There is no two-fold symmetry perpendicular to c.
    (d) $a = b = 1.542/0.58 \times 0.866 = 3.07$ Å
There is two-fold symmetry perpendicular to c, but it is not possible to say whether it is 2 or $\bar{2}$.

    ((b) Rider, p. 118, If the lattice is primitive, the absence of l odd in $h0l$ indicates a c-glide plane perpendicular to b. An $h1l$ photograph would distinguish between the two possibilities.)

Bibliography

Suggestions for further reading

(1)   General introductions

Elementary:

Lipson, H. S., with Lee, R. M., *Crystals and X-rays,* Wykeham, London (1970).

Lonsdale, K., *Crystals and X-rays,* Bell, London (1948).

Wheatley, P. J., *The Determination of Molecular Structure,* O.U.P., London (1968) (Chapters V–IX).

Wormald, J., *Diffraction Methods,* O.U.P., London (1973).

More advanced:

Buerger, M. J., *Elementary Crystallography: An Introduction to the Fundamental Geometrical Features of Crystals,* Wiley, New York (1963).

Bunn, C. W., *Chemical Crystallography* (2nd edn.), O.U.P., London (1961).

Gay, P., *The Crystalline State: An Introduction,* Oliver and Boyd, Edinburgh (1972).

James, R. W., *X-ray Crystallography* (5th edn.), Methuen, London (1965).

Jeffery, J. W., *Methods in X-ray Crystallography,* Academic Press, London (1971).

McKie, D. and McKie, C., *Crystalline Solids,* Nelson, London (1974).

Phillips, F. C., *An Introduction to Crystallography* (4th edn.), Oliver and Boyd, Edinburgh (1971).

Wilson, A. J. C., *Elements of X-ray Crystallography,* Addison-Wesley, New York (1969).

Woolfson, M. M., *An Introduction to X-ray Crystallography,* C.U.P., Cambridge (1970).

(2)   Crystal optics

Gay, P., *An Introduction to Crystal Optics,* Longmans, London (1967).

Hartshorne, N. H. and Stuart, A., *Practical Optical Crystallography* (2nd edn.), Arnold, London (1969).

Hartshorne, N. H. and Stuart, A., *Crystals and the Polarising Microscope* (4th edn.), Arnold, London (1970). [More advanced than the above book by these authors.]

Stoiber, R. E. and Morse, S. A., *Microscopic Identification of Crystals,* Ronald, New York (1972).

Wood, E. A., *Crystals and Light: An Introduction to Optical Crystallography,* Van Nostrand Reinhold, New York (1964).

(3)   X-ray diffraction

Recording techniques:

Arndt, U. W. and Willis, B. T. M., *Single Crystal Diffractometry,* C.U.P., Cambridge (1966). [Includes material on neutron diffraction.]

Buerger, M. J., *The Precession Method in X-ray Crystallography,* Wiley, New York (1964).

Buerger, M. J., *The Photography of the Reciprocal Lattice.* ASXRED Monograph number 1, The American Society for X-ray and Electron Diffraction [now The American Crystallographic Association] (1944). This brief account of the principles is unfortunately now out of print.

Henry, N. F. M., Lipson, H. and Wooster, W. A., *The Interpretation of X-ray Diffraction Photographs* (2nd edn.), Macmillan, London (1960).

Powder techniques:

D'Eye, R. W. M. and Wait, E., *X-ray Powder Photography in Inorganic Chemistry,* Butterworths, London (1960).

Klug, H. P. and Alexander, L. E., *X-ray Diffraction Procedures for Polycrystalline and Amorphous Materials* (2nd edn.), Wiley, New York (1974).

Lipson, H. and Steeple, H., *Interpretation of X-ray Powder Diffraction Patterns,* Macmillan, London (1970).

Peiser, H. S., Rooksby, H. P. and Wilson, A. J. C., *X-ray Diffraction by Polycrystalline Materials,* published on behalf of the Institute of Physics by Chapman and Hall, London (1960).

With a more or less specialized aspect:

Alexander, L. E., *X-ray Diffraction Methods in Polymer Science,* Wiley–Interscience, New York (1969).

Brown, G. (Editor), *The X-ray Identification and Crystal Structures of Clay Minerals,* Mineralogical Society, London (1961).

Cullity, B. D., *Elements of X-ray Diffraction.* Addison–Wesley, Reading, Mass. (1956). [Emphasis on metallurgical applications.]

Guinier, A., *X-ray Diffraction: In Crystals, Imperfect Crystals and Amorphous Bodies,* Freeman, San Francisco (1963). [Emphasis on imperfections and disordering.]

Warren, B. E., *X-ray Diffraction,* Addison–Wesley, Reading, Mass. (1969). [Emphasis on disordered materials.]

Wilson, A. J. C., *X-ray Optics* (2nd edn.), Methuen, London (1967). [Emphasis on diffraction by imperfect crystals.]

(4)   Crystal structure analysis

General:

Buerger, M. J., *Crystal Structure Analysis,* Wiley, New York (1960).

Glusker, J. P. and Trueblood, K. N., *Crystal Structure Analysis: A Primer,* O.U.P., New York (1972). [Excellent introduction.]

Lipson, H. and Cochran, W., *The Determination of Crystal Structures* (3rd edn.), Bell, London (1966).

Stout, G. H. and Jensen, L. H., *X-ray Structure Determination: A Practical Guide,* MacMillan, New York (1968).

Special methods:

Buerger, M. J., *Vector Space: and its Application in Crystal Structure Investigation,* Wiley, New York (1959).

Lipson, H. and Taylor, C. A., *Fourier Transforms and X-ray Diffraction,* Bell, London (1958).

Taylor, C. A. and Lipson, H. S., *Optical Transforms,* Bell, London (1964).

Woolfson, M. M., *Direct Methods in Crystallography,* O.U.P., Oxford (1961).

Special applications:

Holmes, K. C. and Blow, D. M., *The Use of X-Ray Diffraction in the Study of Protein and Nucleic Acid Structure,* Wiley–Interscience, New York (1966).

Kitaigorodskii, A. I., *Organic Chemical Crystallography,* Consultants Bureau, New York (1961).

Nyburg, S. C., *X-Ray Analysis of Organic Structures,* Academic Press, New York (1961).

Robertson, J. M., *Organic Crystals and Molecules: Theory of X-Ray Structure Analysis, with Applications to Organic Chemistry,* Cornell U.P., Ithaca, New York (1953).

(5) Neutron diffraction

Bacon, G. E., *Neutron Diffraction* (2nd edn.), O.U.P., Oxford (1962).

Bacon, G. E., *Applications of Neutron Diffraction in Chemistry,* Pergamon, Oxford (1963).

Willis, B. T. M. (Editor), *Chemical Applications of Thermal Neutron Scattering,* U.K.A.E.R.E. Harwell Series, O.U.P., London (1973).

(6) Electron diffraction

Gard, J. A. (Editor), *The Electron Optical Investigation of Clays,* Mineralogical Society, London (1971) (Chapters 1 and 2).

Hirsh, P. B., Howie, A., Nicholson, R. B., Pashley, D. W. and Whelan, M. J., *The Electron Microscopy of Thin Crystals,* Butterworths, London (1965).

Rymer, T. B., *Electron Diffraction,* Methuen, London (1970).

(7) Miscellaneous background material

Bernal, I., Hamilton, W. C. and Ricci, J. S., *Symmetry: A Stereoscopic Guide for Chemists,* Freeman, San Francisco (1972).

Bijvoet, J. M., Burgers, W. G. and Hägg, G., *Early Papers on Diffraction of X-rays by Crystals,* published for the International Union of Crystallography by Oosthoek, Utrecht (Vol. I, 1969, Vol. II, 1972).

Bragg, W. L. (Edited by Phillips, D. C.), *The Development of X-ray Analysis,* Bell, London (1975).

Harburn, G., Taylor, C. A. and Welberry, T. R., *Atlas of Optical Transforms,* Bell, London (1975).

Macgillavry, C. *Symmetry Aspects of M. C. Escher's Periodic Drawings,* published for the I.U.C. by Oosthoek, Utrecht (1965).

Verma, A. R. and Krishna, P., *Polymorphism and Polytypism in Crystals,* Wiley, New York (1966).

Watson, J. D., *The Double Helix,* Penguin, London (1970).

REFERENCE SOURCES

International Tables for X-Ray Crystallography
> Vol. I Symmetry Groups (1952).
> Vol. II Mathematical Tables (2nd edn. 1965).
> Vol. III Physical and Chemical Tables (2nd edn. 1967).
> Vol. IV Revised and Supplementary Tables (1974).

Published by the International Union of Crystallography at the Kynoch Press, Birmingham.

World list of Crystallographic Programs, (edited by G. C. Bassi); J. Appl. Cryst. **6**, 309- 346 (1973).

Molecular Structures and Dimensions (series), published for I.U.C. by Oosthoek, Utrecht.

BIDICS—Bond Index to the Determinations of Inorganic Crystal Structures (edited by I. D. Brown), Institute for Materials Research, McMaster University, Hamilton, Ontario, Canada. (Series beginning 1969.)

Structure Reports (edited by W. B. Pearson), published for I.U.C. by Oosthoek, Utrecht. [Continuing series covering structures from earliest days of X-ray crystallography.]

Index of Crystallographic Supplies 3rd edn. (edited by R. Rudman), published for I.U.C. by Oosthoek, Utrecht (1972).

The Powder Diffraction File (edited by W. L. Berry), published by the Joint Committee on Powder Diffraction Standards, 1601 Park Lane, Swarthmore, Pennsylvania 19081, U.S.A.

Donnay, J. D. H. and Ondik, H. M., *Crystal Data Determinative Tables* I Organic Compounds (1972); II Inorganic Compounds (1973); published jointly by the U.S. Dept. of Commerce, the National Bureau of Standards and the Joint Committee on Powder Diffraction.

Fang, J. H., and Bloss, F. D., *X-Ray Diffraction Tables,* Southern Illinois University Press, Carbondale, Ill. (1966). [Tables of 2θ v d-spacing for a variety of X-ray wavelengths.]

Porter, M. W. and Spiller, R. C., *The Barker Index of Crystals,* Vol. I (1951), Vol. II (1956), Vol. III (1964), Heffer, Cambridge.

Winchell, A. N., *The Optical Properties of Organic Compounds,* University of Wisconsin Press, Madison, Wis. (1943).

Winchell, A. N. and Winchell, H., *The Microscopical Characters of Artificial Inorganic Solid Substances.* Academic Press, New York (1964).

Wyckoff, R. W. G., *Crystal Structures* (2nd edn.), Vols, 1- 6, Wiley- Interscience, New York (1963-71).

Index